Core Themes in Geography
Physical

Eddie Broadley
Depute Rector, Glen Urquhart High School
and
Ritchie Cunningham
Rector, Inverness High School

Oliver & Boyd

Acknowledgements

The publishers thank the following for permission to reproduce photographs or other copyright material:
University of Dundee (1.3); New Scientist (1.6, 1.38, 1.41, 1.42, 1.44, 1.47, 1.53, 1.54, 1.63, map p.46); Tony and Marion Morrison (1.17, 6.7, 6.24 E. Parker); US Weather Bureau (1.20); Geographical Magazine (1.45); Daily Telegraph (1.49); Panos Pictures (1.62a,b Alain le Garsmeur, 1.64b Jiri Polacek, 6.11 Paul Harrison, 6.13 Jeremy Hartley, Oxfam, 6.14 Paul Harrison, 6.15 Ron Giling); M. Nimmo (1.64a, 3.21a, 4.57); Klaus Albrectsen (cartoon 1, p.39); Nils Forshed (cartoon 3, p.39); Andrew Skinner/Outram Magazines (2.7); Highland River Purification Board (2.19, 2.20, 2.21, 2.22, 2.26, 2.32); Scottish Hydro-Electric PLC (2.23, 2.24, 2.25, 2.28); Alan Clowes (2.33); Aberdeen Journals Ltd (2.29); A.S. Pollock (2.30); The Glasgow Herald and Evening Times (2.31); John Dewar Studios (2.45); Landform Slides (2.51, 3.6, 3.13, 3.14 inset, 3.29, 3.42, photo p.103, 4.31, 5.10, 5.11, 6.5, Fig. 7, p.170); Eric Kay (2.46, 2.49, 3.19, 3.25, 3.48, 3.52, 4.1, 4.35, 4.48, 4.52, 6.2); Aviemore Photographic (3.6); Highlands and Islands Development Board (3.17); Eddie Broadley (3.18, 5.26); British Geological Survey (3.21b); British Museum (Natural History) (3.30); Simon Warner (3.36, 3.37, 3.38); Tom Parker (3.39, 5.19); Mike Williams (3.40); Rex Features (3.43, 6.32); Cambridge University Collection (3.47b, 5.5 (© Crown copyright 1991/MOD); 5.13); Tony Waltham (3.54, 4.38, 5.1); Mark Edwards/Still Pictures (4.41, 6.6, 6.9, 6.12, 6.16, 6.17, 6.21, 6.23, 6.27, 6.28); TASS (4.46); Nature Conservancy Council (4.56 Richard Lindsay); Frank Lane Picture Agency (4.59, 6.8 D.A. Robinson); the various National Park Authorities (5.4); David Hunter (5.21, 5.22, 5.28); Exxon Chemical Geopolymers Ltd (5.34); Holt Studios Ltd (6.4a, b); Friends of the Earth (6.25); Central Independent Television plc (6.30); Hutchison (6.34 Moser/Taylor); Roger Leakey (6.35); Science Photo Library (photos 1 and 2, p.168); Greg O'Hare (Figs 2, 3, 5, 6, 8, p.170); Geoscience Features (Figs 1, 4, p.170).

The authors and publishers would like to acknowledge the following sources which were used as a basis for figures or text:
Natural Environmental Research Council, *Our Future World* (1.2, 2.3); N. Mayers (ed.), *Gaia Atlas of Planet Management*, Pan Books (1.9, 4.29, 4.30, 4.40, p.131, 6.1, 6.3); A.N. Strahler, *Physical Geography*, John Wiley 1969 (1.11, 1.12, 1.13, 2.12); R.A. Muller, *Physical Geography Today: A Portrait of a Planet*, CRM Books (1.26, 1.28); H.J. Critchfield, *General Climatology*, Prentice Hall 1974 (1.29); David Wilcock, *Physical geography*, Blackie 1983 (1.39); The Department of the Environment, Environment in Trust, *Air Quality*, May 1989 (1.40, 1.50, 1.52, 1.55); Press Association (1.46); *New Scientist*, Inside Science Supplement 'Acid Rain', 5 November 1987 (1.58, map p.46); *Geofile* (1.60 Jan 1988, 1.61 April 1984, 1.73 Jan 1988, diagram p.47); Leslie F. Musk, *Weather Systems*, Cambridge University Press (1.69); *Geographical Magazine* (graph p.38, 2.6, 6.19, 6.29); HMSO weather charts (2.27); B.J. Knapp, *Earth and Man*, Allen & Unwin (3.1); I. Galbraith & P. Weigand, *Landforms*, Oxford University Press (3.2, 3.10); Brunsden, Goudie et al., *Landshapes*, David & Charles (3.3, 3.4, 3.7, 3.11); HMSO Geology Report 'Grampian Mountains' (3.15); Eric Young, *The Scenery of Britain*, Edward Arnold (3.26); work by A. Doherty, Linlithgow Academy (3.27); material from Yorkshire Dales National Park Authority (3.32, 3.34); A. Goudie, *Nature of Environment*, Blackwell Scientific, and M.J.Readman & F.M.Mayers, *The Dynamic Landscape*, Oliver & Boyd (3.51); J. Small, *Slopes*, Cambridge University Press (4.19); Roy Collard, *Physical Geography of Landscape*, Unwin Hyman (graph p. 101); J. Sissons, *Evolution of Scotland*, Oliver & Boyd (map 2, p. 102); B.J.Knapp, *Systematic Geography*, Unwin Hyman (4.1–4.9); Bridges, *World Soils*, Cambridge University Press (4.19); material from Dartmoor National Park Authority (4.27, 4.28); Hilton, *Physical Geography*, Unwin Hyman (map p.121); Nature Conservancy Council (4.49, 4.50, 4.55); Countryside Commission (5.3); Lake District Special Planning Board (pp. 140–145); Mel Rockett, *Themes in Human Geography*, Arnold-Wheaton (5.27); 'Landscapes of Tomorrow', university research project into the future of the Yorkshire Dales, 1989–90 (5.28–5.35); *New Scientist*, 16 December 1989 (6.33). E. Broadley would also like to thank Ruth Bankhead and Dougie Strachan of of Plockton High, and Jimmy Roberts, for their invaluable help with his research and writing.
Every effort has been made to trace copyright owners. The publishers apologise if there are any omissions.

Figures 1.30–1.32, 1.35–1.37, 1.74–1.77 are from G. O'Hare & J. Sweeney, *The Atmospheric System*, Oliver & Boyd. The diagram on page 21 is from *GCSE Geography Copymasters: The Physical Environment*, Oliver & Boyd. Figures 2.9, 2.10 and 2.16 are from P. Comfort & A. Clowes, *Process and Landform*, 1st edition, Oliver & Boyd. Figures 2.35, 2.37, 2.40, 2.42, 2.43, 2.47, 2.48, 2.50, 2.53, 2.54 are from P. Comfort & A. Clowes, *Process and Landform*, 2nd edition, Oliver & Boyd. Figures 1.34, 1.43, 1.56, 1.59, 2.1, 2.2, 2.55, 6.10, 6.20, 6.26 were supplied by Gemini News Service, 9 White Lion Street, London N1 9PD (Tel. 071 833 4141) The map on p.167 is an extract from OS Outdoor Leisure Series 1:25 000 Southern Area map (Malham), reproduced with the permission of the Controller of Her Majesty's Stationery Office, Crown Copyright Reserved.

Cover and book design by Lynda McNee. Cover photograph by R.J. Pipes

Illustrated by Valerie Lewis, Bob McAllister, Will Rankine, Ann Rooke and Tim Smith

Oliver & Boyd
Edinburgh Gate
Harlow
Essex CM20 2JE
An Imprint of Longman Group Ltd
ISBN 0 05 004556 3
First published 1991
Sixth impression 1996

Typeset in 10pt Helvetica Narrow on the Apple Macintosh; styled by Word Power, Berwickshire
Produced by Longman Singapore Publishers Pte Ltd
Printed in Singapore

The Publisher's policy is to use paper manufactured from sustainable forests.

CONTENTS

INTRODUCTION

Physical geography is concerned with the study of patterns and interrelationships between the various aspects of the physical environment. The four major aspects of physical geography dealt with in this book are the atmosphere, hydrosphere, lithosphere and biosphere. Although these are dealt with in separate chapters, they are inextricably linked by exchanges of energy and mass. The interaction of the processes described is examined in two further chapters, on rural land resources; and rural land degradation.

This book adopts a **systems approach** because the study of physical geography is concerned with a complex functioning system which centres on the relationship between people and the land.

A system is simply a set of interrelated characteristics or components, within a boundary, between which energy and/or material flows. These related components provide a structure for describing and understanding complex interrelationships. Within a global earth–atmosphere system there are clearly identifiable sub-systems such as the hydrological cycle, the rock cycle and the plant–soil cycle (1.1).

Components within systems are linked by flows of energy, water, people, etc. giving a distinctive structure. Topics such as vegetation succession, soil formation and landform development can be better understood as sytems. Many systems are able to withstand altered conditions within certain limits, although some systems are more resilient than others. This idea helps when studying topics such as soil degradation, deforestation and climatic change.

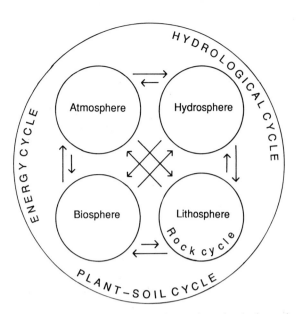

1.1 The earth–atmosphere system.This diagram shows that the four major components in the system, the atmosphere, hydrosphere, biosphere and lithosphere, are linked to each other by exchanges of energy and material.

The global hydrological cycle is one example of a system which can easily be used to illustrate the various attributes of a systems approach (1.2). The simplest way of illustrating this cycle is by a straightforward flow diagram. In this cycle there is a fixed amount of water within the boundary of the system (the earth and its atmosphere)and the circulation of this water is powered by energy from the sun (which is outside the system). Although the total amount of water in the cycle is fixed, there have been and will continue to be changes in the distribution of water through the cycle, because of climatic change, such as the glaciations. Water is held in storage at different points of the cycle: for example, groundwater, ocean storage and ice caps.

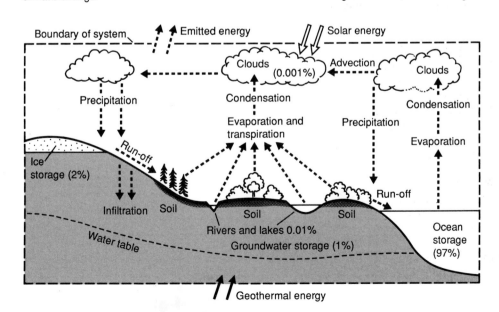

1.2 The global hydrological cycle. Most water within the cycle is held in storage, with 97% in ocean storage.

THE ATMOSPHERE

The Atmospheric System

We are all aware of the importance of the atmosphere for all human activity. In a sense we live in an ocean of air, as fish do in water, and the atmosphere is as important to us as water is to the fish. We are bombarded with information on the atmosphere's activity, from news reports of winter blizzards to summer droughts, particularly the events which cause destruction and death.

An ever-improved understanding of atmospheric processes is required if popular interest in the weather and climatic change is to be satisfied. Satellites with a range of remote sensing devices can now give us almost instantaneous pictures of global weather (1.3). This vast increase in information has had to be matched by improved computer capacity and software, in order to arrive at some understanding of the atmosphere's behaviour.

Although our knowledge of atmospheric processes is increasing rapidly, unfortunately action to remedy atmospheric damage such as ozone depletion, acid rain or increased volumes of 'greenhouse' gases is not so rapid. Even our ability to communicate crucial weather warnings has on many occasions been inadequate. For example, the 1970 flood in the Ganges delta, which killed almost half a million people, had been predicted but the warnings did not reach the people in their rural communities.

International concern about global warming has highlighted the need for further research into the workings of the atmosphere. The results of this research will reach a wide audience outside the scientific community, because the implications may be very significant. The concept of an enhanced 'greenhouse effect' and ozone depletion were debated theories some years ago, whereas now they are accepted as a reality.

1.3 Meteosat image. Images from space can give us pictures of global circulation and weather. This photograph shows the Inter-tropical convergence zone at X, a depression off the west coast of Spain(Y) and the bright sand of the Sahara, under a cloudless sky. The grasslands of southern Africa (C) are noticeably darker than the coastal desert sands of Namibia(D).

The earth and its atmosphere can be viewed as a closed system (earth–atmosphere system), dependent on continuing inputs of energy from the sun. There are also some very small energy contributions from the earth's interior (geothermal energy) and tidal energy (1.4). The solar energy which drives the earth–atmosphere system is received and transformed in a series of energy transfers, most of these within the atmosphere itself (1.5). Some of the solar energy is reflected back into space by the atmosphere (25%) while some is absorbed (23%), transformed into heat and is then emitted as long-wave radiation. 52% of the original solar energy finally reaches the earth's surface where 46% is absorbed (and later radiated back into the atmosphere), and a small amount is reflected into space (6%). For every 100 units of energy provided by the sun, 31 are reflected back into space while 69 are absorbed by the earth and its atmosphere. The 31% lost by reflection is termed the earth's **albedo**.

The radiation received by the earth's surface causes its temperature to rise and, like any other hot body, it radiates energy. This energy is emitted as long-wave radiation into the atmosphere and here certain trace gases (carbon dioxide, methane and water vapour) play an important role in absorbing it. These gases are heated and emit radiation in all directions. Much of this energy is returned to the surface while clouds effectively block some from escaping into space. This return of energy to the earth's surface maintains warm temperatures which would be some 30 °C colder without this effect. This maintenance of high temperatures by the atmosphere, allowing in short-wave radiation and trapping the bulk of outgoing long-wave radiation, is sometimes called the 'greenhouse effect' (1.6). The increase in carbon dioxide and other greenhouse gases which trap the outgoing heat is currently causing much concern.

1.5 Solar energy distribution in the earth–atmosphere system. (Data from Natural Environment Research Council)

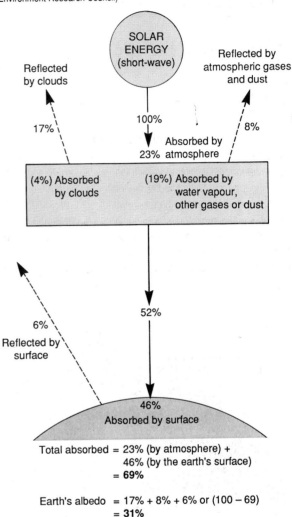

Total absorbed = 23% (by atmosphere) +
46% (by the earth's surface)
= **69%**

Earth's albedo = 17% + 8% + 6% or (100 − 69)
= **31%**

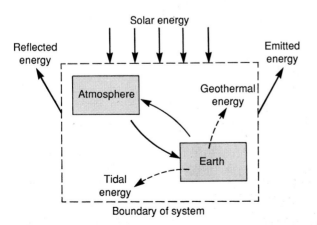

1.4 Energy exchange in the earth–atmosphere system. Energy comes into the system from the sun, while within the system energy is exchanged between the earth and its atmosphere.

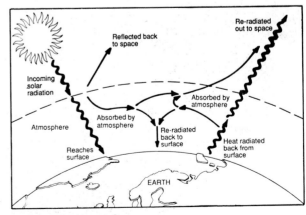

1.6 Details of energy exchange in the earth–atmosphere system

The Global Heat Budget

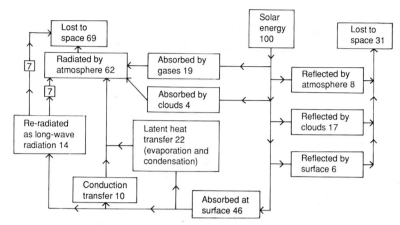

1.7 The global heat budget. The earth's surface transfers 39 units of energy to the atmosphere while the atmosphere only absorbs 23 units of solar energy. The 39 units transferred from the earth is made up of 22 units transferred by latent heat, 10 by conduction and 7 re-radiated as long-wave radiation.

If there was no human interference with the atmosphere, the earth as a planet would not be getting appreciably hotter or colder. It would neither lose energy nor store energy and therefore the total output of energy from the earth–atmosphere system would equal its input from the sun (1.7). The right hand side of the diagram shows the radiation initially reflected into space as indicated in 1.5. The left hand side of the diagram illustrates the routes to space made by the remaining 69%.

Of the 46 units of short-wave solar radiation which reach the earth's surface 14 units are re-radiated as long-wave radiation (7 into space and 7 to the atmosphere), 10 units are returned to the atmosphere by **conduction** and 22 units are transferred by **latent heat**. Conduction is the transfer of heat between the earth's surface and the atmosphere it is in contact with. However only the lowest portion of the atmosphere is warmed in this way as air is a poor conductor. Transfer by latent heat is where water is evaporated at the earth's surface, rises in the atmosphere and transfers heat energy as it condenses (1.8).

Of the 46 units received by the earth's surface 39 units are transferred to the atmosphere. As was mentioned earlier the atmosphere only manages to absorb 23 units of short-wave solar radiation; therefore the atmosphere receives most of its energy from the earth's surface. The most significant aspect of the earth's **heat budget** is that the atmosphere is largely heated from below.

1.9 summarises the earth's energy cycle illustrating that over 99% of all energy in the system comes from the sun, 46% warms the sea and land while 22% powers the hydrological cycle.

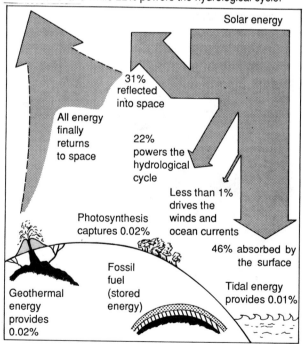

1.9 The energy cycle. Energy from the sun drives the earth–atmosphere system and all its sub-systems such as the hydrological cycle, plant–soil cycle, oxygen cycle and other geochemical cycles, that sustain life on earth. Indirectly the sun provides our food by powering photosynthesis in plants (which only captures 0.02% of incoming solar energy). Even the power we obtain from fossil fuels, such as coal and oil, is in effect stored solar energy.

1.8 Energy transfers from the earth's surface in the earth–atmosphere system

Global insolation

Because the earth is spherical the sun's radiation (**insolation**) only strikes the earth's surface on the perpendicular between the Tropics of Cancer and Capricorn. The further away from the Tropics, the larger the surface area hit by the insolation (1.10) and therefore surface heating is much less. Also the sun's radiation must pass through more of the atmosphere, because of the oblique angle, and hence this reduces the heating still further. This difference in global insolation helps to explain the variation and distribution of air temperatures over the earth.

The inclination of the earth's axis causes the **angle of incidence** (the angle that the sun's rays strike any point on the earth's surface) to change throughout the year and therefore the insolation changes with the seasons. At the poles, where there are six months of light and six months of night, the variation in insolation is most extreme (1.11). The three-dimensional diagram (1.12) shows how insolation varies with latitude and time of the year. At the equator there are two maxima (when the sun is directly overhead) at the equinoxes and two minima (when the sun is overhead at either of the Tropics) at the solstices. At the Arctic Circle (66.5° N) insolation is zero on the winter solstice (22 December) and this period of zero insolation lengthens with increasing latitude. The measurements of insolation illustrated in 1.11 and 1.12 are measurements of energy received at the outer limits of the atmosphere.

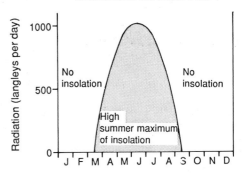

Insolation at the North Pole

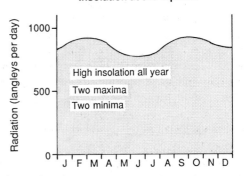

Insolation at the equator

1.11 Latitudinal variations in insolation. At the equator insolation is high all year round with two maxima when the sun is overhead. At the North Pole there is no insolation for six months of the year.

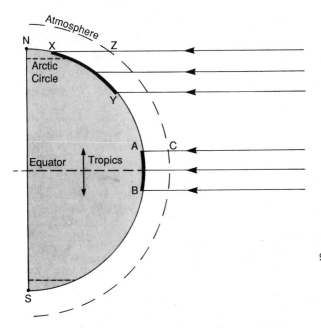

1.10 Variation in insolation across the globe. Both bands of solar radiation are equivalent, but this energy is received over a greater area nearer the North Pole (XY) than at the equator (AB). The further north or south the greater the depth of the atmosphere the radiation has to penetrate (XZ against AC).

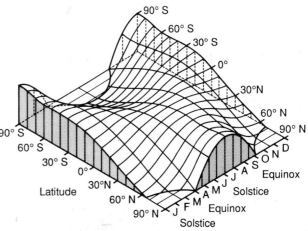

1.12 Effect of latitude and season on intensity of insolation. At any given latitude and month of the year the relative insolation received is proportional to the height of the surface above the base of the block.

Atmospheric Circulation 1

Redistribution of energy

As well as energy transfers between the earth's surface and the atmosphere there are also energy transfers at a horizontal level, between low latitudes and high latitudes. Poleward of latitude 38° in both hemispheres there is less solar energy absorbed than terrestrial energy emitted; whereas between 38° N and 38° S there is more energy absorbed than emitted (1.13). Energy is

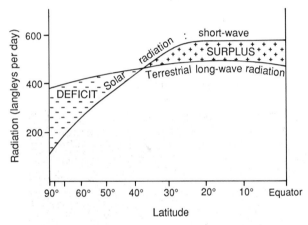

1.13 Radiation budget. More energy is absorbed in low latitudes than is re-radiated, while the opposite is true in high latitudes. Energy is therefore transferred from low latitudes to high latitudes.

transferred from the low-latitude energy surplus areas to the high-latitude energy deficit areas. Without this transfer of energy the low latitudes would get even hotter and the high latitudes even colder.

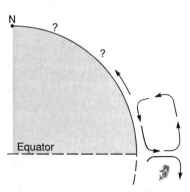

1.14 Hadley's circulation model, 1735. Energy is transferred to higher latitudes by winds generated by tropical heat.

As early as 1735, George Hadley, a British scientist, suggested that a tropical heat source powers global circulation and effects a transfer of energy from the Tropics to the poles (1.14). Hadley proposed that direct heating of air at the equator causes upward convection and this air then moves poleward to sink at the subtropics. He indicated that other similar cells might exist in mid and high latitudes, however it was left to William Ferrel in 1856 to put forward a three-cell model for each hemisphere (1.15).

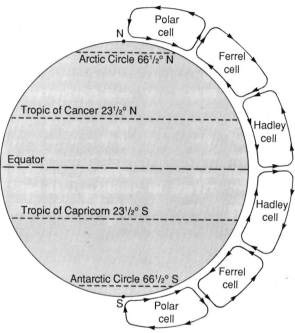

1.15 Ferrel's circulation model, 1856

Atmospheric circulation

The simple three-cell model of atmospheric circulation (1.15) proposed by Ferrel included the tropical **Hadley cell** with rising equatorial air and descending air at the subtropics (around 30° latitude). This cell also includes air movement at ground level between the subtropics and the equator to replace the rising equatorial air, which has created a zone of **low pressure**. This area of low pressure is caused by the heated air at the equator which expands, becomes less dense (heavy) and rises (1.16). As the heated air rises through the atmosphere the 'weight of air' on the surface is lessened and this results in a low-pressure area.

Differences in air pressure create air movement (wind) and in this case the wind moves from the high-pressure subtropics to the low-pressure equatorial zone.

The rising equatorial air carries with it considerable amounts of latent heat in the evaporated water from the oceans and land surface. Some of this energy is released as the water vapour condenses in the form of cumulonimbus clouds (1.16 and 1.17). The expansion of the rising air in the upper atmosphere creates an air flow in both northward and southward directions. More of the water vapour condenses and releases energy as the air moves poleward, warming the atmosphere in the middle latitudes. The poleward-moving air sinks (subsides) in the subtropics because the space available in the upper atmosphere decreases poleward. This subsidence causes a subtropical high-pressure zone at about 30° latitude.

A **polar cell** in this model is due to cold, dense air subsiding in polar regions (polar high-pressure zone) and moving to lower latitudes where it expands as it moves into more space and is warmed by the earth's surface.

The **Ferrel cell** between the other two is a response to the two **thermally direct cells** (circulation cells which owe their origin to temperature differences) and obtains its energy from them. This cell feeds warm air to high latitudes and transfers cold air back to the subtropics for warming.

This simple three-cell model is a useful simplification of reality at the spring and autumnal equinoxes. It does not take into account the seasonal shifts in pressure belts or other forces governing global circulation.

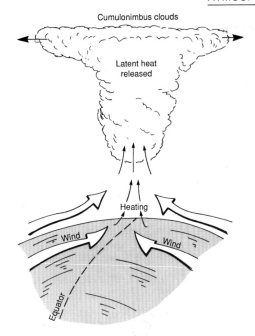

1.16 Equatorial heat machine. Surface heating at the equator drives the tropical Hadley cells, with latent heat being released as the air rises.

1.17 Cumulonimbus clouds over Brazil. Equatorial heat generates these towering clouds over Brazil in South America.

Atmospheric Circulation 2

Forces governing global circulation

As was mentioned earlier, air moves away from high-pressure areas towards low-pressure areas. This is sometimes called the **pressure gradient force**. It ought to cause the winds to blow directly between the high and low pressure areas, at right angles to the **isobars** (lines of equal pressure). However, other forces deflect the winds.

The **Coriolis force**, named after the nineteenth-century French scientist, Coriolis, is the effect produced by the earth's rotation. It must be allowed for when studying objects that move with respect to the earth's surface. From space, winds (or other moving objects) are seen to be moving in a straight line with the earth rotating beneath. But from the earth's surface the effect of the Coriolis force appears to deflect the movement. (for this reason the force is sometimes called 'apparent'.) It acts at right angles to the direction of motion, deflecting winds towards the right in the northern hemisphere and to the left in the southern hemisphere. This force affects all objects and fluids and therefore also influences the ocean currents. The Coriolis force is zero at the equator (because the earth's surface is spinning in a plane almost parallel to the axis of rotation) but increases poleward.

At high altitude the wind direction tends to find a balance between the pressure gradient force and the Coriolis force. When the air begins to move from high to low pressure it becomes subject to the Coriolis force which displaces it to the right. As it speeds up the deflection increases until the two forces are exactly balanced and the wind flows parallel to the isobars. This is known as the **geostrophic wind** (1.18a). Near ground level however

there is another force that comes into play: **friction**. The friction of the air against the ground partly counteracts the Coriolis force and causes the wind to cross the isobars at an angle of between 20° and 45° (1.18b). The more rugged the terrain the larger the angle, while for smoother surfaces such as water the angle is smaller. Friction also has the effect of reducing the speed of the wind.

Improvements in atmospheric circulation models

Research early this century revealed the existence of large-scale belts of fast-moving winds. These wind belts follow a wave-like pattern, first poleward then towards the equator and so on (1.19). These wave-like patterns are known as planetary waves or **Rossby waves** and occur at altitudes of 10 000 to 12 000 metres Within these wind belts there is a core of very fast-moving air (the **jet stream**) where the wind can reach speeds of up to 350–450 km per hour (1.20). There are two jet streams in each hemisphere: the polar jet stream which lies between about 30° and 50° latitude and the subtropical jet stream at about 20° to 30° latitude. In the northern hemisphere the polar jet stream flows west to east and the subtropical jet stream east to west. The jet streams and their associated Rossby waves are a mechanism for mixing air of different temperatures and are located at key locations in the atmosphere for the transfer of energy.

The jet streams are generated by the temperature differences between polar and subtropical air and between subtropical and equatorial air. The polar jet stream is the most vigorous of the two because the temperature difference between polar and subtropical air is more marked than the difference between subtropical and equatorial air.

The Rossby waves themselves are linked to pressure changes at the surface and rotation of the earth but major physical barriers like the Rocky Mountains and the Andes have a great influence on the wave pattern and wind speed. The compression of air as

1.18 Forces affecting the wind

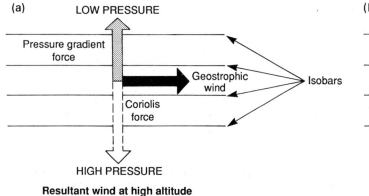

Resultant wind at high altitude

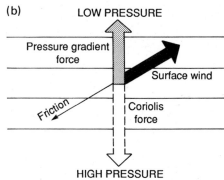

Resultant wind at the surface

the wind blows over the Rockies causes the wind first to blow south-eastward and then north-eastward (1.21). This deflection results in approximately 4 or 5 waves which encircle the earth. The wave-like pattern would appear to have a life cycle of about 6 weeks. 1.22 illustrates the development and breakdown of Rossby waves. The wave amplitude and wind speed increase to the point where the polar air transfers southward in cells and the subtropical air moves into higher latitudes. Increased knowledge and understanding of Rossby wave activity and its influence on surface weather has enabled an improvement in forecasting reliability.

1.19 Rossby waves. These winds are generated by temperature differences and are important mechanisms for the mixing of air masses and thus transfer of energy.

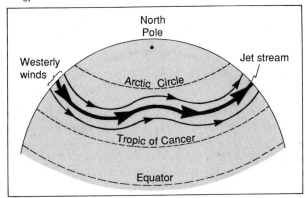

1.20 The jet stream. The jet stream has a central core of high-velocity winds (From US Weather Bureau, Aviation Series No.3)

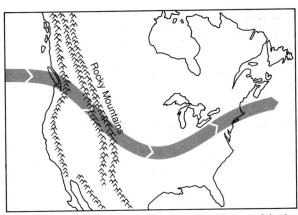

1.21 Deflection of upper air flow by the Rocky Mountains. Major mountain barriers like the Rockies and the Andes deflect upper air flow and generate a wave-like pattern.

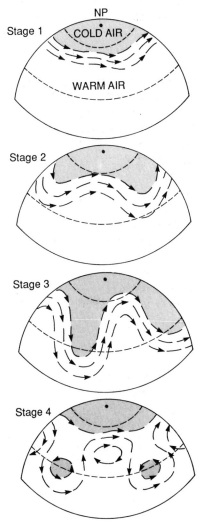

1.22 Life cycle of Rossby waves. Wave amplitude increases to the point where cold cells of air become detached and the cycle repeats. This re-distributes energy by mixing warm and cold air.

The addition of jet streams and a **polar front** (a boundary between the cold polar air and warm subtropical air) to the simple three-cell model of atmospheric circulation gives us the model shown in 1.23.

Further improvements in our understanding have led to modifications of the Rossby model (1.23). The model of global circulation proposed by Palmen in 1951 is the one that is still generally accepted today (1.24). This plan view of atmospheric circulation is a simplification of reality; the simple pattern is influenced by the distribution of land and ocean as well as high mountain barriers.

Planetary wind circulation

The major wind systems largely conform to broad latitudinal zones (1.25). There are two main wind belts in each hemisphere. The **trade-wind** belt covers nearly half the earth's surface and is found between latitudes 30° N and 30° S. The trade winds are fairly constant and predictable because of the relative permanence of the subtropical high-pressure zones, from where they emanate. The second major wind belt in each hemisphere is the **mid-latitude westerlies** which develop from the poleward sides of the subtropical high-pressure zone. The westerlies in the southern hemisphere are more persistent than those in the northern hemisphere because of the relative absence of large land masses. Poleward of the mid-latitude westerlies are smaller polar zones of easterly winds. In the Arctic these easterlies tend to occur only in winter while in Antarctica they tend to be less seasonal.

The trade winds from both hemispheres meet near the equator in what is called the inter-tropical convergence zone (**ITCZ**). The ITCZ moves between the tropics with the seasonal shift of the equatorial low pressure. Because this zone is an area of convection (uplift of air) the winds are weak and are called the 'Doldrums'. The other two **zones of convergence** are the polar fronts in both hemispheres, where the westerlies meet the polar easterlies. There are also two important **zones of divergence**, the subtropical high-pressure zones, which are areas of relatively light winds usually referred to as the 'horse latitudes'.

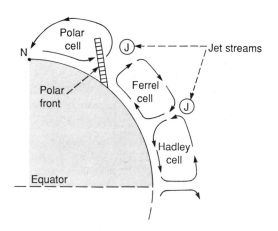

1.23 Three-cell model of atmospheric circulation. This is essentially Ferrel's model with the addition of a polar front and jet streams.

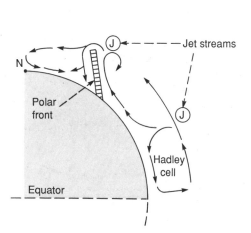

1.24 Palmen's global circulation model, 1951. This model of atmospheric circulation is the one in current usage. It is a useful simplification of reality at this scale.

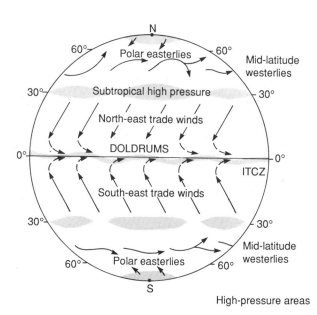

1.25 Global wind belts

These idealised wind belts rarely exist in reality because of seasonal changes in insolation and the distribution of oceans, continents and major relief features. Average wind and pressure patterns for January and July are shown in 1.26. Prominent pressure features are present at both times of the year and are therefore relatively permanent. The most noticeable features are the subtropical high-pressure cells at about 30° N and 30° S with the equatorial low-pressure trough in the vicinity of the equator.

The larger land masses in the northern hemisphere tend to break down the latitudinal belts of similar pressure. For example, in summer the warmer land masses of southern Asia generate a low-pressure cell in subtropical latitudes, while in winter a high-pressure cell develops over northern Asia, in contrast to the Icelandic and Aleutian Lows.

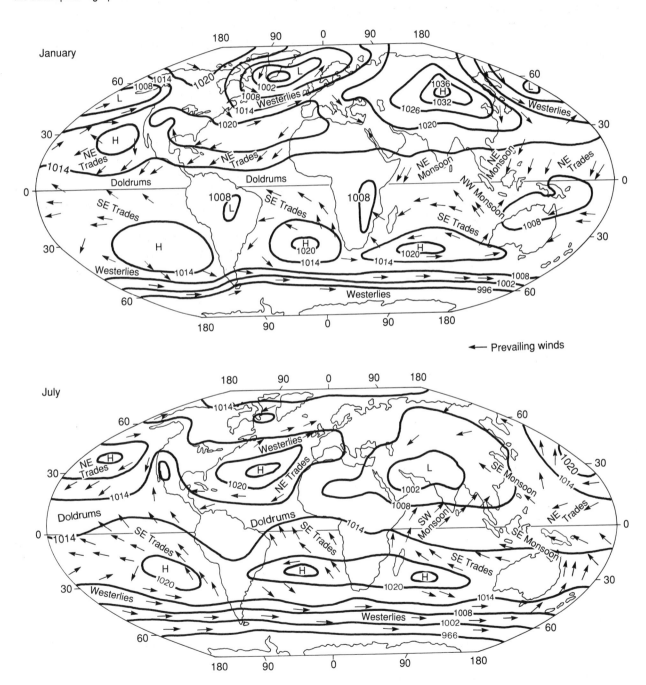

1.26 Global wind and pressure patterns at ground level in January and July

Ocean Currents

Land and water differences

Land and water have quite different properties in the absorption and radiation of heat. In general, land surfaces heat faster and to a higher level than water surfaces. However land surfaces also cool faster and reach lower temperatures when solar energy is absent. Oceans cool at a slower rate because the heat is dispersed through some depth, so they act as a store of energy. Temperature ranges over large land masses are therefore greater than over large areas of water. This difference in properties leads to contrasting amounts of energy being transferred to the atmosphere from land and water.

The difference in properties between land and water can be explained by the fact that water is transparent and allows solar radiation to penetrate to a depth of several metres. The water in the oceans is mixed by rising and sinking motions and therefore the heat is distributed through a great volume of water. More heat is also lost by surface evaporation over water than over land (1.27). The land only absorbs heat at the surface and can therefore reach higher temperatures.

Two-thirds of the earth's surface is water and this receives two-thirds of the insolation. Therefore the redistribution of energy from the equator to the poles by the oceans is significant. **Ocean currents** are the mechanism for this exchange of energy.

1.27 Land and ocean heating characteristics. Land surfaces heat faster and to higher temperatures than water surfaces because of their different properties. Solar radiation penetrates the ocean's surface and the waters mix, distributing the heat. Evaporation over the ocean also cools the surface.

Ocean currents

Atmospheric and oceanic circulation are so closely connected and have such an influence on each other, that it is necessary to have some knowledge of ocean currents in order fully to understand global climate patterns. The ocean, like the atmosphere, acts as a great heat machine transferring energy from the tropics to higher latitudes.

If there were no land masses, the ocean circulation would be largely controlled by the surface wind systems and would look like 1.28 where there are three closed loops in each hemisphere. The distribution of the major land masses breaks down this pattern and only in the Pacific and Atlantic Oceans, where there is sufficient room, do we see elementary development of these loops or **gyres** (1.29) which are controlled by the subtropical high-pressure cells.

An interesting feature of ocean currents which results from the circulation pattern is that, below a latitude of about 30°, the west coasts of continents have contact with cold currents (e.g. Canaries Current and California Current) whereas the east coasts are in contact with warm currents (e.g. Gulf Stream, Brazil Current). Above about latitude 45° the positions are reversed with west coasts in contact with warm currents (e.g. North Atlantic Drift) and east coasts in contact with cold currents (e.g. Kamchatka and Labrador Currents).

Ocean currents can have a significant effect on climate. For example the United Kingdom owes its relatively mild winters and ice-free waters to the North Atlantic Drift which is an extension of the Gulf Stream. This warm current keeps the average January temperature in Valentia (western Ireland) at about 7 °C while on a similar latitude in Tomsk, central USSR, it is –21 °C (1.29). The influence of ocean currents on climate is examined more fully on page 18 which looks at temperature variations across the globe.

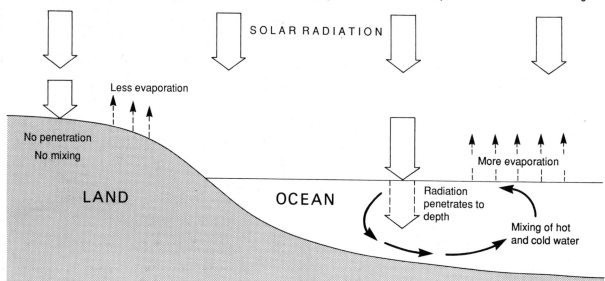

SOLAR RADIATION

Less evaporation

No penetration
No mixing

LAND   OCEAN

More evaporation

Radiation penetrates to depth

Mixing of hot and cold water

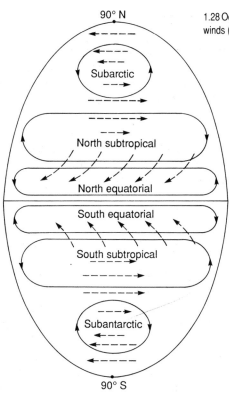

90° N

Subarctic

North subtropical

North equatorial

South equatorial

South subtropical

Subantarctic

90° S

1.28 Ocean currents on a featureless earth. Ocean currents (solid lines). Surface winds (broken lines).

1.29 Simplified ocean circulation around the globe. The ocean currents, like the atmosphere, transfer energy from the Tropics toward the poles.

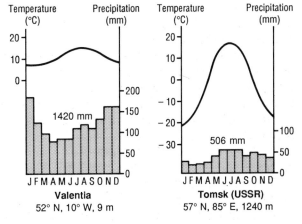

Temperature (°C)   Precipitation (mm)

1420 mm

JFMAMJJASOND
Valentia
52° N, 10° W, 9 m

Temperature (°C)   Precipitation (mm)

506 mm

JFMAMJJASOND
Tomsk (USSR)
57° N, 85° E, 1240 m

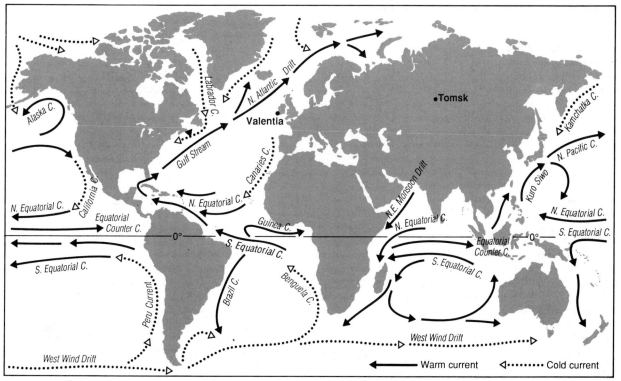

Alaska C.

Labrador C.

N. Atlantic Drift

Valentia

•Tomsk

Kamchatka C.

Gulf Stream

Canaries C.

N. Pacific C.

N. Equatorial C.

California C.

N. Equatorial C.

Kuro Siwo

Equatorial Counter C.

Guinea C.

N.E. Monsoon Drift

N. Equatorial C.

N. Equatorial C.

0°

0°

S. Equatorial C.

S. Equatorial C.

Equatorial Counter C.

S. Equatorial C.

Peru Current

Brazil C.

Benguela C.

S. Equatorial C.

West Wind Drift

West Wind Drift

◄─── Warm current   ◁····· Cold current

Temperature Variations across the Globe

Global **isotherm** maps for January and July, 1.30 and 1.31, show that the mean (average) monthly air temperature decreases away from the equator, reflecting the decrease in solar insolation. The east–west trend and parallelism of the isotherms is best developed in the southern hemisphere where the land masses are smaller than in the northern hemisphere. In the northern hemisphere the isotherms are deflected where they pass from land to ocean.

The January map shows isotherms deflected poleward over ocean and equatorward over land, in the northern hemisphere. The effects of warm ocean currents such as the North Atlantic Drift are clearly shown by the isotherms. This trend is reversed in the July map because continental interiors rapidly heat up in the summer months. In January the east and west coasts of both

South America and Southern Africa illustrate the effect of contrasting warm and cold currents on coastal temperatures.

Throughout the year the isotherms shift with solar insolation changes. Over large water areas the latitude shift is small whereas over substantial land masses the shift can be considerable. This difference between land and ocean can be clearly seen when the temperature range between January and July is examined. The annual range is much greater in continental than in coastal locations. It is over 55 °C in north-east Siberia, while for much of the UK it is about 10 °C.

The impact of continentality and the influence of ocean currents can be examined using the concept of temperature **anomaly**. Temperature anomalies are calculated by subtracting the mean January or July temperatures for the line of latitude from that of individual stations on that line of latitude. The temperature difference whether positive or negative is the anomalous temperature. Temperature anomalies for January are shown on 1.32. The largest anomalies are in the northern hemisphere where the oceans exhibit positive anomalies and the continental interiors negative anomalies. North-west Europe benefits with a positive anomaly while north-east Siberia is over 24 °C colder than the average for its line of latitude.

1.30 January temperatures at sea level (°C). Temperatures over northern continental interiors are very low with marked contrasts between land and ocean. Isotherms are fairly parallel in the southern hemisphere.

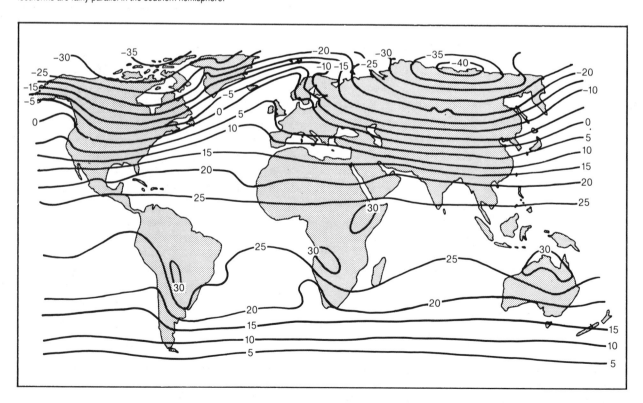

1.31 July temperatures at sea level (°C). Temperatures in northern continental interiors contrast with the low January temperatures. The land/ocean contrast in the northern hemisphere is reversed.

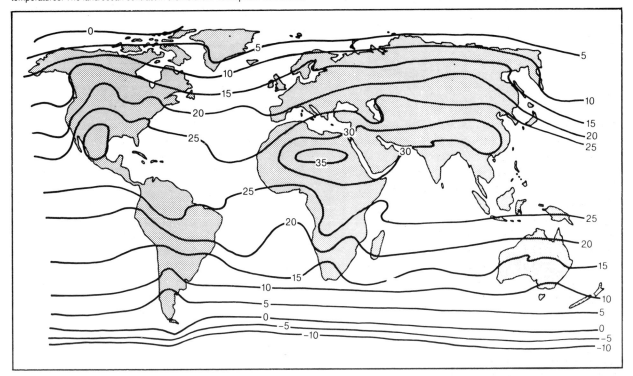

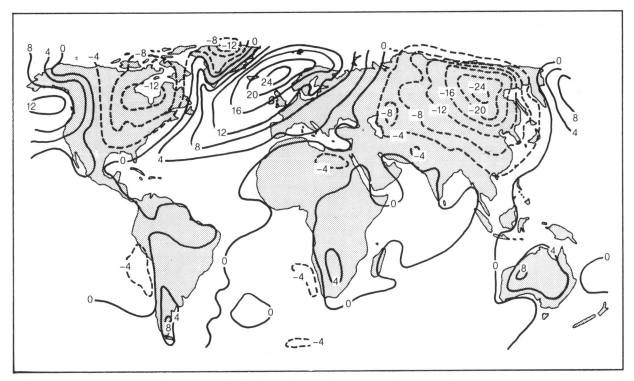

1.32 World January temperature anomalies at sea level (°C). Solid lines indicate positive, and broken lines show negative, values. Notice the difference between the northern and southern hemispheres and also the land/ocean contrast in the northern hemisphere. This map illustrates the different properties of land and water in relation to absorbing and losing energy.

Questions

Q THE ATMOSPHERIC SYSTEM/GLOBAL HEAT BUDGET

1 (a) What is the earth's albedo?
(b) Describe how the 'greenhouse effect' keeps the earth warm.
(c) Make a copy of 1.5.
(d) Using 1.5, describe the distribution of solar energy in the earth–atmosphere system.
(e) In what ways is heat transferred from the earth's surface?
(f) Using 1.7 describe the energy transfers that make up the earth's albedo.
(g) Briefly describe the energy cycle as shown in 1.9.
(h) Write a brief note to explain the global heat budget.
(i) How does solar radiation differ from terrestrial radiation?

Q THE GLOBAL HEAT BUDGET/ATMOSPHERIC
      CIRCULATION 1 AND 2

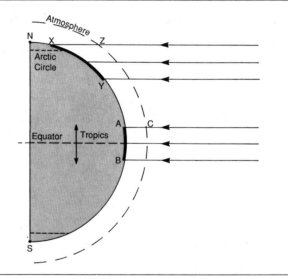

2 (a) Describe the changes in solar insolation at the equator, throughout the year.
(b) Use the diagram on the right to explain the variation in insolation across the globe.
(c) How is surplus energy transferred from low latitudes?
(d) Describe the workings of Ferrel's three-cell model of atmospheric circulation.
(e) What is the pressure gradient force?
(f) What is the Coriolis force and what is its effect?
(g) What force partly counteracts the Coriolis force?
(h) Explain the seasonal shifts in wind and pressure belts.
(i) Which pressure zones are low rainfall zones?

Q ATMOSPHERIC CIRCULATION 2

3 (a) How and where do geostrophic winds occur?
(b) What are Rossby waves?
(c) Where would you expect to find the jet streams?
(d) Describe the development and decay of Rossby waves.
(e) Why are mountain barriers important in Rossby wave formation?
(f) What is the polar front?
(g) Describe the main components of Palmen's global circulation model.
(h) Why do the major wind systems correspond to broad latitudinal zones?
(i) Why are the trade winds so predictable?
(j) What are zones of convergence and where are they found?
(k) What weather conditions would you expect at zones of divergence?
(l) Why are jet streams of importance to aircraft pilots?

OCEAN CURRENTS/TEMPERATURE VARIATIONS ACROSS THE GLOBE

4 (a) What properties enable the oceans to act as heat stores?

(b) How is heat transferred to high latitudes by the oceans?

(c) Describe the pattern of ocean currents in the North Atlantic as shown in 1.29.

(d) In what ways do the ocean currents in the Atlantic differ from the idealised pattern in 1.28?

(e) Look at the diagram below and explain the temperature differences between the places shown on the map.

(f) What effect does the North Atlantic Drift have on climate in the British Isles?

(g) Look at 1.30 and 1.31; why does the 20 °C isotherm in the southern hemisphere take a southerly bend over each land mass?

(h) Describe a route from Britain to Australia making full use of ocean currents.

(i) Define the term 'temperature anomaly'.

(j) Describe the distribution and character of temperature anomalies for January, shown in 1.32.

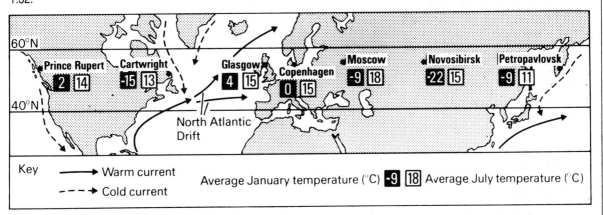

Research and Further Work

(a) Of what gases is the atmosphere composed? List these in a table.

(b) What are the main layers of the atmosphere? Draw a diagram to show them and the variation in temperature with height.

(c) What modern advances have enabled us to gain a better understanding of climate and the atmosphere?

(d) Explain the past and present importance of ocean currents to people.

(e) Describe one potential use to which the oceans could be put, concerning future food supplies.

(f) What is an El Nino event, and where and when do they occur?

(g) What factors, other than the wind, influence the flow of ocean currents?

(h) Why are ocean currents important in relation to iceberg warnings?

(i) Why is sea water salty?

Climatic Change

The recent record-breaking extremes of Britain's weather conditions including the drought in 1976, harsh winter of 1978–9 and hot summer of 1989, have stimulated public interest in the whole question of climatic change. The more extreme climatic disasters, such as Hurricane Hugo and the drought in the Sahel, have captured the attention of the general public, anxious for explanations. 1.33 shows some weather extremes throughout the world in 1988–9, while 1.34 shows the location of major natural disasters in 1988, all but one caused by the weather.

There is a wide variety of evidence which tells us that activity in the earth–atmosphere system has changed over the centuries. Many of these changes have left their mark on the landscape. Of the wide variety of techniques which can be used to investigate past climatic change, **pollen analysis**, **dendrochronology** and **isotope analysis** (ocean floor analysis and ice core analysis) are the most widely used.

Pollen analysis is concerned with examining the pollen found in sediments, particularly peat bogs which preserve the pollen grains for a long time. This analysis can identify the past vegetation of an area and hence indicate past climates because many plant species have particular climatic requirements. This form of analysis is particularly useful in detecting the climatic changes since the last glaciation (which ended about 10 300 years ago) (1.35). The rapid rise in temperature between 10 000

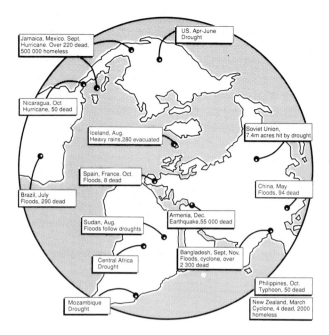

1.34 Natural disasters in 1988. All but one of these was caused by the weather.

years before present (BP) and 8000 years BP is particularly striking.

Dendrochronology is the study of growth rings in cross-sections of tree trunks: thick rings indicate a favourable climate and thin rings indicate poor conditions. Each ring represents one year's growth. To obtain an accurate climatic reconstruction

1.33 Weather extremes 1988–89. Extreme variability in world weather has been characteristic of the 1980s.

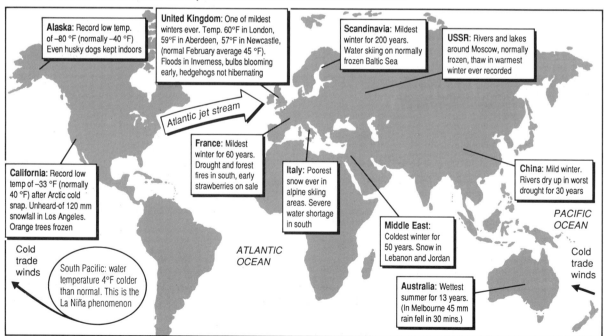

using this method, cores are taken from a number of trees and their rings cross-matched, to enable rings to be dated (1.36). Samples of timber are not restricted to living trees and by using old timbers or tree stumps buried in peat the record can extend back many centuries. In California some bristlecone pines which are over 4000 years old have been used for this sort of analysis. A reconstructed climatic record for the British Isles using oak timbers is shown in 1.37.

Isotope analysis in climate study has concentrated on the examination of oxygen isotope ratios. The two main isotopes of oxygen, ^{16}O and ^{18}O, occur in water, ice and water vapour but they move through the hydrological cycle differently. The difference in their behaviour is related to their weight: ^{16}O being slightly lighter passes into the water vapour stage more readily. This results in the remaining water being enriched in ^{18}O. Condensation reverses this process and restores the balance. However, during cold periods more precipitation is locked up in ice sheets and the return flow is diminished. The colder the climate is the greater the ^{18}O concentration in sea water. Isotope ratios can therefore indicate temperature.

Ice core analysis measures the oxygen isotopes in the polar ice sheets where snow has accumulated over thousands of years. These ice cores are in effect a record of past precipitation and the relative abundance of ^{18}O indicates the temperature of the time: abundant ^{18}O indicating warm conditions and vice versa.

Ocean floor sediment analysis is another isotopic method of obtaining information about past climates. The remnants of tiny organisms are buried in sediment, their skeletons containing ^{16}O and ^{18}O. The relative proportions of these indicate the temperature of the sea water at the time. Higher ratios of ^{18}O to ^{16}O indicate warmer temperatures.

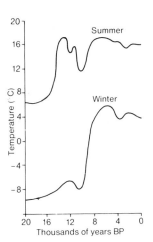

1.35 Average British temperature trends derived from pollen analysis

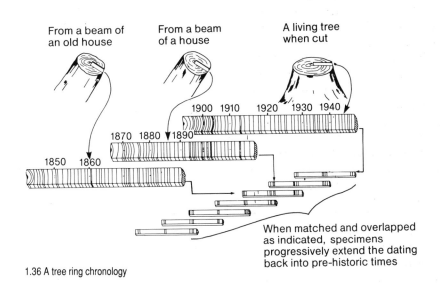

1.36 A tree ring chronology

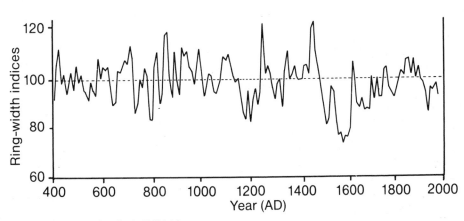

1.37 An oak ring chronology for the British Isles

Reasons for Climatic Change

Astronomical theories for climatic change enjoy wide scientific support. These theories regard the amount and distribution of insolation as the main factor controlling climate, on the grounds that it drives atmospheric circulation.

The idea of built-in climatic change in the earth–atmosphere system was first proposed by a Scot, James Croll, in 1860, and a Yugoslavian astrophysicist, **Milankovitch** reintroduced this theory in the 1930s. The fact that the shape of the earth's orbit around the sun, the angle of tilt of the earth, and the time of year when the earth is closest to the sun, change through time in well-defined cycles (1.38) led Milankovitch to argue that, when the lowest phases of insolation in all cycles combine, glaciations would occur. His predictions for past Ice Ages have received some support from ocean floor sediment analysis since the 1930s (1.39). Despite the accuracy of his predictions, Milankovitch's theory does not offer a full enough explanation to satisfy all scientists.

There are other factors which influence climatic change, such as continental drift (plate tectonics), volcanic emissions and, of most recent significance, human activity. Recent work on a link between carbon dioxide levels and the astronomical cycles has given the Milankovitch theory added strength (a fuller explanation of this link will be found on page 27).

The periods of glaciation which Milankovitch was able to predict so closely are examples of climatic change on a massive scale, but smaller-scale changes on shorter timescales are also highly significant (1.40). There is considerable historical evidence to support significant climatic changes over the last 10 000 years. The evidence from historical sources can also be checked and confirmed by pollen analysis and dendrochronology. All evidence points to a gradual warming after the last Ice Age (10 000 years ago) until around 5000 BCE (before common era, or BC before Christ), with occasional reversions to colder conditions. From 5000 BCE to 3000 BCE, conditions in northern Europe were warmer than today and mild all year round. Since about 2000 BCE, temperatures have been in general decline although there have been some interruptions of very warm conditions. The climatic worsening which started about CE 1300 (CE common era, or AD) resulted in many medieval villages being abandoned. The very cold period between 1550 and 1750 is known as the 'Little Ice Age', when glaciers in Northern Europe started to re-advance and the River Thames froze over frequently. After 1800 the climate warmed until about 1945 after which temperatures dipped slightly until the early 1970s. The increase in air temperatures since the early 1970s and the very variable weather we experienced in the 1980s, may have more to do with the impact of human activity on climate than natural rhythms.

Oxygen – 18 analyses[1] (years before present)	Milankovitch[2] (years before present)
20 000	20 000
65 000	70 000
110 000	115 000
	180 000
245 000	230 000
330 000	330 000
420 000	
505 000	

1.39 Comparison of Milankovitch's predictions with glaciation datings from ocean cores

1.38 Astronomical cycles. Milankovitch suggested that these three known cycles combine to determine the onset of the glaciations.

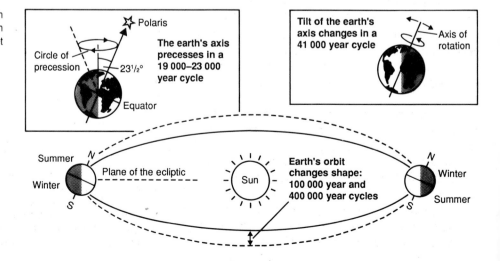

There are other earth-bound theories of climatic change which have been suggested. One of these proposes that periods of volcanic activity trigger off cold periods because volcanic dust and sulphur dioxide blown into the atmosphere reduce insolation by scattering solar radiation. Some large individual volcanic eruptions in the past few thousand years have had a significant effect on climate on local, regional and global scales. Evidence for this effect is found in historical sources and confirmed by pollen analysis and dendrochronology.

Some scientists now believe that the cooling between 1945 and 1970 was due to atomic testing and a large volcanic eruption in 1963, at Mt Agung in Indonesia. An eruption of the Icelandic volcano, Heckla, in about 1159 BCE appears to have caused significant deterioration of the weather in much of northern Europe. One result was the abandonment of the Highlands of Scotland by its Bronze Age population, which is estimated to have been as large as 600 000. The largest recorded volcanic eruption at Tambora (in the Pacific) in 1815 resulted in poor weather throughout Europe in 1816. It became known as the year without a summer and inspired Byron's poem 'Darkness' and Mary Shelley's story 'Frankenstein'. However not all volcanic eruptions have a significant effect on climate. The Mount Saint Helens eruption on 18 June 1980 did not appear to cause a widespread climatic effect, probably because the eruption was largely a lateral one and very little of its dust and sulphur dioxide reached high into the atmosphere. Computer analysis of this eruption has calculated that it caused a temperature decrease of less than 0.1 °C in the northern hemisphere.

Another theory of climatic change is based on possible shifts in Rossby waves which could cause a redistribution of temperature along lines of latitude without causing a fall in average temperature. This under certain conditions could cause an increase in snowfall to the point where a glaciation would proceed. A change in the path of Rossby waves can under certain conditions cause areas of high pressure to remain almost stationary for days or weeks. The type of extreme condition this creates depends on the position of the **blocking high pressure**. During 1982 a blocking high pressure over south-east Australia caused a severe drought by deflecting the rain-bearing depressions.

This factor in climatic change became more evident in the 1980s with extremes of weather conditions being apparently commonplace.

None of the above theories answers all of the questions about global climatic change or can conclusively account for the glaciations and other long-term climatic events. Whatever the causes, one thing is clear and that is that extreme variability in climate is possible in any direction. Some factors seem to be pointing to global cooling while others are indicating global warming. However, human activity on the present scale seems capable of promoting some climatic alteration; whether it be in nature's direction or against it is yet to be seen.

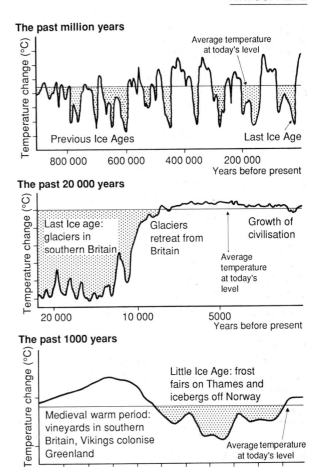

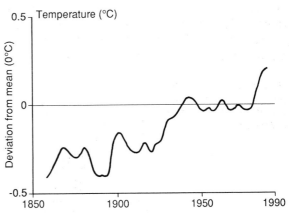

Note: The mean is the average temperature for 1950–79

1.40 Temperature changes on four different scales. When looking at the past million years the regular ice ages are the most striking feature. The past 20 000 years illustrate the warming since the last Ice Age, while the last 1000 years shows that even small temperature variations can persist for several hundred years. The fourth graph showing the warming over the last hundred years also shows periods of falling temperatures within the overall upward trend.

The Greenhouse Effect

As was explained on pages 8 to 9 and in 1.6, the greenhouse effect is the effect that the atmosphere has in keeping the earth warmer than it would be without this protective blanket.

The moon, which has no protective atmosphere, has an average surface temperature of about −18 °C while the earth has an average temperature of about 15 °C (33 °C warmer).

The earth's atmosphere consists mainly of nitrogen and oxygen but there are small proportions of other gases such as **carbon dioxide**, **methane**, **water vapour** and **chlorofluorocarbons (CFCs)**. These greenhouse gases let short-wave solar radiation in, absorb some of the long-wave radiation leaving the earth and re-radiate it back to the surface. Without the greenhouse gases the earth's temperature would be about −15 °C. If more greenhouse gases are added to the atmosphere the earth's surface temperature will rise. 1.41 shows the relative contribution of the main greenhouse gases which play an important part in warming the earth above natural levels.

Over the past 100 years, levels of greenhouse gases have risen substantially, giving rise to concern over an enhanced greenhouse effect. Carbon dioxide levels have risen by about 25%, from 0.0265% of the atmosphere to about 0.034% (6.7 billion tonnes added each year by human activity) and are expected to rise to 0.06% by CE 2050 (1.42 shows the build-up of carbon dioxide in the atmosphere as observed from Mauna Loa Observatory, Hawaii). This increase in carbon dioxide levels is almost entirely due to human action including the burning of fossil fuels (coal, oil and natural gas) and **deforestation** of large areas, in particular the tropical rainforests (1.43). The burning of the rainforests has produced more carbon dioxide as well as removing the trees which convert carbon dioxide into oxygen. Other greenhouse gases have also increased dramatically.

Methane is currently increasing at 1% a year and is the second most important contributor to the greenhouse effect. Molecule for molecule it traps 25 times as much heat in the atmosphere as does carbon dioxide. Methane comes from a variety of sources including rubbish tips, rice fields, burning of forests, domesticated livestock, bogs and marshes. Human activity has created new sources of methane and disturbed many of the natural sources.

As the human population increases so does the need for increased food production and this in turn increases levels of methane. There is roughly one head of cattle for every four humans and this large number of animals can produce more methane than the wild herbivores did before humans domesticated

cattle. The bacteria in the guts of cattle convert between 3 and 10% of the food they eat into methane and they expel it from both ends. A West German chemist has calculated that the world's cattle emit 100 million tonnes of methane into the atmosphere each year.

Another major source of methane is natural wetlands (bogs and marshes) and artificial wet landscapes such as rice fields. The rice paddies which have increased in line with human population are now thought to contribute up to 150 million tonnes of methane per year. Although natural wetlands have diminished as people have reclaimed them for agriculture there are vast tracts of bogland in the Arctic Tundra which are an enormous reservoir of methane. As world temperatures rise the permafrost in the Arctic will melt and this will allow the bogs to release more methane. Indeed some scientists believe that their measurements show this is already happening.

The other major greenhouse gases, CFCs, are increasing even faster than methane: at 6% per year. This is especially worrying since CFCs are up to 10 000 times more efficient at trapping heat than carbon dioxide. Worldwide concern about CFCs has led to international agreements to reduce CFC levels but it is likely to be many years before this will effect a reduction of the gas in the atmosphere.

1.41 The greenhouse gases and their contribution to global warming

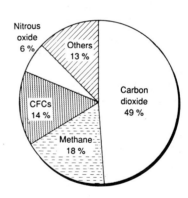

How greenhouse gases contribute to global warming: carbon dioxide comes largely from burning fossil fuels but also from the destruction of forests. Chlorofluorocarbons (CFCs) are synthetic chemicals that also destroy the ozone in the stratosphere. Nitrous oxide comes largely from agricultural activity. Other gases include ozone in urban smogs and halons in fire extinguishers.

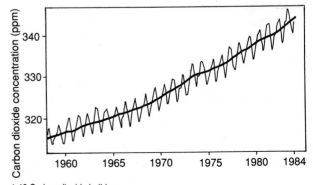

1.42 Carbon dioxide build-up

1.43 The greenhouse effect

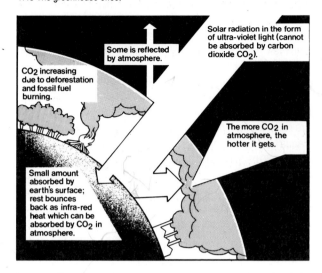

1.44 The link between carbon dioxide and global temperatures

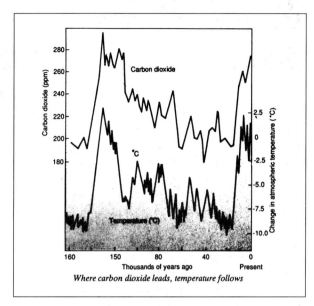

Where carbon dioxide leads, temperature follows

Evidence for the greenhouse effect

Evidence for a link between carbon dioxide and global temperatures was established in 1982 when research into past carbon dioxide levels was matched against global temperatures (1.44). This research shows that, when carbon dioxide levels rise, a rise in temperature follows and, when carbon dioxide levels fall, a temperature fall follows. When the Milankovitch cycles, carbon dioxide levels and global temperatures are examined, it is evident that the changes in the earth's orbit precede changes in carbon dioxide levels which in turn precede temperature changes. It would appear that the astronomical cycles cause a change in carbon dioxide levels to occur and low levels of carbon dioxide trigger off the glaciations. How this mechanism works is still conjecture but, although we might have expected a *fall* in carbon dioxide levels following orbital changes, the opposite is true at present. Human activity producing greenhouse gases could be making the world warmer, when we might have expected signs of global cooling, preceding the next Ice Age.

Although the 0.5 °C rise in global temperatures over the last century is consistent with the greenhouse effect and the six warmest years on record occurred in the 1980s some scientists are reluctant to accept categorically that the enhanced greenhouse effect is here. Dr James Hansen of NASA is not so reluctant; he and his colleagues have used a computer simulation of global circulation to produce year-by-year predictions of global temperature (1.45). Hansen has produced predictions for three scenarios:

1.45 A warmer world in the twenty-first century

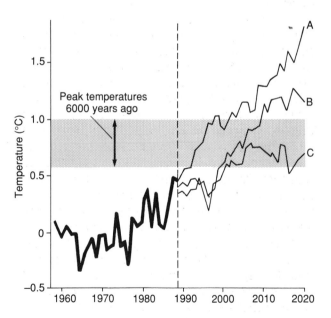

A emissions of carbon dioxide growing at their present rate.
B decreasing emissions
and
C drastic cuts in emissions over the next ten years.
Hansen's predictions are that, whichever of the scenarios is followed, global temperatures will match or exceed peak temperatures 6000 years ago within ten years.

Impact of the Greenhouse Effect

Apart from a rise in temperature what else might the greenhouse effect do to the earth? One effect of increased temperatures that we can already see is a rise in sea levels. During this century sea levels have risen by about 15 centimetres; most of this rise is due to the expansion of sea water because of higher temperatures. Very little extra water has been added by melting ice – in fact there is no evident shrinkage of the polar ice caps because of increased snowfalls. Continued global warming could cause sea levels to rise by another 30 centimetres in the next 40 years, by thermal expansion of sea water alone. It would take a global warming of a further 4 °C to cause significant melting of the ice caps.

Even a 30 centimetre rise in sea level would necessitate a

1.46 The greenhouse threat highlighted by the press

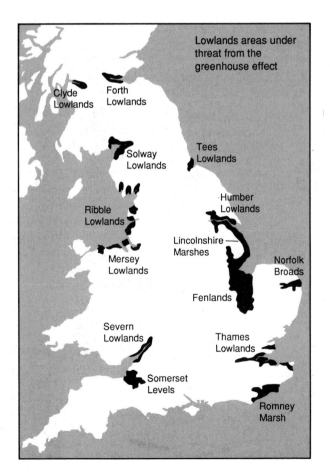

Lowlands areas under threat from the greenhouse effect

Clyde Lowlands
Forth Lowlands
Solway Lowlands
Tees Lowlands
Ribble Lowlands
Humber Lowlands
Lincolnshire Marshes
Mersey Lowlands
Norfolk Broads
Fenlands
Severn Lowlands
Thames Lowlands
Somerset Levels
Romney Marsh

strengthening of Britain's coastal defences and if a greater rise in sea level were to occur a number of coastal lowlands would be threatened with inundation. The British press carried a number of warnings about the possible flooding caused by the greenhouse effect (1.46) in 1988 and 1989.

However serious the effects might be in Britain, they would be much worse in countries such as the Netherlands, Bangladesh and Egypt which are lower lying. Already some parts of the world are suffering from rising sea levels. The tiny Carteret Islands off Papua New Guinea are shrinking each year as the sea level rises. The first 60 people had to be evacuated from their homes in 1989; the islands may have to be abandoned altogether in a few years' time. In the United States, 25% of Florida's coast has already suffered from rising sea levels and the famous Miami Beach had to be artificially recreated at a cost of 60 million dollars in the 1980s. The richer countries may be able to afford the cost of keeping the sea at bay for some time but the developing countries will not be so lucky. With one-third of the world's population living less than 60 km from the sea the consequences of rising sea levels could be very serious.

The rainfall pattern in a warmer world, created by the greenhouse effect, would also be different from that of today's. The Climatic Research Unit at the University of East Anglia has predicted the pattern shown on 1.47. This prediction expects a decrease in rainfall over much of the United States, Southern Europe, the USSR and Japan. If these and the other rainfall predictions prove to be correct, present agricultural practices for large parts of the earth's surface will have to change. In 1988 the Mid-West of the United States, which under greenhouse conditions is likely to become drier, suffered its worst harvest. If this proves to be a long-term problem it will have a serious effect on the world's food supply and cost of food.

Another side-effect of greenhouse conditions would be a change in the natural vegetation zones. The pollen record has demonstrated that even small changes in climate have altered vegetation communities, and changes in climate brought on by an enhanced greenhouse effect would also alter vegetation. 1.48 shows one possible redistribution of world vegetation zones.

Wildlife in general is very sensitive to changes in temperature and the rapid changes envisaged in a greenhouse world could wipe out up to 100 species a day. Some animals depend on very specific habitats and feeding patterns. So, if these are disrupted, extinction for many is a real possibility. Polar bears hunt for their food over the sea ice in the Arctic : early thaws or thinning of sea ice could cut the bears off from their food (seals). Migrating birds, crocodiles, sea elephants and many other animals will suffer if temperatures rise steeply.

Economically the greenhouse effect could have serious financial costs. The 1988 drought in the United States caused serious disruption to transport on the Mississippi River which handles vast quantities of cargo, including half of the country's

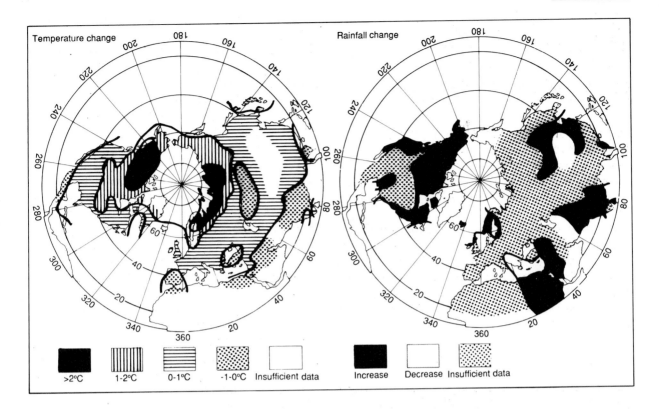

Temperature change

Rainfall change

>2°C   1-2°C   0-1°C   -1-0°C   Insufficient data

Increase   Decrease   Insufficient data

1.47 Climatic change in the greenhouse world

1.48 Natural vegetation changes in a greenhouse world

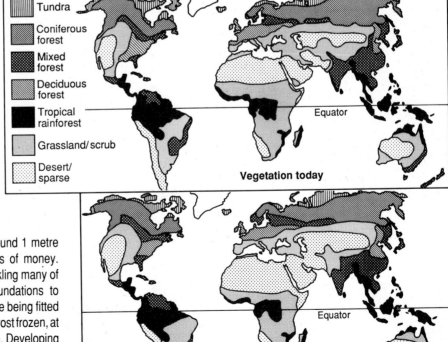

Tundra

Coniferous forest

Mixed forest

Deciduous forest

Tropical rainforest

Grassland/scrub

Desert/sparse

Equator

Vegetation today

Equator

Greenhouse world

grain. The drop in river level of around 1 metre cost many industries vast amounts of money. Melting permafrost in Alaska is buckling many of the roads and causing house foundations to collapse. Some stretches of road are being fitted with freezer units to keep the permafrost frozen, at a cost of one million dollars per mile. Developing countries which rely on single cash crops for much of their earnings could be the worst affected if these crops failed as a result of climatic change.

Solutions to Global Warming

Scientists continue to study the greenhouse effect in order to understand it better: for example, there is a British project to examine the role of the oceans in altering carbon dioxide levels in the atmosphere (1.49). The British scientists are interested in finding out if the oceans and their **plankton** are playing a role in keeping the greenhouse effect in check. Whatever current or future research may tell us there are some ways the greenhouse effect can be combated.

Already governments have agreed to phase out production of CFCs.

Carbon dioxide levels could be reduced in a number of ways:
1. preserve forests (which take in carbon dioxide and breath out oxygen),
2. plant new forests (one energy company, Applied Energy Services, has contributed to the planting of 52 million trees in Guatemala which will consume as much carbon dioxide as their new power station will produce),
3. conserve energy, thereby reducing the need for power, which consumes vast quantities of fossil fuels,
4. use alternatives to fossil fuels for heat and power production,
5. reduce car exhaust emissions,
6. help developing countries to industrialise; otherwise they will clear more forests, produce more methane from their farms and use cheap technology that produces more carbon dioxide.

In itself the greenhouse effect is not all 'doom and gloom'. It is preferable to the onset of a new Ice Age. But what matters is the way that human society adapts and responds to this environmental challenge. The greenhouse effect will be a factor in all long-term planning whether it be for agricultural planning, flood protection or water supply. There are also contentious choices to be made between fossil fuels and nuclear power. At present there is a certain irony in that nuclear power offers the only large-scale 'environmentally clean' alternative to fossil fuels.

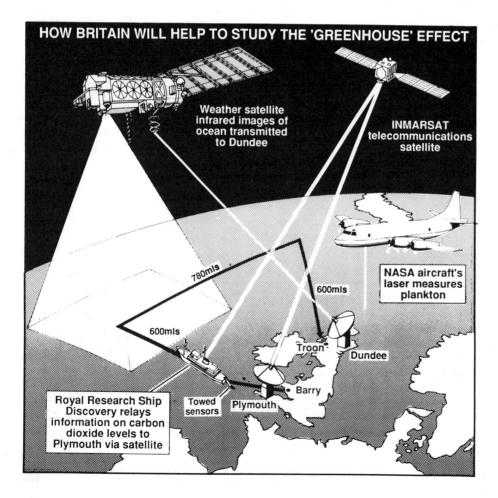

HOW BRITAIN WILL HELP TO STUDY THE 'GREENHOUSE' EFFECT

Weather satellite infrared images of ocean transmitted to Dundee

INMARSAT telecommunications satellite

NASA aircraft's laser measures plankton

780mls

600mls

600mls

Troon

Dundee

Barry

Royal Research Ship Discovery relays information on carbon dioxide levels to Plymouth via satellite

Towed sensors

Plymouth

1.49 How Britain is helping to study the greenhouse effect

The Ozone Layer

Ozone is a form of oxygen which has three atoms in each molecule instead of the usual two. The ozone layer is the part of the atmosphere where most ozone is concentrated. This layer lies in the **stratosphere** which is between 10 and 50 km above the earth's surface. Oxygen (O_2) is broken into individual oxygen atoms in the stratosphere by ultraviolet radiation. These 'free' atoms of oxygen are very reactive and some combine with oxygen (O_2) to form ozone (O_3). Ozone itself is broken down by ultraviolet and so ozone is continually being created and destroyed in the ozone layer. The ozone layer is very important because it shields the earth from much of the sun's ultraviolet radiation which could cause serious damage to the environment and human health. Excessive ultraviolet can cause fatal skin cancers and it has been calculated that for every 1% decrease in ozone there is likely to be a 5% increase in skin cancers. An increase in ultraviolet will also cause significant decreases in crop yields.

In 1974 two American scientists, Sherwood Rowland and Mario Molina, warned that chlorofluorocarbons (CFCs) could destroy ozone in the atmosphere. They were convinced that CFCs (which are found in aerosols and refrigerants: see 1.50) could rise in the atmosphere until sunlight breaks them down to release chlorine, which in turn destroys ozone. CFCs are synthetic gases which are inert, relatively non-toxic, non-flammable, and are without smell or colour. CFCs can last in the atmosphere for over 100 years and one molecule of CFC can destroy thousands of ozone molecules (1.51). What is worrying is that it now appears that ozone is being destroyed by synthetic chemicals faster than

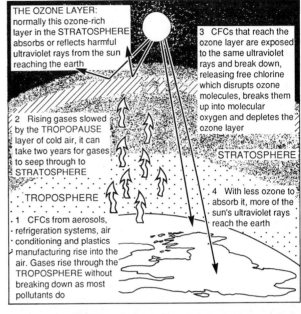

THE OZONE LAYER: normally this ozone-rich layer in the STRATOSPHERE absorbs or reflects harmful ultraviolet rays from the sun reaching the earth

3 CFCs that reach the ozone layer are exposed to the same ultraviolet rays and break down, releasing free chlorine which disrupts ozone molecules, breaks them up into molecular oxygen and depletes the ozone layer

2 Rising gases slowed by the TROPOPAUSE layer of cold air, it can take two years for gases to seep through to STRATOSPHERE

STRATOSPHERE

TROPOSPHERE

4 With less ozone to absorb it, more of the sun's ultraviolet rays reach the earth

1 CFCs from aerosols, refrigeration systems, air conditioning and plastics manufacturing rise into the air. Gases rise through the TROPOSPHERE without breaking down as most pollutants do

1.51 Destruction of the ozone layer

it is being created. The United States banned the use of CFCs in aerosols in the 1970s following warnings from scientists, but already CFC production in the UK has climbed above its mid 1970s level, because CFCs are used in so many products (1.52).

1.50 The uses of CFCs in the UK

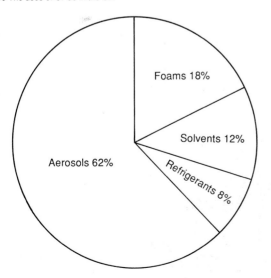

Foams 18%

Solvents 12%

Aerosols 62%

Refrigerants 8%

1.52 Annual production of CFCs in the UK. (CFC 11 and CFC 12 are the two most common CFCs.)

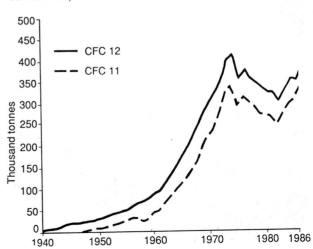

CFC 12
CFC 11

Thousand tonnes

The Ozone Hole

The first evidence that something was actually happening to the ozone layer came in 1982. J.C.Farman of the British Antarctic Survey noticed a 'hole' in the ozone layer over Antarctica. The British Antarctic Survey, at Halley Bay, has been monitoring ozone levels since 1957 and every year since 1982 there has been a massive depletion of ozone in the Antarctic's spring (September and October), with a recovery in the summer (1.53). These findings were later confirmed by satellite data from NASA which had been overlooked in earlier computer analyses. Although it has been called a 'hole' in the ozone layer it is in fact a large area (the size of the USA) which is seriously depleted of ozone: up to 50% less than normal levels and up to 97% less in some parts of the ozone layer (1.54).

The American weather satellite *Nimbus 7* recently provided measurements of ozone levels over the Arctic which suggest that the ozone layer over this region also thins. Scientists have also detected other areas of the world where ozone is thinning rapidly, such as northern Norway and over the Alps, but nowhere as dramatic as over Antarctica.

The discovery of the ozone hole has brought about a number of scientific experiments to determine its cause and, although some suggested causes seem less likely now, the effect of CFCs cannot be ruled out. In the last six years ozone levels globally have dropped by 3%.

Similar reactions in the ozone layer to those caused by CFCs can be stimulated by dust from volcanic reactions. Recent volcanic eruptions such as El Chichon have noticeably reduced ozone levels and there is a fear that current CFC levels may enhance the ozone depletion effect of future eruptions.

Effect of ozone depletion

While some scientists are trying to determine the cause of ozone depletion, others are examining the effects a reduction in ozone levels may have on plants and animals. For humans any decrease in ozone will cause increased incidence of skin cancer, cataracts and a depression of the immune system. If ozone decreases by 25%, crop yields are likely to decrease by the same amount, causing serious food shortages. Oceanic plankton might also suffer and this would disrupt the entire food chain in the oceans and possibly cause other environmental damage. Since fish account for 18% of human consumption of animal protein (40% in Asia) the repercussions would affect most societies.

Plankton have an important geochemical role in the oceans. They take up inorganic carbon from the upper waters of the oceans and some of this eventually sinks to the ocean floor, so removing carbon from the upper ocean. This creates a deficit of

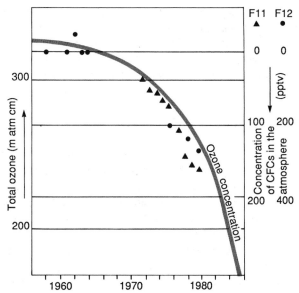

1.53 October ozone levels over Antarctica matched with CFC production. The curved line shows the drop in ozone concentration from 1957 to 1985. The ozone depletion matches closely the build-up of CFCs in the southern hemisphere since the 1970s. The major CFCs are plotted on a reverse scale with dots and triangles indicating concentrations of the two main CFCs F11 and F12.

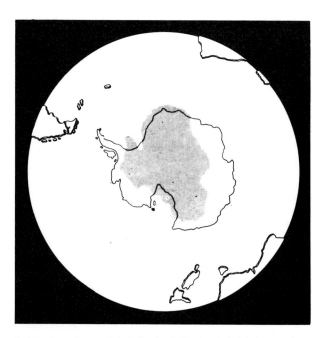

1.54 The Antarctic ozone hole. In October 1987, when the hole in the ozone layer (shaded) above Antarctica was at its biggest, it covered an area the size of continental United States

carbon in the upper ocean which is replenished by carbon dioxide from the atmosphere. Quite how this part of the carbon cycle works is still under investigation. But the plankton do play a role in regulating carbon dioxide levels in the atmosphere and any reduction in their ability to do so could accelerate the greenhouse effect.

What is being done?

Concern about the threat to the ozone layer led to the Vienna Convention in 1985 which covered matters such as cooperation on environmental research and monitoring. The Montreal Protocol of 1987 which requires cuts in CFCs of 50% by 1999 has been signed by 30 countries and is an important indication to industry to find alternatives to CFCs.

In 1989, because of scientific advice, the European Community agreed to cut production by 85% and phase out CFCs by the end of the century. The scientific evidence of CFC damage to the ozone layer led to a strengthening of the Montreal Protocol in 1990. However, many countries have yet to sign the Protocol and there is a danger that developing countries will use CFCs in industry unless the developed nations help them to find cost-effective alternatives. The UK and other developed nations are prepared to use overseas aid programmes to assist developing countries that wish to play their part in global efforts to protect the ozone layer. As Mr Zuil Rahman, Indian Minister of the Environment and Forests, said in March 1989 when arguing for technology transfer to the Third World, 'I think the excellent principle of "polluter pays" should be applied to the developed world'.

The Montreal Protocol gave industry a clear signal to develop substitutes for CFCs and new technologies that can do without them. Until economic alternatives to CFCs are available, practical methods to reduce leaks, eliminate unnecessary uses and improve handling of CFCs have had to be pursued.

1.55 illustrates what effect four different levels of CFC emissions will have on CFC concentration in the atmosphere. In 1986 760 million aerosol cans were sold in the UK and two-thirds of these contained CFCs. Elimination of CFCs from aerosol production in the UK by the end of 1989 was one step to achieve a significant reduction in CFCs. The McDonalds hamburger chain now have their hamburger cartons blown with hydrocarbons instead of CFCs, and a small American company Petroferm have developed a solvent for the electronics industry to replace CFC-113. Alternative 'ozone friendly' CFCs (CFC-123 and CFC-134A) have been developed and if they complete toxicity tests successfully they may be used in refrigerants. Another substitute for CFCs, HFA134a, is an alternative refrigerant for which new refrigerators are being designed.

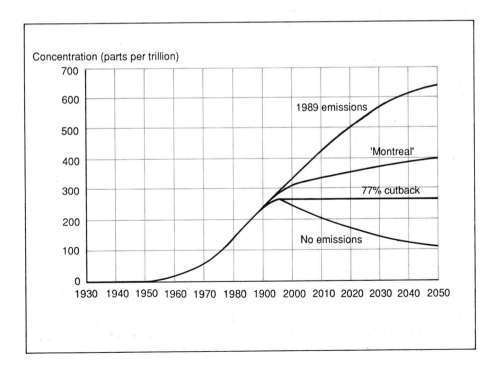

1.55 Projections of CFC concentration in the atmosphere

Acid Rain

Acid rain is not a new phenomenon. In the mid nineteenth century the pollution from coal fires and industry caused acidic rain to attack buildings and vegetation. However, the scale of damage (first seen in the lakes and streams of Scandinavia and forests of Central Europe) since the 1960s has made acid rain a major political issue.

Europe has seen some of the worst acid rain damage with 20% of Swiss forests affected, more than one-third of West Germany's forests affected (resulting in 47 000 lost jobs), 300 000 hectares of forest in Czechoslovakia damaged, 18 000 lakes in Sweden acidified (4000 are totally devoid of fish), and many salmon rivers in Norway too acid for fish to live in. But the problem is also worldwide with pollution damaging rainforest in Brazil, damaging health in Mexico City, eroding marble from the Taj Mahal in India and souring relations between the USA and Canada (1.56).

What is acid rain?

Rain is naturally acidic because water in the atmosphere reacts with carbon dioxide to produce a weak carbonic acid with a **pH** of about 5.6. However, the acid rain which is caused by air pollution can have a pH of less than 3 (1.57). The main culprit causing acid rain is **sulphur dioxide**, a gas that is given off by burning fossil fuels (1.58 shows the main sources of sulphur dioxide in the UK).

In the atmosphere the sulphur dioxide can turn to sulphuric acid resulting in highly acidic rainfall. Other major culprits are **oxides of nitrogen** which are given off by power stations and car exhausts. Nitric oxide converts to nitric acid and ozone in the atmosphere. The nitric acid falls as acid rain and the ozone attacks foliage. Even nitric oxide unconverted in the atmosphere can cause damage. Trees grown near to busy roads can suffer from very rapid growth which eventually will kill them.

1.56 Acid rain 'export' from the USA to Canada

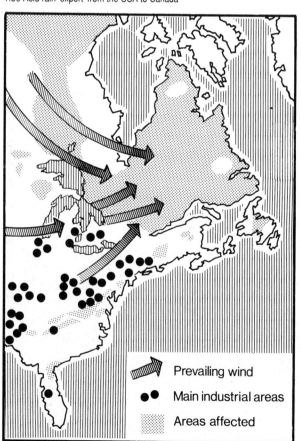

Key:
- Prevailing wind
- ●● Main industrial areas
- Areas affected

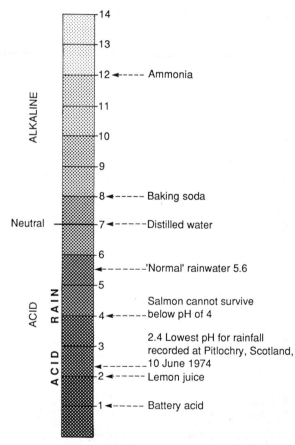

1.57 The acid scale. The scale is logarithmic so rain with a pH of 4 is ten times as acid as rain with a pH of 5 and 100 times as acid as pH 6. Acid rain is rainfall with a pH below 5.6.

The atmosphere over Europe contains many more chemicals than it did years ago and this may also affect the acidification process. Heavily polluted urban air which contains tiny particles of metals such as iron and manganese can speed up the process of turning these gases into acid rain.

The acid rain, which is formed by these pollutants mixing with water vapour in the atmosphere, can fall many kilometres or hundreds of kilometres from the source of the pollution (1.59).

Acid rain damages rivers, lakes, soils and buildings. The droplets of acid which form in clouds can be around ten times more acid than the rain falling from the clouds. Therefore low cloud and acid mist can be much more damaging to the environment, particularly trees, than showers of rain.

The World Health Organisation (WHO) and the United Nations Environmental Programme (UNEP) have collaborated on air monitoring in about 35 countries, since 1974. Their data show some decline in sulphur dioxide and lead pollution since the mid 1970s but carbon monoxide and nitrogen oxide emissions are still increasing in some industrialised countries. The increases can be linked to the continued growth in the number of cars. One worrying aspect of their data is that all types of air pollution are increasing in the developing countries.

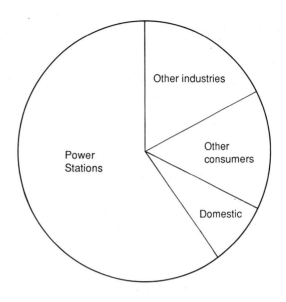

1.58 Sulphur dioxide pollution: its sources in Britain

1.59 The acid rainmakers

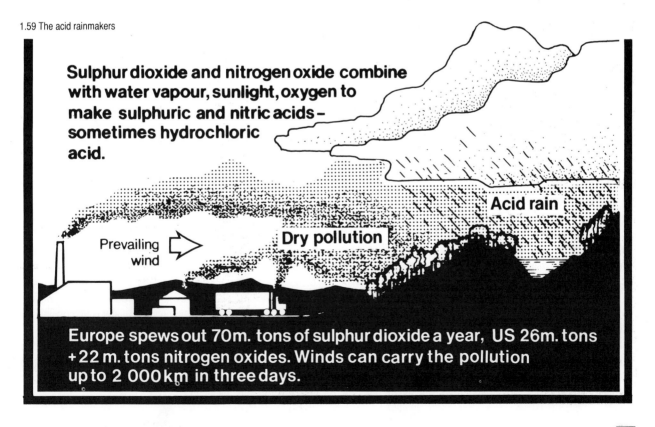

Sulphur dioxide and nitrogen oxide combine with water vapour, sunlight, oxygen to make sulphuric and nitric acids – sometimes hydrochloric acid.

Prevailing wind

Dry pollution

Acid rain

Europe spews out 70m. tons of sulphur dioxide a year, US 26m. tons +22 m. tons nitrogen oxides. Winds can carry the pollution up to 2 000 km in three days.

Europe's Acid Rain Problem

Key
380   Average annual deposits
       of sulphur in 1984
       (thousand tonnes)
(22%) Percentage received from
       other countries

Norway 194 (93%)
Sweden 323 (84%)
Denmark 94 (68%)
United Kingdom 654 (20%)
Netherlands 152 (76%)
East Germany 779 (32%)
Poland 935 (29%)
Belgium 147 (57%)
West Germany 781 (55%)
Czechoslovakia 685 (41%)
Austria 206 (81%)
Switzerland 103 (89%)
France 781 (55%)
Italy 851 (23%)

1.60 Sulphur deposition in Europe, 1984

1.61 Sweden: sources of sulphur deposition, 1978 (thousand tonnes)

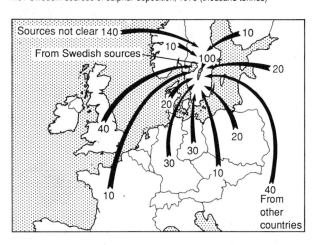

Sources not clear 140
From Swedish sources 100
10 10 20
20 20
40 20
30 30 10
10 40 From other countries

1.62 The effect of acid rain on stone

Europe currently produces most of the world's acid rain and many countries have suffered serious damage from this scourge. 1.60 shows the annual deposits of sulphur in tonnes and the percentage of this pollution received from other countries. The Scandinavian countries have suffered from serious acid rain damage for 30 years and blame much of this on the UK and other European neighbours (1.61). Many of Scandinavia's streams and lakes are acidified by pollution and some are only kept habitable for fish by extensive **liming** to neutralise the acid. This is not a long-term solution, however, and it doesn't protect all water life from the effects of the pollution.

Some lakes in the UK have also suffered from acidification. Studies at Loch Enoch in Scotland have shown that acidity has increased markedly since the Industrial Revolution (1.63), despite the fact that this loch is remote from roads and towns.

A serious side-effect of acid rain, and a very lethal one, is the way the rain washes metals, especially aluminium, into the rivers and lakes. Normally aluminium and other metals are insoluble and stay in the soil, but acid rain can dissolve these metals and wash them into the streams. Aluminium damages the gills of fish and they eventually die. In Sweden several kidney dialysis patients have also died because of high aluminium levels in dialysis water. Now hospitals in Sweden have had to be fitted with water purification plants to avoid this problem. Some Swedish scientists also suspect that aluminium in water is responsible for the high numbers of deaths through senile dementure.

The acidified water has effects that extend throughout the food chain. For example, birds that eat contaminated insects from acid lakes have a reduced capacity to lay eggs and once one species dies its predators follow.

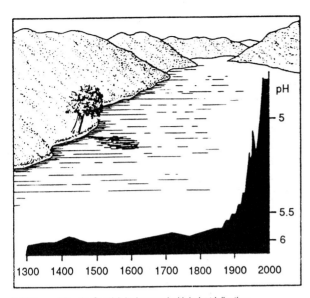

1.63 How acidity of a Scottish loch soared with industrialisation

In Europe's forests acid rain is causing extensive damage(1.64). Even in the UK, which until now has escaped the worst of the effects, it is estimated that 67% of conifers have some damage while 29% have moderate to serious damage. In Sweden studies have shown that soil acidity has increased ten-fold since 1927 and the acid waters draining from the soils wash out nutrients and metals. So the forests suffer from a lack of nutrients as well as attack from the pollutant gases.

International action to clean up acid rain

The Netherlands has already decided to cut sulphur emissions by 60% but until 1986 the UK government did not even officially recognise the link between pollution and acid rain. The cut of 14% offered by the UK was regarded as too little too late by the Scandinavian countries receiving much of the pollution.

The European Community has been discussing proposals to cut emissions of sulphur dioxide by 60% and nitrogen oxides by 40%, but the UK will not make cuts of this magnitude until 2003. In 1979 the United Nations set up a protocol which required 30% cuts in sulphur dioxide. 16 countries in Europe signed the protocol but the UK, Poland, Spain and the USA have not signed. The UK did sign a UN protocol to cut emissions of nitrogen oxides to their 1987 level by 1994.

The European Community has made some progress in reducing car exhaust fumes and expects exhaust levels to be reduced substantially by 1993.

International cooperation on other climatic menaces such as the greenhouse effect and the destruction of the ozone layer do, however, indicate that international agreements and action are possible.

1.64 The before and after of acid rain in Central European forests

Q CLIMATIC CHANGE/REASONS FOR CLIMATIC CHANGE

1 (a) Write brief notes to explain each of the following; pollen analysis, dendrochronology, and ocean floor analysis.
   (b) What did Milankovitch believe controlled the onset of the glaciations?
   (c) Examine the different timescales shown in 1.40. What do the graphs tell you about the earth's climate?
   (d) Other than astronomical theories, what theories have been proposed to explain climate change?
   (e) Describe the changes in global temperature as shown in the graph below.

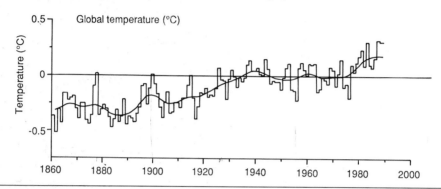

Q THE GREENHOUSE EFFECT/SOLUTIONS TO GLOBAL WARMING

2 (a) List the main greenhouse gases in order of their contribution to global warming.
   (b) Explain the build-up of carbon dioxide in the atmosphere over the last one hundred years.
   (c) Why is the build-up of methane and CFCs even more worrying than the build-up of carbon dioxide?
   (d) What evidence is there for an enhanced greenhouse effect?
   (e) Describe what the greenhouse effect might do to the earth.
   (f) List the possible actions which might help reduce global warming.
   (g) Examine the table listing some of the likely advantages and disadvantages of the greenhouse effect. Should the UK government be concerned? Justify your answer.

Advantages
1. Higher yields from most domestic crops
2. Agricultural land can extend to higher altitudes
3. Some new crops could be grown in southern Britain
4. Longer growing season
5. Less severe winters

Disadvantages
1. Coastal regions face increased threat from flooding, including most cities
2. Disappearance of some coastal environments e.g. salt marshes
3. Increased spending on coastal defences: £5 billion
4. More agricultural pests because of milder weather
5. The world's grain growing regions (e.g. Great Plains) decline
6. Deserts expand
7. Developing countries worst affected by sea level rise

Q THE OZONE LAYER/THE OZONE HOLE

3 (a) Which gas poses a serious threat to the ozone layer?
   (b) Why is the ozone layer so important for life on earth?
   (c) Where was the first ozone hole identified and when?

   (d) What international action is being taken to preserve the ozone layer?

Q ACID RAIN/EUROPE'S ACID RAIN PROBLEM

4 (a) Why has acid rain soured relations between some countries? Give examples.

(b) What gases produce acid rain and where do they come from?

(c) What evidence is there that acid rain causes environmental damage?

(d) What message is cartoon 1 trying to put over?

(e) Describe the acid rain chain (as shown in diagram 1).

(f) Why is liming lakes not a long-term measure against acid rain?

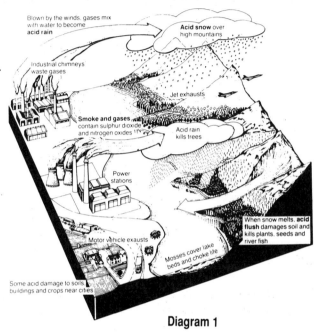

Diagram 1

Cartoon 1

ACCELERATION

Research and Further Work

(a) Find out what life was like in Europe, during the 'Little Ice Age'.

(b) Research items from the press on climatic change.

(c) What is industry using instead of CFCs in its products?

(d) What do environmental pressure groups like 'Friends of the Earth',' Greenpeace' and the 'World Wide Fund for Nature' say about the dangers of climatic change?

(e) 'Weather appears to be worsening in the UK. According to the records of one big insurance company the past 13 years have seen:

-the worst drought for 250 years
-the wettest spring for 200 years
-the worst winter in 250 years
-the mildest winter for 100 years
-the most devastating "hurricane" this century'
(*The Guardian*, 21 January 1989)

With this evidence why is it still acceptable to say that recent climatic events are within expected variability?

Air Masses

Origin and movement

Global wind circulation and the pattern of ocean currents are important determinants of climatic patterns but to get a fuller understanding of day-to-day weather some knowledge of the origin and characteristics of **air masses** is essential.

The source regions for these air masses are usually places where surface geography is fairly uniform, such as over deserts, oceans, large plains and ice-covered areas. Air which is slow moving or gently subsiding over these areas can acquire uniform temperature and humidity characteristics. These large volumes of air with relatively uniform characteristics are called air masses.

Air moving from the source regions of the air masses influences the weather of adjoining regions. The main source regions for air masses are shown in 1.65, which shows their average position at the equinoxes. Air moves from these source regions in response to pressure differences (pressure gradient force), to areas of lower pressure. The air tends to retain its characteristics of heat and humidity for some time, but is gradually modified by the earth's surface and by solar insolation. Because the earth's surface plays such an important part in the modification of the air, the lower layers are affected first. An air mass moving equatorward from the poles is heated in its lowest layers. This makes the air **unstable** because the temperature gradient is steepened and convective cloud is likely to develop. Conversely air moving polewards is cooled in the lowest layers lessening the temperature gradient and making the lower air more **stable** (1.66).

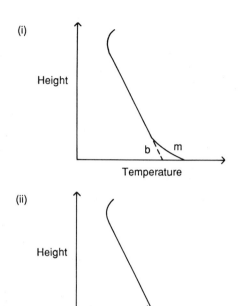

1.66 Air mass modification.
(i) Polar air modified as it moves equatorwards: unstable base providing convective cloud and rain.
(ii) Tropical air modified as it moves polewards: stable base producing low cloud and sea fog.
b Temperature gradient before modification
m Temperature gradient after modification

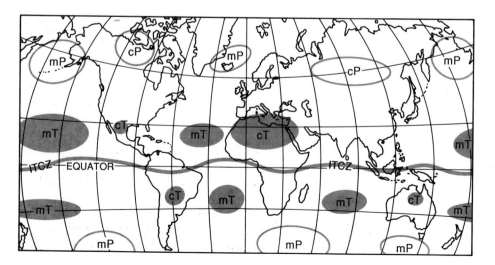

1.65 Air mass source regions. Air masses are classified by their origin – continental (land) or maritime (ocean) – indicated by a lower case 'c' or 'm' respectively; with capital letters referring to the region: 'A' Arctic; 'P' Polar; 'T' Tropical and 'E' Equatorial. Therefore mT air has a maritime origin in the Tropics.
This map shows the average locations of air masses at the equinoxes. The ITCZ, which is a zone of convergence, is shown in its equatorial location.

Air masses and the inter-tropical covergence zone

The inter-tropical convergence zone (ITCZ: see pages 14–15) is where the trade winds converge; it is an area of uplift of air. The air that converges on the ITCZ does not have the differences in temperature and density that are typical of convergence at the polar front, and therefore there are no weather fronts. Equatorial weather, despite this, is far from placid. Heating of the tropical air can cause instability and periods of heavy rainfall, which is of vital importance to some tropical regions. This rainfall occurs when mT air is drawn in over the land but, when the source region is a continent, dry weather persists. This conflict between mT and cT is played out each year over the west coast of Africa.

The tropical Hadley circulation which transfers energy to middle latitudes is maintained by the release of latent heat of condensation in the ITCZ. The trade winds feed into this zone of convergence which is a zone containing clusters of deep convective clouds which produce heavy precipitation (1.67). The ITCZ doesn't migrate much over the ocean but over land the position reflects the latitude of maximum insolation (1.68).

Clouds in the ITCZ form clusters which are separated by cloud-free areas. These cloud clusters form where the weak trade-wind inversion is broken through and convection occurs to great heights, forming towering cumulonimbus clouds. The cloud clusters are 100–1000 km across and within these are convective cells 10–100 km across with individual cumulonimbus clouds of 1–10 km across. The clusters move slowly westwards within the ITCZ producing heavy precipitation (1.69).

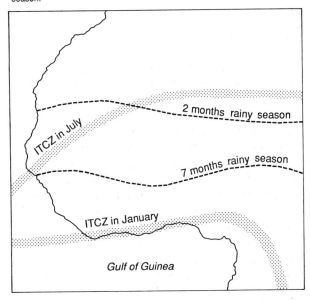

1.68 Migration of the ITCZ over West Africa. This map shows the location of the ITCZ in January and July (for 'normal' years) and indicates the length of the rainy season.

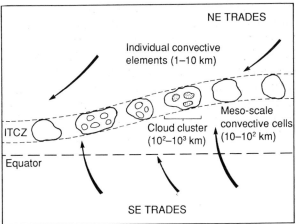

1.69 A diagrammatic representation of convective cloud clusters in the ITCZ. This diagram indicates the scale of cloud clusters in relation to convective cells and individual clouds.

From March to July the ITCZ moves northwards across West Africa bringing cloudy humid conditions. As the moist air surges northwards rain storms develop. This moist air gives rise to little rainfall at its northern edge where it meets dry subsiding cT air from the Sahara desert. This air overlies the mT air giving stability and dry conditions. Further to the south, where the airstream is deepest, belts of cumulonimbus clouds give stormy conditions with heavy rain (1.70).

In winter the cT air over the Sahara extends southwards, almost to the coast. This allows the dry **Harmattan wind** (north-east trades), blowing from the north to desiccate the **Sahel** zone.

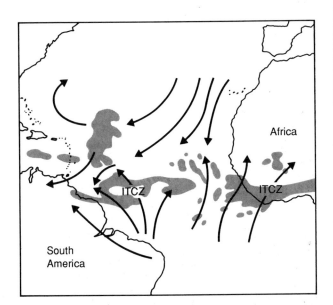

1.67 Low-level winds and cloud cover in the ITCZ. This map shows a typical July position of the inter-tropical convergence zone in the drought years of the 1970s and 1980s. Low-level winds and cloud cover as seen from space are indicated.

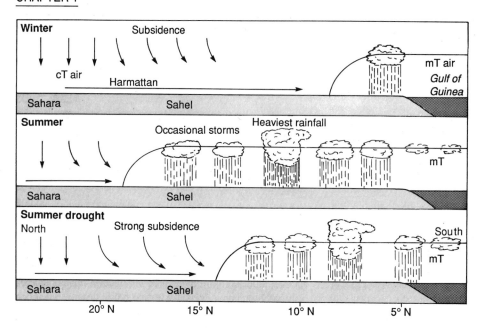

1.70 Seasonal migration of the ITCZ over West Africa. Dry winds from the north dominate much of West Africa in the winter. In 'normal' summers heavy rains migrate northwards but decrease in frequency and duration towards the northern edge of the mT air. Summer droughts are characterised by strong subsidence over the Sahara and northern Sahel. The mT air doesn't reach as far north as in 'normal' years.

ITCZ migration and its effect in West Africa

The marginal lands bordering the Sahara desert have suffered over the 1970s and 1980s from a combination of overpopulation (of humans and livestock) and drought which has **desertified** large tracts of land. During the 1950s greater than average rainfall encouraged the extension northwards of agriculture and the increase in livestock numbers. But average rainfall in the 1960s and drought throughout the 1970s and 1980s has brought about southward migration as **desertification** has claimed marginal lands (1.71). In 1975 alone over 1 million people migrated southwards in western Africa. There has been severe starvation and millions of animals have died (about 80% of original livestock total has died).

The climate of the Sahel has been variable over the last 100 years and many climatologists consider that runs of dry or wet years are a part of the natural variability of the Sahel's climate. Others, however, believe that the region is going through a climatic change which will lead to the southward extension of the Sahara Desert.

During the drought years there has been an equatorward shift in the ITCZ of some 200–300 km. The shift does vary from place to place but this shift has caused the failure of the rains in many Sahel countries. The subtropical high-pressure zone has also drifted south causing strong subsidence over the Sahara and stronger, dry north-east trade winds into the Sahel (1.70).

In West Africa the length and severity of the dry season is the most important factor influencing agriculture(1.72). Humid conditions, where there is no dry season (for example, Monrovia, Axim) enable cultivation year round. Crops such as sweet potato,

yams and cassava are important subsistence crops under these conditions. Once the dry season extends to 3–5 months (for example, at Minna) grain crops such as maize become important and, for dry seasons as long as 6–8 months, drought-resistant crops such as millet, sorghum, cotton and ground nuts are grown. Areas with a dry season of more than 8 months are limited to short-term drought-resistant crops including millet and sesame. In areas with dry seasons of more than six months cattle rearing is more common and these are kept for the most part by nomadic pastoralists.

The Sahel droughts of the 1970s and 1980s were the result of several years of poor rainfall, not just one bad year. Since the early 1970s millions of people in the Sahel zone have had to depend on food aid for years at a time. To tackle the long-term problem of drought there are several possible responses:
(i) accept the situation and be prepared for large-scale migration out of the Sahel;
(ii) attempt to increase rainfall by cloud-seeding;
(iii) plant trees and shrubs to improve atmospheric humidity, by **transpiration** (see page 105);
(iv) develop new sources of water for irrigation;
(v) attempt to change the customs of the inhabitants (for example, reduce cattle herds, introduce grazing control, re-settlement, land reform and family planning).
Many of the possible responses will be difficult to implement for economic or social reasons.

In the meantime scientists continue to study the climate of West Africa to determine the cause of the variability in rainfall.

1.71 Variations in annual rainfall in the Sahel. The shaded area represents the Sahel region. The graph shows that rainfall in the Sahel is highly variable, with wet years (above the 'average' line) and dry years (below the 'average' line).

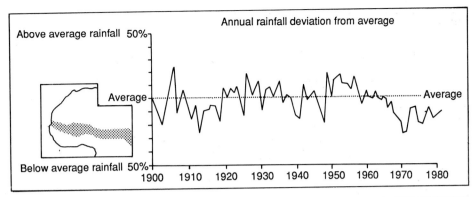

One recent discovery in 1972 by J.M. Walker was the identification of another cell-like circulation in West Africa, but this operates in an east–west direction (1.73). Convection of air to high altitudes, caused by intense heating, is followed by movement westwards in the subtropical jet stream and then descent. These cells play a role in the weather and climate of this tropical zone and when understood more fully may provide a fuller explanation of climatic events in the tropics. Another piece of research suggests that there is a link between **sea surface temperatures** (SSTs) and periods of drought. One theory is that abnormally warm temperatures in the southern Atlantic weaken the equatorial low pressure and hence weaken the airflow over West Africa. There appears to be a strong correlation between SSTs and drought but how the two are linked is still a matter for debate.

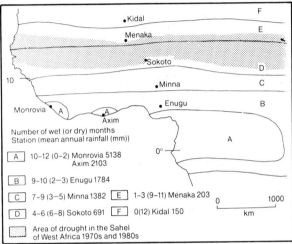

1.72 Average duration of wet and dry seasons in West Africa

1.73 Walker circulations. East–west circulations which influence local weather and climate. (Crown copyright, reproduced with the permission of the Controller of Her Majesty's Stationery Office)

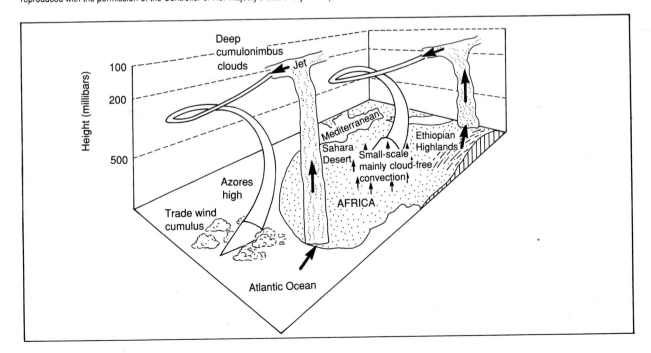

Variability of Rainfall

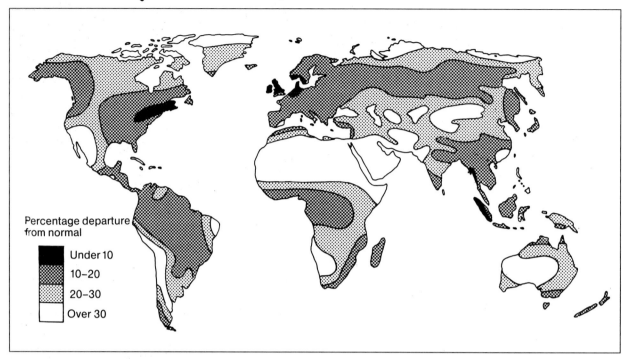

1.74 World map of annual relative rainfall variability

The **variability of rainfall** is the extent to which the precipitation of individual years varies from the average value. Not surprisingly hot desert areas lying near to the Tropics have the highest variability, with some years having no rainfall and others with 3 or 4 times the average.

Monsoon regions also have a high variability because of the nature of monsoon rainfall, which depends on the strengths of regional air circulation. The rainfall in Bombay has ranged from as low as 600 mm in 1918 to 3400 mm in 1933. On the other hand wet equatorial climates have a low variability because of high convectional rainfall produced by the inter-tropical convergence zone. Map 1.74 shows the global pattern of rainfall variability.

As has been shown on page 41 the Sahel and savanna regions in North Africa suffer from variability in annual rainfall which is linked to the equatorward shift in the inter-tropical convergence zone (1.70). Long-term trends indicate that groups of dry or wet years occur together. This is illustrated by the data from Ed Dueim (1.75) in semi-arid east Sudan. Dry spells occurred in the 1940s, late 1960s and 1970s with wet spells in the 1930s and 1950s.

1.75 Annual rainfall trends at Ed Dueim in central Sudan

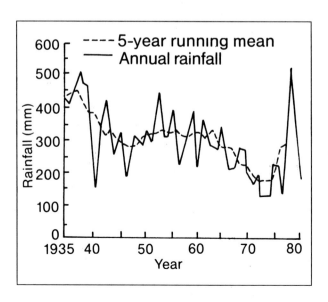

Even in the British Isles, which tends to have a low variability of rainfall, there can be extreme years. The period between May 1975 and August 1976 gave England and Wales the driest 16 month period since weather records began in 1727. Map 1.76 shows the rainfall expressed as a percentage of average rainfall for the five month period from April to August 1976. This drought like so many others did not have one single cause but was a result of several factors. One major cause that is evident on a weather map is that of a **blocking anticyclone** (1.77). This blocking anticyclone is a complete anticyclonic cell that broke away from the Azores anticyclone and established itself in higher latitudes. Once established a blocking anticyclone can persist for weeks, diverting the rain-bearing fronts to the north and south of it (1.78).

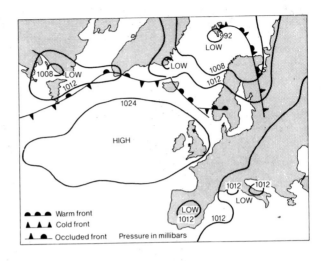

Warm front
Cold front
Occluded front   Pressure in millibars

1.77 Weather map of 26 August 1976: at the height of the 1976 drought

1.76 Rainfall distribution in the UK, April–August 1976 as a percentage of average rainfall

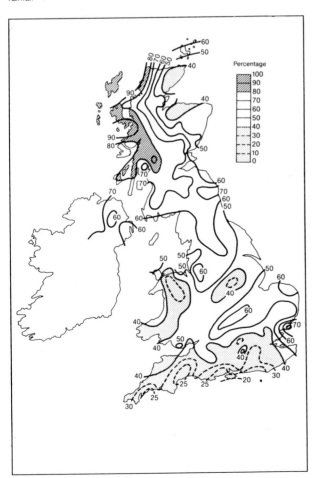

1.78 The influence of a blocking anticyclone, diverting depressions and their associated rainfall

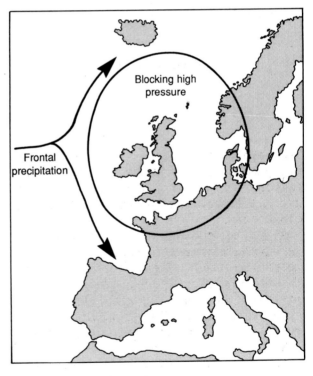

Q

The total fallout of sulphur (g/m²) over Europe in one year

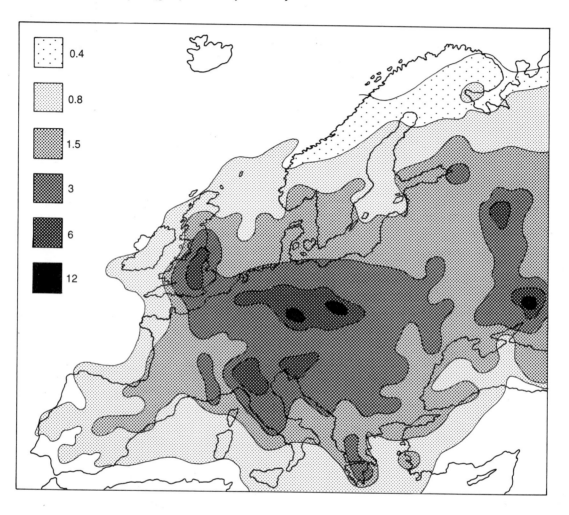

0.4
0.8
1.5
3
6
12

1 (a) What is meant by the term 'acid rain'? (3)
   (b) What sort of environmental damage can this sort of pollution be responsible for? (6)
2 (a) The map shows the sulphur deposition over Europe, much of it by acid rain. Discuss the geographical factors
        which account for the distribution of this pollution. (5)
   (b) Describe the international efforts at pollution control and comment on their success so far. (4)

Q

Highly simplified model of global wind and pressure belts

Major pressure/wind belts	Major lines of latitude	Description

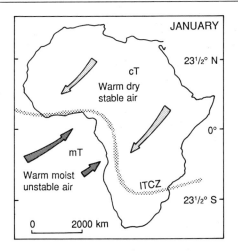

Polar high
Polar easterlies
Polar front
South-westerlies
Subtropical highs
North-east trade winds
Inter-tropical convergence zone (ITCZ)/equatorial low
South-east trade winds
Subtropical highs
North-westerlies
Polar front
Polar easterlies
Polar high

Arctic Circle
Tropic of Cancer
Equator
Tropic of Capricorn
Antarctic Circle

High latitudes
Mid latitudes
Low latitudes
Mid latitudes
High latitudes

High-pressure regions
Winds
Convergences

3 (a) Describe and explain the distribution of the principal pressure belts of the globe, giving the latitude for each. (5)

    (b) Explain fully why pressure belts shift in latitude throughout the year. (4)

4 either

    (a) Why do the land masses of North America and Asia disrupt the belted pressure pattern of the globe? (4)

    or

    (b) Why do the idealised winds shown on the diagram rarely exist in reality? (4)

    and

    (c) Why don't the winds flow directly between the main pressure belts? Explain the forces which influence the winds. (5)

Q

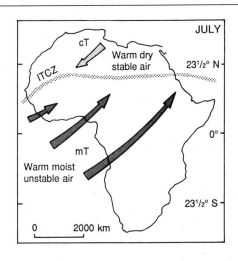

5 (a) Explain the changing position of the inter-tropical convergence zone (ITCZ) between January and July. (4)

    (b) Explain why the seasonal pattern of rainfall is related to the migration of the ITCZ. (5)

6 (a) Account for the variation in annual rainfall for the Sahel region of Africa. (4)

    either

    (b) Identify and explain the main problems caused by the seasonal pattern of rainfall in West Africa. (5)

    or

    (c) What human problems have the droughts of the 1970s and 1980s in the Sahel caused? (5)

THE HYDROSPHERE

Introduction

Water is a vital component of the earth's atmosphere and surface. It is essential for all life on earth and even in its gaseous form it plays a significant role in absorbing radiation and transferring energy between the earth and its atmosphere.

Despite the fact that only 3% of the water on earth is fresh water and only a third of that is available for use, the usable hydrosphere contains more than enough water for all current needs. However, water like other resources is not evenly distributed around the world. Some parts suffer regular droughts while others experience floods.

In developed countries where each person consumes over 100 litres of water per day (for all uses, washing, cooking, etc.) people tend to take water for granted. But in developing countries less than 25 litres per day per person is not unusual. Water consumption ranges from 5.4 litres per day in Madagascar to over 600 litres per day in the USA (2.1).

Of the total water use, irrigation uses 73%, industry uses 21% and domestic use only 6%. The water used by industry and in people's homes is often returned to rivers and can be reused (up to 90%). 70% of the water used for irrigation, on the other hand, is lost into the atmosphere or ground, but this irrigated land produces about 20% of global food supplies (2.2).

2.1 Water supply and use

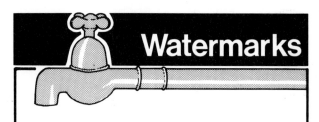

Watermarks

- 97% of water is sea water
- less than 1% of fresh water is available for human use; rest is locked away in glaciers and polar ice caps
- over 70% of irrigation water never reaches the crops
- domestic water accounts for only 6% of total fresh water consumption
- 1700m. people do not have an adequate supply of drinking water; 3000 m. lack proper sanitation

2.2 Water: some facts

The landscapes of the earth are sculpted in an environment in which water plays a significant role. The continual cycling of water in the global hydrological cycle has created a range of landscapes produced by the erosional, transportational and depositional work of water.

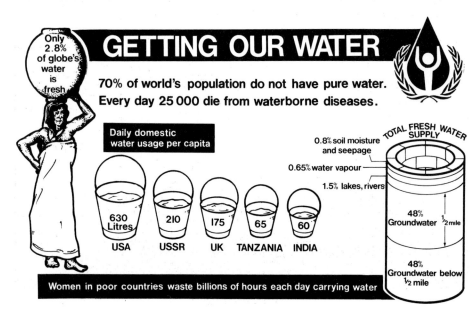

GETTING OUR WATER

Only 2.8% of globe's water is fresh

70% of world's population do not have pure water. Every day 25 000 die from waterborne diseases.

Daily domestic water usage per capita

630 Litres — USA
210 — USSR
175 — UK
65 — TANZANIA
60 — INDIA

0.8% soil moisture and seepage
0.65% water vapour
1.5% lakes, rivers

TOTAL FRESH WATER SUPPLY

48% Groundwater ½ mile
48% Groundwater below ½ mile

Women in poor countries waste billions of hours each day carrying water

The Global Hydrological Cycle

The passage of water in its liquid, solid and vapour states plays an important role in all aspects of the earth–atmosphere system. Therefore the **global hydrological cycle** which describes the distribution and movement of water is a major system which links all elements of our environment (2.3). The flow of water in the global hydrological cycle is linked with the transfer of energy at all points in the cycle.

The sun provides the energy (latent heat) to wet surfaces (oceans, lakes, rivers, etc.) to cause **evaporation**. The rate of evaporation is dependent on the continual replacement of moist air with dry air. Without the wind to continually move the air in contact with the earth's surface, the air would become saturated with water vapour and unable to hold any more moisture. Also warm air can hold more water vapour than can cold air. Therefore warm windy conditions cause more evaporation than cold calm conditions.

Evaporation varies across the globe with the highest evaporation rates over the tropical portion of the oceans. Evaporation over equatorial oceans is high but slightly less than in the tropical areas to the north and south, because of greater cloud cover over the equatorial regions. The tropical deserts, however, give very low rates of evaporation because there is almost no surface water to be evaporated.

As moist air moves upwards in the atmosphere it may become unable to hold all the water vapour. Clouds form from the resulting **condensation** and some of the energy that was used to power

the uplift is released. Precipitation in the form of rain or snow will eventually return this water to the earth's surface.

Water is stored at several points in the global hydrological cycle with the vast majority of all water in the oceans (97%). Glaciers and ice caps hold 2%, while terrestrial waters (groundwater, soil water, lakes and rivers) constitute 1%, of which the majority is groundwater. The atmosphere itself contains only 0.001% of the total.

With 97% of all water in the oceans and a further 2% frozen as ice, life on the land surface of the earth has to make do with a very small proportion of the total. Indeed the earth is a very suitable environment for fish; humans have to interfere with the hydrological cycle in order to colonise much of the land surface.

Of all the water in the hydrological cycle 84% is evaporated from the oceans while 16% is evaporated or transpired (**evapotranspiration**) from the land. While 76% of all precipitation falls on the oceans 23% falls on the land. This results in a transfer at the surface of 7% from land to sea and this is matched by a 7% transfer in the atmosphere (2.4).

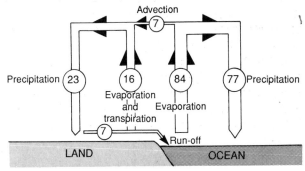

2.4 Transfers of water in the hydrological cycle. There is an exchange of 7% of global water from land to the ocean at the surface and a corresponding transfer in the atmosphere to match this.

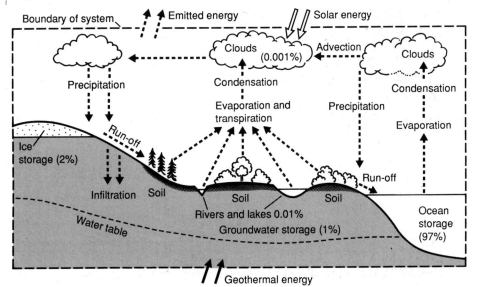

2.3 The global hydrological cycle. Most water is held in storage within the cycle, with 97% in ocean storage and approximately 2% as ice.

The Water Budget

The idea of a water budget is analogous to a monetary budget where precipitation represents the income and the **potential evapotranspiration** represents the expenditure. Potential evapotranspiration is the maximum possible evapotranspiration that would take place under given climatic conditions if there was sufficient moisture for it to do so. Both potential evapotranspiration and precipitation can be considered on a month to month basis.

2.5 shows the data for a typical weather station in southern England. The two graphs are superimposed, with precipitation shown as shaded columns and potential evapotranspiration as blank columns with a broken border. Precipitation is highest in the winter months, declining in the summer. Potential evapotranspiration has low values in winter rising to a maximum in summer. The rise is due to longer summer days and higher temperatures. In winter the precipitation is much greater than potential evapotranspiration and there is a large water surplus. This surplus either infiltrates the soil or flows as run-off. As the spring approaches the water surplus is reduced month by month until in May the potential evapotranspiration is greater than precipitation. By July all the soil water has been used up, trying

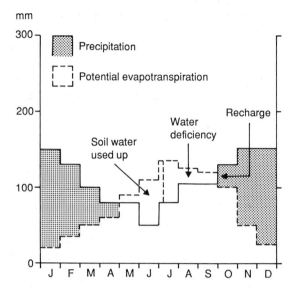

2.5 Water budget for a typical weather station in southern England. The figures for potential evapotranspiration and precipitation are long-term averages. There is a small water deficit for three months, once soil water is used up, in the summer. Precipitation outstrips potential evapotranspiration in seven months of the year.

2.6 Soil moisture deficit. (a) Mean annual rainfall, (b) mean annual potential evaporation and (c) mean annual soil moisture deficit in Britain

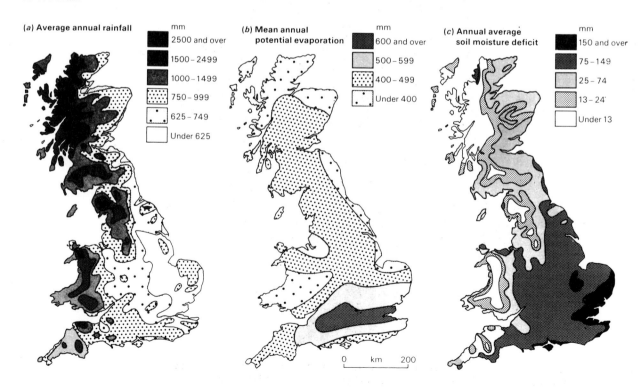

(a) Average annual rainfall

| mm |
| 2500 and over |
| 1500 – 2499 |
| 1000 – 1499 |
| 750 – 999 |
| 625 – 749 |
| Under 625 |

(b) Mean annual potential evaporation

| mm |
| 600 and over |
| 500 – 599 |
| 400 – 499 |
| Under 400 |

(c) Annual average soil moisture deficit

| mm |
| 150 and over |
| 75 – 149 |
| 25 – 74 |
| 13 – 24 |
| Under 13 |

0 km 200

to make up for a lack of precipitation, and for the months of July, August and September there is a water deficit. During this time it would be beneficial for farmers to irrigate crops. By October the precipitation has again overtaken potential evapotranspiration, recharging the soil water.

Over most of Britain, despite its maritime climate, potential evaporation exceeds precipitation in one or more of the summer months. The south-east of England suffers from the greatest deficit (2.6) but this is not normally so severe that sprinkler irrigation cannot alleviate the problem. The areas with the most severe water deficit in England and Wales are also the areas with the highest percentage of arable land (2.7).

Contrasting climatic regimes provide very different water budgets with a range of water deficits and surpluses. For example, hot desert climates are characterised by significant water deficits, often over 1300 mm; while the wet tropical climate of the rainforests is characterised by a water surplus, often over 1500 mm.

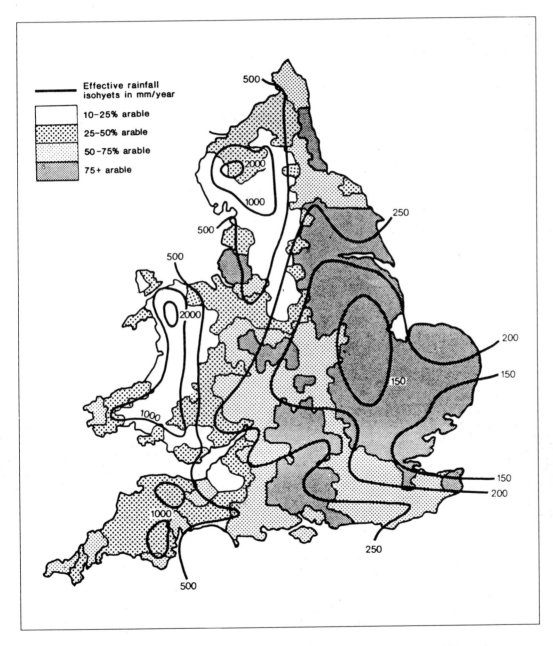

Effective rainfall isohyets in mm/year

10–25% arable
25–50% arable
50–75% arable
75+ arable

2.7 The relationship between arable land and effective rainfall in England and Wales. Arable land in England and Wales tends to be found in areas with low effective rainfall. Effective rainfall is the precipitation minus that which has been evaporated.

The Basin Hydrological Cycle

A drainage basin is the catchment area of a stream bounded by a **watershed**; the watershed is the high ground which separates different drainage systems. Streams, however, join together forming tributaries of longer rivers and the river system has a much larger catchment incorporating the drainage basins of all its tributaries (2.8).

Each drainage basin can be viewed as a system comprising a set of characteristics (streams, slopes, soil, etc.) which are interrelated. The drainage basin has as its boundary the watershed, with inputs of precipitation and solar energy and outputs of evapotranspiration and channel **run-off**. Each drainage basin is simply the result of water being returned to the oceans as part of the global hydrological cycle. The processes and transfers within the river basin can be seen as a series of inputs and outputs. The input of precipitation is transferred into outputs of channel run-off, deep basin outflow (flow of groundwater beyond the boundaries of the drainage basin) and evapotranspiration (2.9).

Precipitation over land may be **intercepted** by vegetation; this means the vegetation surfaces (leaves, etc.) become wet with any surplus water flowing over or into the ground. Densely vegetated areas intercept large amounts of water. Measurements

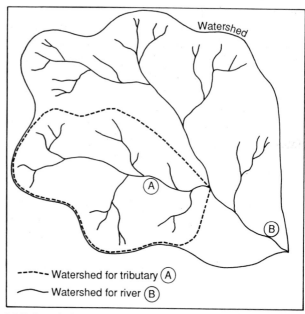

2.8 Drainage basin and watershed. The watershed is the high ground which separates different drainage systems. Within any river system each tributary will have its own watershed.

in German Beech forests during the summer months suggest that over 40% of precipitation is intercepted by the trees but this is reduced to just over 20% in winter.

Some water soaks into the ground (**infiltration**) flowing through the natural passageways between poorly fitting soil particles as

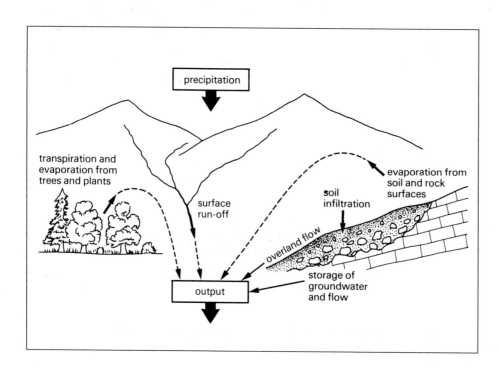

2.9 A simplified diagram of the river basin run-off system. This indicates the main outputs of the system with precipitation as the main input and some water held in storage as groundwater.

well as larger openings.

If rainfall is greater than the capacity of the soil to soak up the water, or too rapid to be be passed downwards, the excess will flow over the surface as run-off. This run-off flowing as a sheet of water downhill is called **overland flow**. As the soil becomes saturated with water its capacity to soak up more decreases to an almost constant level. The reason for the rapid drop in infiltration capacity is that the soil's openings rapidly become clogged by particles or by clays as they take up water and expand. This explains why a sandy soil does not suffer so great a drop in infiltration capacity as a clay-rich soil such as silt (2.10).

Overland flow can be produced by low rainfall over a period of time or sudden high rainfall near the beginning of a storm (2.11). A soil's infiltration capacity also depends on how **permeable** it is (i.e. how fast water can pass through it). Certain farming practices can reduce the infiltration capacity of a soil. Burning grass or crop stubble destroys vegetation cover and surface litter which protect the soil, leaving it open to direct **rainsplash** which closes soil openings and compacts the soil. Over-use by grazing animals which trample the soil also compacts it. Both these farming practices can reduce infiltration capacity, and increase run-off and erosion.

The reduction in infiltration will also in time result in a reduction of soil water reserves. Some soil water is intercepted by plant roots which take up water in response to losses by evaporation from leaves, etc., a process called **transpiration**. In summer rapid transpiration can cause roots to remove water from the soil faster than it is replaced by rainfall, greatly reducing water flow in rivers and streams. One hectare of maize can transpire 3.6 million litres of water in a growing season.

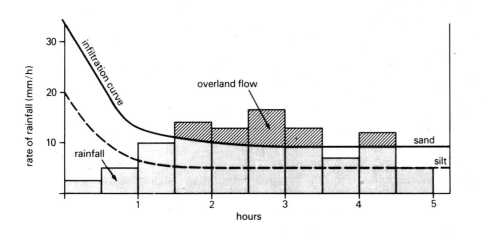

2.10 Infiltration rates and rainfall. More water can infiltrate sandy soil than can infiltrate silt. Infiltration rates rapidly fall off with time, as the soil becomes saturated.

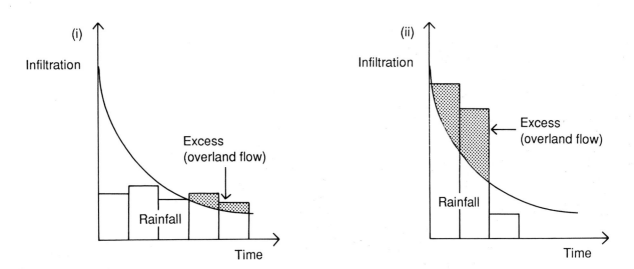

2.11 Infiltration and rainfall intensity. Because infiltration rates decrease with time, even low rainfall intensity will result in overland flow eventually. High rainfall intensity can cause overland flow even near the beginning of a storm.

Groundwater and Run-off

In most areas water percolates beyond the reach of plants and will move through the soil to stream or lake banks. This throughflow is very slow and this is why rivers remain at high levels for several days after heavy rain. Rocks as well as soil can transfer water and the storage capacity of permeable rocks is many times that of the soil. Water may pass into a permeable rock from the soil or directly at surface outcrops of the rock. Permeable rocks which have beneath them **impermeable** rocks (through which water cannot pass) are called **aquifers**. They can hold large quantities of groundwater which feeds into rivers, lakes and the oceans in the same way as soil water. The top level of saturation in the aquifer is called the **water table** (2.12). Between the soil and the water table there is an **aeration zone** which is not fully saturated. It changes in depth as the water table rises or falls.

Groundwater is held in rocks for a very long time, so this reservoir of water can sustain rivers through long dry spells. A simple representation of a drainage basin is shown in 2.13 while 2.14 shows the linkage between the various sub-systems without reference to solar energy input. The output from one sub-system becomes in turn the input of the next sub-system. The exchange of water that is able to flow within each sub-system is limited to the

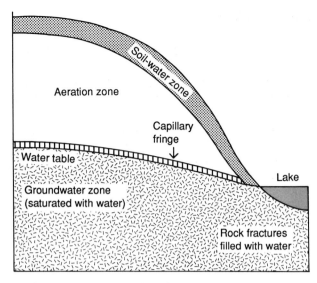

2.12 Soil-water and groundwater belts. Groundwater fully saturates the pore spaces in the rock, while the zone of aeration is not fully saturated. The capillary fringe between the groundwater zone and zone of aeration is a thin layer of water which has been drawn up from the groundwater by capillary force. Soil water is retained in the soil by capillary force and it is this water that is available for plants.

capacity of the system and any surplus must move along an alternative route. For example, if infiltration capacity is low, overland flow is an alternative route and subsequent erosion is likely.

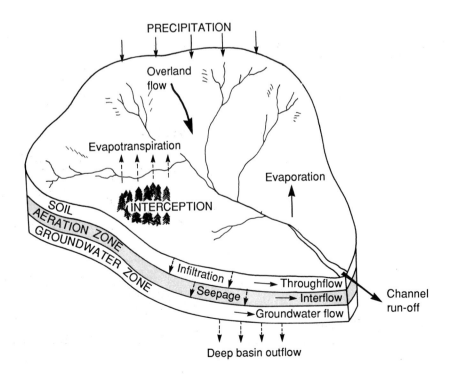

2.13 Goundwater components in the basin hydrological cycle. Flow in the three groundwater zones is shown on the diagram. Soil zone : throughflow. Aeration zone: interflow. Groundwater zone: groundwater flow.

Channel run-off

Eventually some of the precipitation that falls on a drainage basin reaches a river channel and becomes **channel run-off**. Some of the water which falls as precipitation reaches the river or stream channel fairly rapidly (**quickflow**) as overland flow or soil throughflow.

Groundwater flow on the other hand is much slower and can arrive some considerable time after the precipitation. Groundwater tends to arrive continuously at river channels and maintains a steady flow, even through some lengthy droughts.

The nature of quickflow and groundwater flow gives rise to three categories of stream in a drainage basin (2.15). Perennial streams are supplied by a more-or-less constant level of groundwater flow from the permanent water table and hence the stream's **discharge** (the volume of water flowing through the stream, measured in cubic metres per second, cumecs) is uninterrupted. Intermittent streams at higher elevations are supported by quickflow, and groundwater flow when the water table rises. Therefore these streams tend to be seasonal in nature. Ephemeral streams only flow when they are supplied by quickflow, immediately after precipitation and therefore their discharge fluctuates greatly.

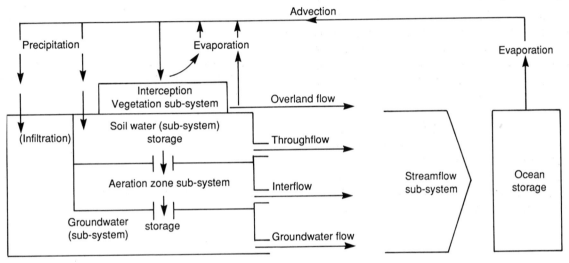

2.14 Systems diagram for water transfer in the basin hydrological cycle. This diagram reveals the constituent parts of the basin hydrological cycle but takes no account of solar energy input or sediment transfer.

2.15 Stream types in a drainage basin. This sequence of stream types tends to occur between the main 'trunk' stream and the watershed.

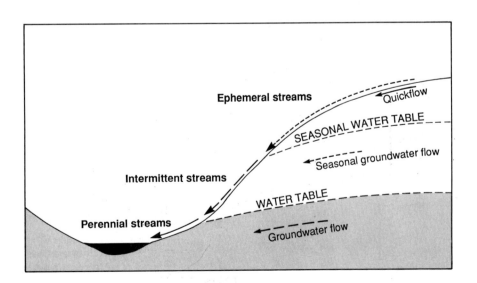

Stream Hydrographs

A **hydrograph** is a record of **channel flow** in a stream or river, which shows the variation of discharge with time. 2.16 shows some of the typical features of a hydrograph following a shower of rain. The **baseflow** is the flow that is supplied by groundwater while the peak is produced by quickflow. The quickflow may be in the form of overland flow or throughflow.

The water is provided by groundwater at the beginning of the time period shown, which will have been decreasing since the last period of rain. When the rain storm occurs there is a time lag between the peak of rainfall and the peak flow; this is called **basin lag**. The lag time will depend partly on the characteristics of the storages in the system and also on how full they are at the time of the rain storm. The rising limb of the graph is the steepest limb and its steepness depends on the speed of transfer of water to the river channel.

Human activity can have a marked effect on run-off, altering the steepness of the rising limb. Urbanisation and drainage improvements increase run-off, steepening the limb and reducing the basin lag, while **afforestation** can reduce the steepness of the limb. Skiing developments in the Alps accompanied by deforestation and abandonment of agricultural land have markedly steepened the rising limb of some alpine streams, causing severe flooding and erosion (2.17).

The shape of the hydrograph is also influenced by the nature of the precipitation and the physical characteristics of the drainage basin (2.18). Prolonged light rain will give a lower flatter hydrograph than a short heavy shower, even if both storms produce the same total rainfall. Intense rainfall may produce considerable quickflow if the soil is incapable of soaking the water in and storing it. Long periods of rainfall can result in a rising of the water table and a resultant increase in overland flow.

The direction in which a rain storm moves also influences the hydrograph, as can the shape of the drainage basin. A long narrow drainage basin with tributaries joining the main channel at regular intervals can produce a hydrograph with a less steeply rising limb than a wide basin with tributary streams closely spaced. Larger basins also have a longer basin lag time which could amount to days while small basins may have a lag of only an hour or so.

The recession limb of the hydrograph is determined solely by the nature of the drainage basin and is therefore more predictable than the rising limb. The recession limb represents the water draining out of the system, through the soil, over the surface and in channels, with the water level falling as the effects of the storm die away.

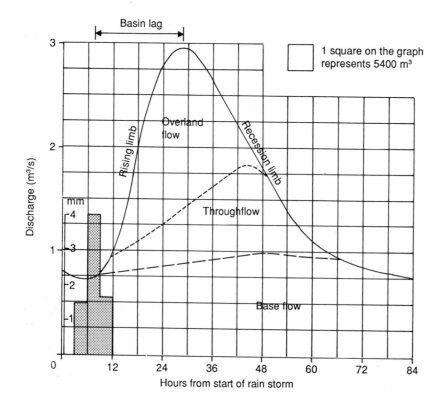

2.16 The storm hydrograph is the pattern of channel flow plotted against time. Base flow is the water released from groundwater sources. The remaining water is supplied by run-off, throughflow and overland flow. If the soil is dry at the beginning of a storm the first rain will be used to recharge the soil water. The time between peak discharge of the stream and the peak of precipitation is called the basin lag or lag time.

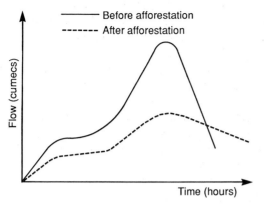

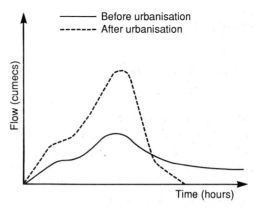

2.17 Impact of afforestation and urbanisation on storm hydrographs. Afforestation reduces the peak discharge in storm conditions because the trees intercept some of the precipitation and quickflow is reduced. Tree roots also help the water to penetrate the soil reducing the likelihood of overland flow. Urbanisation has the opposite effect, covering land with impenetrable tarmac and concrete, thereby increasing run-off dramatically.

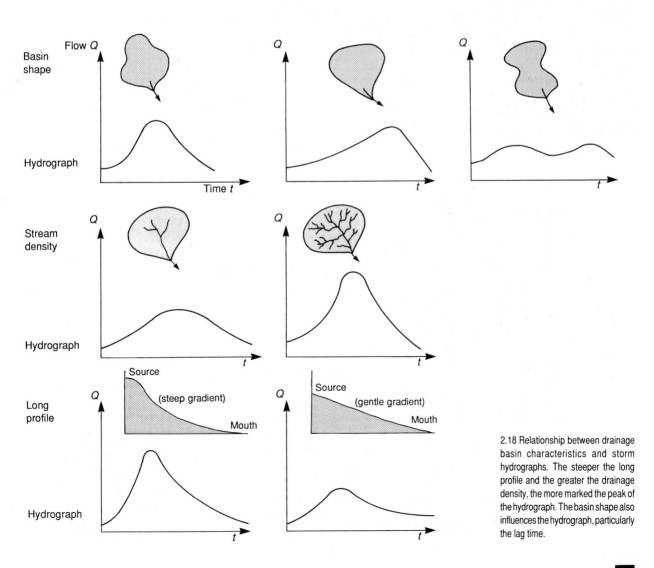

2.18 Relationship between drainage basin characteristics and storm hydrographs. The steeper the long profile and the greater the drainage density, the more marked the peak of the hydrograph. The basin shape also influences the hydrograph, particularly the lag time.

CHAPTER 2

Annual Hydrographs

Water authorities and companies carry out continuous monitoring of river discharge for most major rivers. 2.19 shows the 1983 annual hydrograph for the River Conon at Moy Bridge Ross-shire. The peaks indicate storm flow (periods of heavy rain). In 1983 there was one storm event which resulted in flooding.

The flooding occurred on 31 December when the River Conon breached its embankments at about 9.30 p.m. The sudden breach of embankments led to the drowning of one man on the A862 road. At its lowest point the A862 was under 2.9 metres of water.

Comparing river flows in 1983 and 1984 (2.20) we can see that the river had fewer storm peaks in 1984 and flow exceeded 100 cumecs on fewer occasions. There was also a long period of low flow in 1984 between June and August.

The mean daily or monthly discharge measured over a period of years shows a pattern. In the British Isles the lowest discharges usually occur in late summer when soil-water flow is at its lowest. This mean or 'average' situation is referred to as the **regime** of the river. The regime of a river is analogous to 'climate' with the annual hydrograph as the 'weather' of the river.

The mean monthly flows for the River Conon (2.21) 1980–89 shows that highest flows are normally recorded in winter when evapotranspiration is low and snowmelt from the catchment area releases some stored water. The major flood events over the last 100 years have all occurred in either December or January or February. The period of lowest flow is between May and July when rainfall is low and soil water is at its lowest. The regime of the River Conon is shown in 2.22

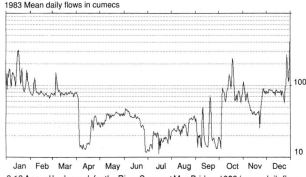

Station 110: River Conon at Moy Bridge
1983 Mean daily flows in cumecs

2.19 Annual hydrograph for the River Conon at Moy Bridge, 1983 (mean daily flows in cumecs)

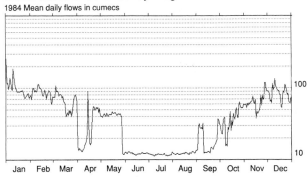

Station 110: River Conon at Moy Bridge
1984 Mean daily flows in cumecs

2.20 Annual hydrograph for the River Conon at Moy Bridge, 1984 (mean daily flows in cumecs)

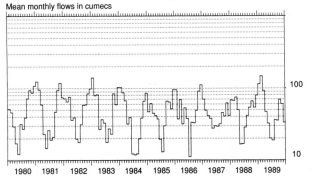

Station 110: River Conon at Moy Bridge
Mean monthly flows in cumecs

2.21 Mean monthly flows in cumecs for the River Conon at Moy Bridge, 1980–89

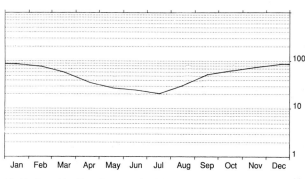

2.22 Regime of the River Conon at Moy Bridge (flows in cumecs)

Q THE GLOBAL HYDROLOGICAL CYCLE

1 (a) What is the global hydrological cycle?
(b) Describe the distribution of water in the global hydrological cycle.
(c) Make a copy of 2.3.
(d) How is water transferred from land to sea and how is this transfer matched?
(e) Describe the uneven distribution of water resources as illustrated in 2.1.

Q THE WATER BUDGET

2 (a) Explain what is meant by the term potential evapotranspiration.
(b) What group of people would be interested in the sort of data shown in 2.5?
(c) Describe the average rainfall pattern for Great Britain and compare this with the soil moisture deficit.
(d) What is the relationship between percentage of arable land and soil moisture deficit?

Q THE BASIN HYDROLOGICAL CYCLE

3 (a) What is a watershed?
(b) Make a copy of diagram 1 and mark on the watershed.
(c) Describe the basin hydrological cycle in terms of inputs and outputs.
(d) What impact would widespread deforestation have on the outputs of a drainage basin?
(e) How is precipitation intercepted?
(f) Explain infiltration, run-off and overland flow.
(g) What does a soil's infiltration capacity depend on?

Diagram 1

Q GROUNDWATER AND RUN-OFF

4 (a) What is an aquifer?
(b) Describe the zonal distribution of soil water and groundwater as shown in 2.12.
(c) Describe the transfers of water between the sub-systems in a drainage basin (2.14).
(d) Explain the nature of each of the three types of stream shown in 2.15.

Q STREAM HYDROGRAPHS

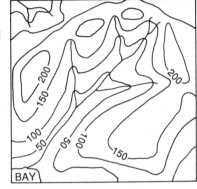

Diagram 2

5 (a) Describe the components of a stream hydrograph.
(b) Calculate the total volume of water which passes the gauging station (for 2.16) as quickflow (each square under the curve represents 5400 m³).
(c) What is basin lag?
(d) Why do afforestation and urbanisation affect stream hydrographs?
(e) Draw graphs to estimate the shape of storm hydrographs for the characteristics shown in diagram 2.
(f) What effect would improved artificial drainage on arable land have on a stream hydrograph?
(g) What methods could be used to slow up the passage of water through a drainage basin?

The Highland Floods of 1989: A Case Study

During January 1989 much of the Highlands of Scotland experienced exceptional rainfall culminating in a particularly severe storm during 5 and 6 February. Both January and February saw flood events in many Highland rivers. The February event was the most dramatic with precipitation for the first week in February exceeding the monthly average (with most precipitation concentrated within one 48 hour period).

In February Loch Ness and Loch Lochy rose to their highest levels since the construction of the hydro-electric schemes in the 1950s. Many rivers reached their highest peaks on record including the Rivers Ness, Ewe, Blackwater, Broom and Meig; with the Rivers Inver, Enrick, Shin, Conon and Glass equalling previous record levels.

The exceptionally wet January raised some reservoir levels to near maximum capacity and consequently their capability to moderate the effects of the February storm was less than normal. The January rainfall was particularly heavy in the West Highlands; the upper parts of the Ness and Beauly catchments experiencing about 800 mm in January, equivalent to an average of about 25 mm per day (2.23).

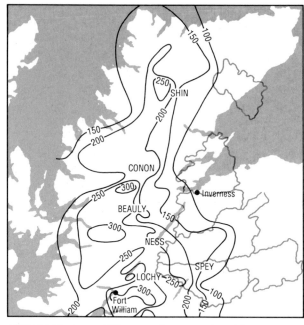

2.24 Rainfall for January 1989 expressed as a percentage of the average

Much of the Highlands had twice the average monthly rainfall with some areas recording over three times the average (2.24). The return period for a twice than average rainfall has been estimated at about 50 years with a three times average rainfall every 1000 years. Therefore the rainfall in January 1989 was exceptional over large areas.

2.23 Rainfall for January 1989 in millimetres

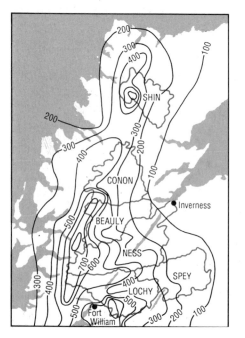

2.25 Raingauge data for 4–7 February 1989

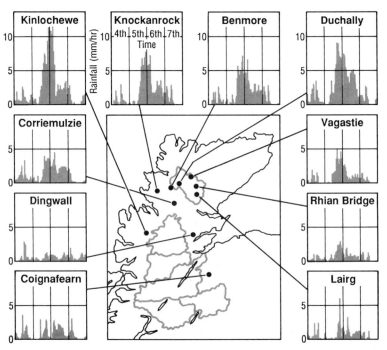

The February event caused more damage than the January rainfall and consequently received more publicity. It began at about 9.00 a.m. on 5 February and lasted for about 48 hours. The rainfall data show the clear contrast between the East and West Highlands in terms of rainfall intensity but the period of rainfall was broadly similar in length (2.25).

The heaviest precipitation rates recorded exceeded 10 mm per hour between 2200 h on 5 February and 0700 h on 6 February. The rainfall intensity for Corriemulzie is shown on 2.26 and although this station was outwith the area of the most intense rainfall, very high levels were recorded for the two-day period. The heaviest rain occurred in the warm sector of a depression and further rain was received as the cold front progressed slowly over the Highlands on 6 February (2.27). The high rainfall in the warm sector of the depression was due to very high humidity of the air and strong winds which drove the air over the rugged terrain of the West Highlands producing heavy orographic rainfall.

The two-day rainfall totals exceeded 100 mm for a large area of the north-west. The highest rainfall recorded for this period was 306 mm at Kinloch Hourn: the highest two-day total ever recorded in the UK (2.28).

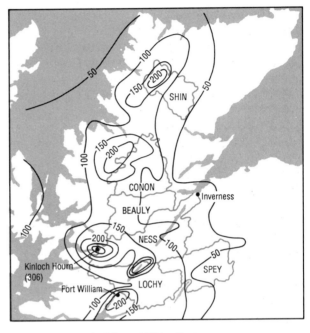

2.28 Rainfall for 5 and 6 February 1989 in millimetres

Station 45: Corriemulzie

1989

Rainfall intensity (mm/h)

Days commence 0900 GMT

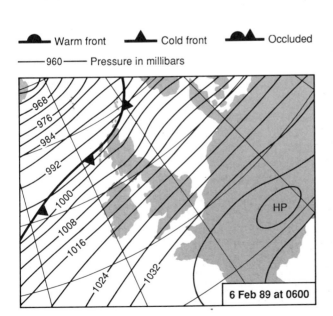

2.26 Rainfall intensity for Corriemulzie 3–6 February 1989

2.27 Synoptic charts for 5 and 6 February 1989

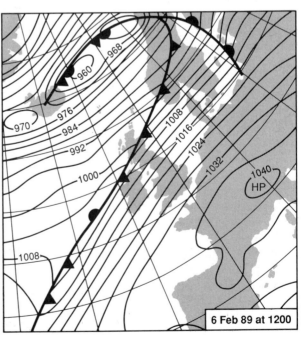

6 Feb 89 at 0600

6 Feb 89 at 1200

The Highland Floods of 1989: A Case Study

(continued)

The flooding which accompanied the the February storm:
- destroyed the only rail bridge to the north over the River Ness (2.29)
- destroyed two fish farms on the River Orrin
- flooded the Ord Distillery to a depth of 1.2 metres
- caused widespread damage to property (2.30)
- blocked a number or roads with mudslides
- caused severe flooding in the Conon and Spey valleys (2.31)
- drowned a number of livestock
- placed Inverness on high flood alert with large sections of the river bank through the town having to be reinforced with sand bags

The hydrograph for the River Conon at Moy Bridge for 1989 has been superimposed on the 1988 hydrograph (2.32) and this shows the very high flow level in 1989 in comparison with 1988. The river flow in January and February 1989 was especially high with significant flood peaks in both months, corresponding to the floods on 13–15 January and 5–6 February.

2.29 Ruins of the rail bridge over the River Ness

2.30 Flooding in Muir of Ord

2.31 Flooding in the Spey valley

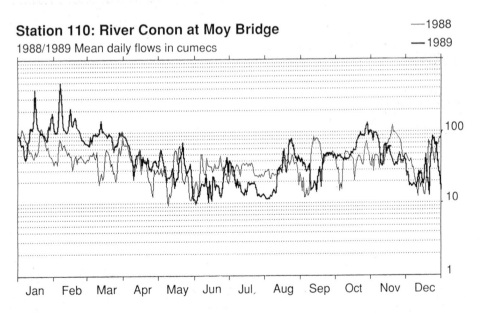

Station 110: River Conon at Moy Bridge
1988/1989 Mean daily flows in cumecs

—— 1988
—— 1989

2.32 Superimposed hydrographs for the River Conon at Moy Bridge 1988 and 1989 (mean daily flows in cumecs)

Research and Further Work

Explain the reasons for the Highland floods of 1989 and describe some of the effects of the storm.
Research the causes and effects of a flood in an area other than the Highlands of Scotland.

Erosion, Transport and Deposition

Rivers are agents of erosion, transport and deposition. Although these three processes are described separately they are interrelated. These processes alter slope, width, and depth of rivers, and the amount of sediment and load in rivers. They respond to the amount of energy the river discharge provides.

Erosion

The greater the discharge and velocity of a river the more erosive power the river has. Some erosion can be achieved by the force of flowing water alone. The dragging effect of the river removes poorly consolidated or well-jointed material from the river bed and banks. This process is called **hydraulic action**. This removal of unconsolidated material may eventually lead to bank collapse, especially on the outside of bends where the current is strongest.

However the main method of erosion is **corrasion** which is when the river drags particles of sediment across the surface of the river bed. This deepens channels and is particularly effective during floods when larger fragments of bed load act on the river bed. Potholes in the beds of rivers are features of this abrasive

2.33 Potholes in the bed of the Afon Glaslyn, North Wales. Pebbles in the bed load are spun round in eddies and drill potholes in the bed of the stream.

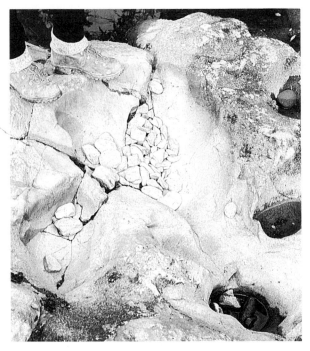

process. The potholes are cylindrical holes 'drilled' into the rock by fragments of load (pebbles) which are rotated by turbulent eddies. Potholes may vary in size from a few centimetres to several metres in diameter (2.33).

Rivers also erode by solution, dissolving any soluble material into their flow. Limestones are particularly susceptible because they are dissolved by carbonic acid, found in rainwater.

The fourth form of erosion (**attrition**) attacks the river's load rather than the channel. The fragments in the load collide with each other in motion and break into smaller pieces. Therefore as fragments of load move downstream they are progressively reduced in size and become more rounded.

Erosion also allows the channel to extend by **headward erosion** at the source of the stream. Undercutting occurs where the water table meets the surface, and sub-surface tunnels and pipes in unconsolidated material collapse, extending the river channel.

Transport

Transport of the eroded material happens in three ways: **suspension**, **bed load** and **solution**.

Suspension: some fine particles such as silt and clay are small enough to be held up by the turbulence within the water. The more turbulent the water the larger the particles that can be transported in suspension.

Bed load: larger particles such as sand and gravel are rolled or bounced along the river bed. The bouncing motion is called **saltation** and the rolling or sliding motion is called **traction** (2.34).

Solution: the dissolved material carried throughout the water is known as the **dissolved load**.

The relative contribution of each type of load varies with the nature of the river and is dependent on its discharge and velocity.

The load carried by a river increases with increased discharge and velocity. Higher velocity makes the river able to carry larger particles. The volume of load that a river can carry is termed its **capacity**, while its **competence** is the weight or size of the largest particles it transports. The relationship between particle size, erosion, transport, deposition and stream velocity has been determined experimentally and is shown in 2.35.

The lowest velocity at which grains of a given size can be picked up is said to be the **critical erosion velocity**. A wide zone rather than a single line is used on the graph to delimit the critical erosion velocity because its value varies with depth and temperature of the water and with density of the particles.

As can be seen on 2.35 sand is more readily picked up than silt or clay. this is because the smaller particles are more cohesive. Once a particle has been eroded from the channel it can be transported at a lower velocity until the velocity decreases to the point where it is deposited. For example a particle of sand

2.34 Sediment transportation. Material in solution is invisible but can be a significant proportion of the total load. Small particles like clay can be kept in suspension by water movement. Slightly larger particles are bounced along the stream bed while the largest particles are rolled along when the discharge is greatest.

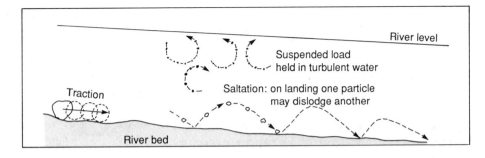

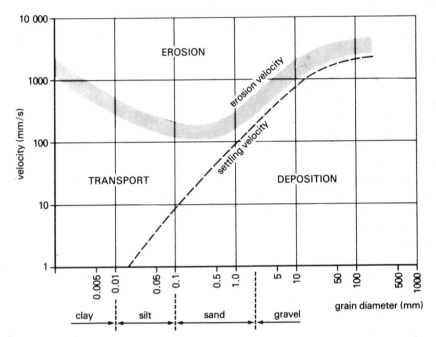

2.35 Velocity and particle movement. This diagram illustrates the relationship between particle size and velocity to erosion, transport and deposition.

0.2 mm in diameter will be eroded if the velocity of flow rises to 300 mm/s but it won't be deposited until the velocity has decreased to about 10 mm/s.

Under flood conditions when greater velocities are experienced all forms of erosion are more effective and the river's load is greatly increased. The increased suspended load often colours the river brown.

Deposition

Deposition occurs when the river is no longer able to carry its load. This may be due to a number of factors including a reduction in gradient of the river channel or an increase in the size of the load, possibly brought in by a tributary. A drop in velocity would also cause deposition. Because a river's load capacity varies through time, sediment is likely to be laid down in categories and this produces a sorted sediment, both laterally and vertically (2.36).

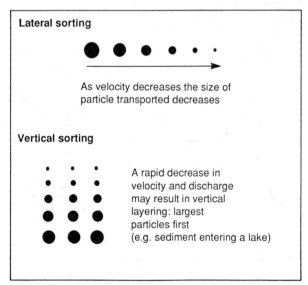

2.36 Sorted sediments. Lateral and vertical sorting are normally found under different conditions but both types of sorting may take place at the same time in delta formation.

River Landscapes: Valleys

Rivers create valleys by eroding the land, but slope processes (see pages 96–7) help by transferring weathered debris down the valley sides to the bottom of the valley. This weathered material is then removed by the river (2.37). The amount of material removed is dependent on the velocity and discharge of the river. Generally speaking the valley sides will be steeper if the river is actively eroding.

V-shaped valleys are usually associated with the upper course of a river. This is partly due to the higher altitudes which provide the potential energy to erode the valley. Excess energy in the lower course is used to erode laterally (sideways) rather than vertically.

Valley shapes depend on the geology, the efficiency of the weathering/slope processes and the capacity of the river. The relationship between weathering and river erosion also influences the valley shape.

The systems diagram 2.38 illustrates the linkage between erosion, transportation and the valley slopes. The steepening of the valley sides allows more weathered material to slide down into the river to be transported downstream. The main inputs into the system are weathered rock, precipitation and gravity with the outputs of river water and transported load.

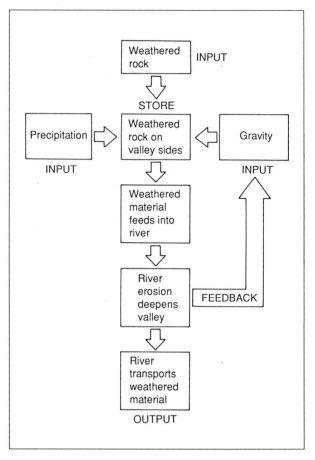

2.38 Simple systems diagram for a V-shaped river valley

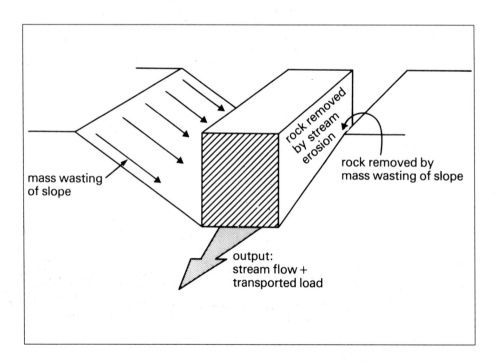

2.37 The slope system, river erosion and transport. The relative contributions of slope processes and river erosion are illustrated for a model V-shaped valley. The precise shape of the valley is determined by the geology, efficiency of slope processes and the speed of downcutting by the river.

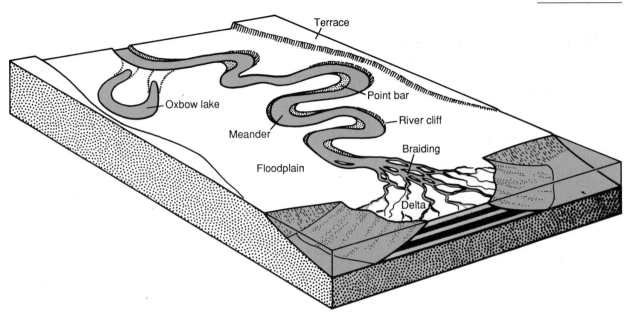

2.39 Landforms of the floodplain. Most of the landforms illustrated in this diagram are associated with the middle and lower courses of a river but can also be found in the upper courses of some rivers, particularly those in upland glaciated areas.

Alluvial landforms

The material deposited by rivers is known as **alluvium** and there is a wide range of alluvial landforms. Some of the main ones are shown in section diagram 2.39.

The most significant feature of a river's deposition is its **floodplain**. The floodplain is the broad, relatively flat valley bottom, most often found in a river's lower course. This floodplain is partly built up by **channel deposits**, such as those laid down in and at the edge of the river channel (for example point bars of a meander: see page 68), and partly by **overbank deposits** which are disgorged during flooding. In most cases channel deposits account for about 80% of floodplain deposits (2.40).

During flooding the coarsest debris is deposited closest to the river channel with the finest silt being spread more widely over the floodplain. The coarser debris can build up along the banks of the river to produce ridges called **levees** (2.40) which are usually the highest ground on the floodplain. The channel bed can be built up between levees and may eventually be higher than the adjacent floodplain.

The levees prevent floodwater returning to the river and the sediment builds up on the floodplain. In most British rivers the floodplain is built up by only a few centimetres every 100 years but tropical floodplains can *accrete* by anything between 10 and 200 centimetres every 100 years.

The floodplains of many of the world's great rivers are susceptible to serious flooding and consequent loss of life. In the 1970s an average of 15.4 million people were affected yearly by flooding. The flooding of Bangladesh in 1988 by the Ganges and Brahmaputra rivers drove up to 30 million people from their homes.

2.40 The formation of the flood plain. Floodplains are strips of land on either side of the river which have been eroded by the river. Flooding and migrating meanders deposit alluvium over the full extent of the floodplain. Repeated floods may build up levees of coarse sand and silt. The river bed may also be raised by deposition.

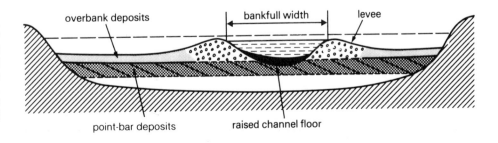

River Landscapes: Meanders

Straight river channels on all but the most gentle of gradients are inherently unstable. Rivers adjust to find a form which can most efficiently transport sediment with the discharge available. Meandering is one such adjustment the river can make. Straight channels can develop into meandering courses (2.41).

Meandering is linked with the development of **riffles** and **pools** in more or less straight channels. Riffles and pools are irregularities in the slope and depth of river beds that develop in both natural and artificial channels. Riffles are shallows of faster flowing water; pools are areas of deeper slower moving water.

The sinuous movement of flowing water in straight channels is enhanced by the deposition of shoals along the channel banks. Erosion along the stream bed causes the development of pools and the deposited coarse material produces the riffles. As the pools and riffles enlarge, the river channel becomes more sinuous and eventually some of the shoals become **point bars** on the inside edge of meanders. Pools and riffles will develop in the

sections of channels between meanders and further meanders will develop from these.

Although the sequence of meander development is fairly well understood there is still debate about the cause of the sinuous flow and the exact role of riffles and pools.

Meanders tend to be associated with alluvial floodplains but they can also be found in the upper courses of rivers and they are a common feature of streams in many glaciated uplands.

The geometry of meanders remains the same for small streams and large rivers. Meander wavelength (see 2.41) has a close relationship to the size of the area drained by the river and **bankfull discharge** (the discharge when the river is full to the top of its banks). Meander wavelength is roughly 7–10 times greater than the channel width.

Flow in meanders

Water moves in a curved path round each meander with the maximum velocity and erosion on the outer concave bank. This erosion on the concave bank is accompanied by deposition of a point bar on the inner convex bank. The flow of water in meanders is **helicoidal** (corkscrew) which transfers eroded material from the **river cliff** (steep bank undercut by erosion: see 2.39) on the concave bank to the point bar on the convex bank (2.42).

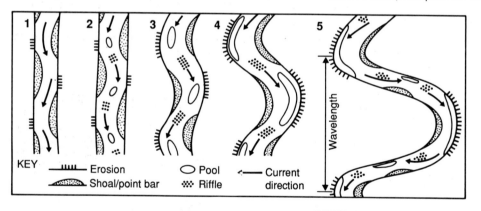

KEY
— Erosion
— Shoal/point bar
○ Pool
░ Riffle
← Current direction

2.41 Stages in meander formation. Sinuous movement of water occurs in all channels, even straight ones. If conditions of gradient and sediment are favourable meanders may develop as riffles and pools enlarge.

2.42 Flow in meanders. (a) helicoidal flow in a curved channel section, (b) flow transverse to the main flow in a meander, illustrating the lateral component of helicoidal flow, (c) position of main flow in a meander.

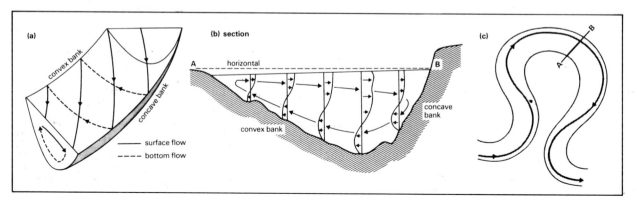

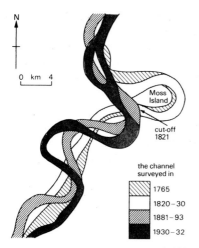

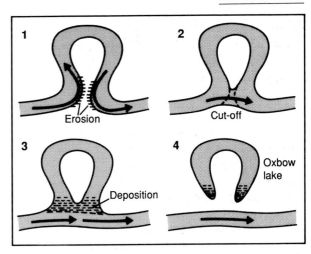

2.43 Channel movements in the Mississippi. The 1881 and 1930 surveys show that the meanders migrated downstream; the meander around Moss Island was cut off in 1821 (After US Army Corps of Engineers, in Strahler, *Physical Geography*, Wiley)

2.44 Formation of an oxbow lake. Erosion at the neck of a meander can enable the river to change course and leave behind a pool of stagnant water called an oxbow lake which is eventually infilled.

More erosion takes place on the downstream section of the meander so the meander gradually migrates downstream. 2.43 shows the migration of meanders on the Mississippi. During a flood in 1821 the river broke through the narrow gap between the two ends of a tightly curved meander, diverting the river to a straighter course, and abandoning the cut-off meander. The abandoned meander became an **oxbow lake**. Oxbow lakes tend to be very temporary features; they soon become infilled until only marshy tracts are left (2.44). Cut-offs shorten channel length causing a steeper river gradient (across the cut-off) than the original gradient along the full length of the meander. The steeper gradient results in some headward erosion and downstream deposition until the river adjusts to its new course and a new equilibrium gradient is achieved.

Former river courses and infilled oxbow lakes can be picked out in aerial photograph 2.45.

2.45 Meandering river with cut-offs, oxbows and scrolls (the River Clyde near Carstairs, Scotland). The marshy tracts of abandoned channels and oxbows can be seen from the air. Indications of former river courses are called scrolls.

River Landscapes: Braiding and Rejuvenation

Rivers with variable discharges or particularly heavy loads are prone to **braiding**, which is where the channel divides itself into several, or many, small channels which flow around 'islands' of deposits (2.46). Braiding can occur when a wide shallow river becomes overloaded with material and this has to deposited in the channel. The overloading can occur because of a drop in discharge or lessening of gradient. Rivers such as the Spey in Scotland have very variable discharges, with high discharge following snowmelt. Islands between the braided channels may become permanent if vegetation establishes before the next high discharge.

Braiding also occurs on slopes that are too steep for meanders to develop and on non-cohesive materials such as sand. Deep channels cannot develop on sandy material and therefore increases in discharge cause the channel to widen and split into smaller channels during stormflow. Because the channel bed is altered with each peak discharge there is not a single stable channel and sediment islands are continually destroyed and created.

Rejuvenation

Rivers can cut their beds no more than a few metres below sea level. This is referred to as **base level**. However base level can change through time as relative sea level changes. A drop in relative sea level increases the potential energy at the river mouth and causes active erosion to resume. This type of change is called **rejuvenation**.

The lower reaches of the river are the first to be affected by the increase in erosion. The river adjusts to the new base level by eroding headwards (towards the source). The headward limit of the rejuvenation at any point in time is termed the **knick point** (2.47). The knick point retreats headward along the length of the river at a very slow rate and by the time it has worked its way along

2.46 A braided channel in a river in northern Iceland

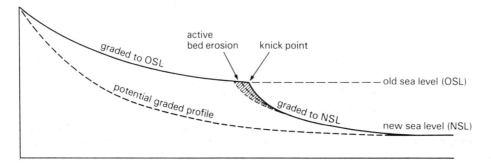

2.47 Sea level changes and the effect on the river profile. A drop in relative sea level results in active erosion in the lower reaches of the river. The headward limit of erosion at any time is indicated by a knick point where the gradient of the river profile changes abruptly.

the full length of the river there may have been several other changes in sea level.

Knick points are not always due to changes in sea level. Variations in rock type can result in different rates of erosion, while lakes can provide an intermediate base level below which rivers feeding into them cannot lower their beds.

Terraces

Terraces are often the remnants of former floodplains (2.48). Floodplain deposits formed by the meltwaters of the last glaciation were built up to considerable depths. Present-day rivers can be seen cutting down through these deposits and forming a new floodplain below the earlier one. The increase in energy which allows the downcutting into the former floodplain is usually due to alterations of the relative levels of land and sea since the last Ice Age. Successive changes in relative levels can result in **stepped terraces**. (Removal of the weight of ice after the last Ice Age has allowed the earth's crust in those areas to rise again – this is called isostatic adjustment – the land has tended to rise in stages and even 8000 years after the last Ice Age some areas are still adjusting.)

2.49 Incised meanders of the San Juan River, Utah, USA. These dramatic goose-neck meanders of the San Juan River are incised into horizontal sedimentary strata.

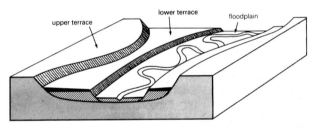

2.48 River terraces. Rejuvenation can result in a river eroding into the floodplain and forming a new one at a lower level. Remnants of the former floodplain are called terraces.

Incised meanders

If the land is rising or the sea level is falling faster than the rate at which the river is downcutting, any meanders in the river course will cut deep trenches in the land. The meander pattern is retained as the river cuts deeper into the surrounding land. Such features are called **incised meanders** (2.49). However if the sea level is falling slower than downcutting there is likely to be some lateral erosion by the river. This produces an asymmetrical trench in which the meander flows. The gentler slopes occur in the meander cores with steeper slopes on the outside of the loop. This is called an **ingrown meander** (2.50).

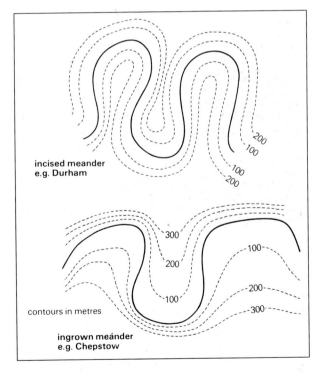

2.50 Incised and ingrown meanders. Incised meanders have a trench which is symmetrical in cross-section, while ingrown meanders have an asymmetrical trench.

River Landscapes: Deltas

Deltas form because rivers lose their energy as they enter the sea (or lakes; see 2.51). They are unable to carry the sediment any further and deposit it at the mouth of the river. However, where tidal currents are strong, deltas may not develop and the sediment is deposited further out to sea.

The river channel discharging into the sea may divide into a number of smaller channels, called **distributaries**, as alluvium is built up in the channel. The distributary network spreads the sediment in different directions giving the delta its characteristic shape.

The two most commonly recognised morphological types are the bird's foot (for example, the Mississippi) and the arcuate (for example, the Nile); see 2.52.

In delta formation the pattern of deposition is determined by a range of factors including: density of river water, type of sediment load and strength of river and sea currents. When there is a high suspended load the coarsest particles are dropped first as the **foreset beds** (2.53) with the finer sediment deposited as the bottomset beds, further out to sea. The fine sediment can be carried some considerable distance from the coast by **turbidity currents**. Topset beds lie on top of the foreset beds and their composition is dependent on the sedimentation conditions prevailing at the time of their formation.

This description of delta formation is very simplistic and can only be treated as one model of deltaic sedimentation. The Mississippi River has formed its present delta through many changes of channel direction and with a relatively low suspended sediment load (2.54).

The formation of deltas and floodplains on numerous river systems has been greatly affected by river management schemes. Dams can trap great volumes of sediment and reduce the sediment load significantly. The effect is to reduce flood-deposited silt on floodplains (which in turn affects fertility of the soil) and restrict the development of the delta. In some cases it would appear that deltas are shrinking as coastal erosion surpasses river deposition.

Deltas are also susceptible to flooding and in 1988 Bangladesh

2.51 The delta of River Etive entering Loch Etive, Scotland

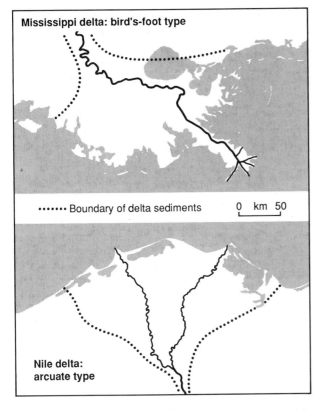

Mississippi delta: bird's-foot type

······· Boundary of delta sediments   0   km 50

Nile delta: arcuate type

2.52 Two main delta forms

2.54 Changes in the distributaries of the Mississippi delta:
channel A approx. 3000 years ago
channel B 1500 years ago
channel C 1000 years ago
channel D 700 years ago
present channel about 400 years old

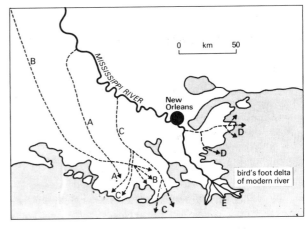

had its worst floods in living memory. More than 1000 people were killed and 25 million were made homeless. Flooding in Bangladesh has become more serious in recent years because of a number of factors (2.55).

- More monsoon rain is falling in the Himalayas.
- Increased deforestation in the Himalayas has increased run-off and soil erosion.
- Increased sediment carried by the rivers has raised channel beds.
- 80% of annual river flow takes place in four months (July–October).

2.53 Structure of a simple delta

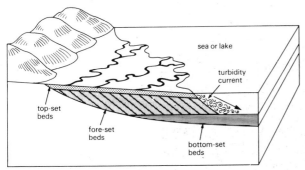

2.55 Why Bangladesh floods

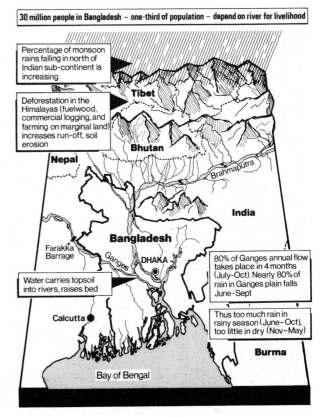

30 million people in Bangladesh – one-third of population – depend on river for livelihood

Percentage of monsoon rains falling in north of Indian sub-continent is increasing

Deforestation in the Himalayas (fuelwood, commercial logging, and farming on marginal land) increases run-off, soil erosion

Water carries topsoil into rivers, raises bed

80% of Ganges annual flow takes place in 4 months (July–Oct). Nearly 80% of rain in Ganges plain falls June–Sept

Thus too much rain in rainy season (June–Oct), too little in dry (Nov–May)

Q EROSION, TRANSPORT AND DEPOSITION

1 (a) Describe the four forms of erosion.

(b) What differences in methods of erosion would you expect in river channels composed of:
   (i) limestone
   (ii) boulder clay (till)
   (iii) gravel

(c) What are the three methods of transporting eroded material?

(d) What is the critical erosion velocity?

(e) What groups of people would find 2.35 a useful diagram and what might some of the possible uses be?

(f) Complete the following table using 2.35 to help you.

Grain size	River velocity	What will happen? (erosion, transport or deposition)
1.0 mm	10 mm/s	
10 mm	100 mm/s	
0.01 mm	100 mm/s	
0.05 mm	1000 mm/s	
0.1 mm	10 mm/s	

(g) Describe conditions which result in sorted sediments.

Q RIVER LANDSCAPES: VALLEYS / MEANDERS

2 (a) Describe the formation of a V-shaped valley.

(b) What is alluvium?

(c) Draw a series of diagrams to illustrate the formation of levees.

(d) Make a copy of 2.41.

(e) Draw a diagram of a meander and indicate the places where active erosion and deposition take place.

(f) Describe the development of a meander from straight channel to ox-bow lake.

(g) Why do meanders migrate downstream?

(h) Draw a sketch of 2.45 showing the present channel and meander scrolls.

(i) Construct a simple systems diagram like 2.38 for a river floodplain.

Q RIVER LANDSCAPES: BRAIDING AND REJUVENATION / DELTAS

3 (a) Why do streams braid?

(b) What is base level?

(c) Where on a river profile would you find a knick point?

(d) Explain how river terraces are formed.

(e) Make a copy of 2.48.

(f) What is the difference between incised and ingrown meanders and why is there this difference?

(g) What conditions may prevent the formation of deltas?

(h) Describe the structure of a simple delta.

(i) Referring to 2.55 explain why flooding is very serious in Bangladesh.

Research and Further Work

(a) Using an atlas estimate the size of the following drainage basins: Amazon, Nile, Mississippi, Thames, Rhine.

(b) What differences in stream velocity would you expect between an artificial (concrete lined) channel and a natural channel?

(c) Find out how gorges and waterfalls are formed and use diagrams to explain their formation.

(d) Find out the main uses of water (other than domestic use) in the UK.

(e) Refer to a geology map of the UK and identify areas which might use groundwater as a major source of water supply.

Q

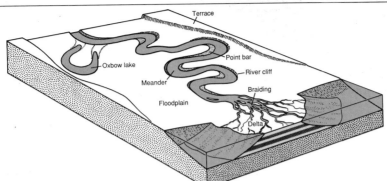

1 (a) Select one of the labelled features on the diagram and describe the processes by which it was formed. (5)
(b) With reference to a named example describe two ways in which a river valley has been modified to reduce the likelihood of flooding. (4)

2 (a) Describe the ways in which weathering and erosion have created the landscape in the diagram. (6)
(b) What is meant by the term rejuvenation and what features might you expect to see in this landscape if it was rejuvenated? (3)

Q

3 (a) Examine the diagram which illustrates the effect of river velocity on erosion, transport and deposition. Describe briefly the relationship between river velocity on erosion, transport and deposition of different material sizes. (6)
(b) Explain how the graph may be of value to hydrologists and engineers concerned with maintaining and controlling river channels and banks. (3)

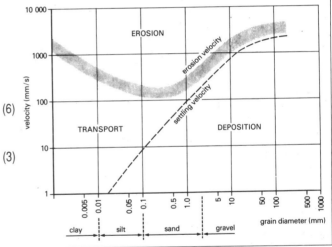

Q

4 (a) With the aid of the diagram explain what is meant by the term **the hydrological cycle**. (5)
(b) How does human activity modify the natural hydrological cycle? (4)

5 (a) 'Water in the UK is in abundance where it is least required.' Explain the uneven distribution of water resources in the UK and indicate how this situation is being tackled. (5)
(b) Account for increasing demand for water in the UK. (4)

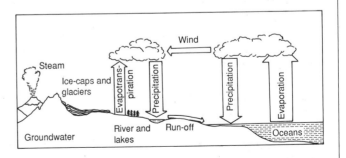

THE LITHOSPHERE

The Geology of the British Isles

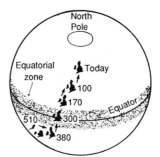

3.1 Continental drift. Britain's slow drift northwards. The numbers are dates in millions of years ago.

Today the British Isles lie far from the edge of the Eurasian plate, so they are spared the threats of volcanic eruption and devastating earthquakes. But this has not always been the case. The British Isles still bear the scars of violent crustal activity.

Because the great plates of the earth's crust have been in continual movement for millions of years, the British Isles have been moved about the globe (3.1). During the past 500 million years, the British Isles have drifted over 9000 km northwards. Evidence for this comes from Britain's varied geology. Tropical and subtropical conditions formed all Britain's coals, sandstones, limestones and salt deposits (3.2). For these rocks to have formed, geologists estimate that the British Isles must have drifted from south of the equator to their present latitude of 50–60°north. At one time, during the Carboniferous period, Britain lay astride the equator!

The British Isles were first brought together by plate tectonic movements which occurred throughout the journey northwards. For example, about 500 million years ago, Scotland was separated from England and Wales by an ancient ocean. As the Iapetus Ocean closed (3.3), its soft sea bed sediments were upfolded into high mountains. This mountain-building period or **orogeny** is called the Caledonian and lasted 200 million years. During this time, much of the British Isles probably looked like the Himalayas do today.

The Hercynian orogeny, which began in the Permian period, lasted 100 million years. It formed new mountains and upfolded the Pennines into a giant **anticline** (arch-shaped upfold).

Ripples caused by the slow convergence of the African and Eurasian plates during the past 70 million years produced waves of folds across south-east England. Plate tectonic movements also disturbed magmas as the American and Eurasian plates diverged.

With the creation of the Atlantic Ocean (3.4), lavas erupted from volcanoes in Western Scotland, for example in what are now the Cuillin Hills of Skye.

In the creation of the British Isles, mountains were thrown up and then partly destroyed by erosion, creating huge volumes of **debris** (rock fragments). This debris was deposited in shallow seas and then compressed over millions of years by overlying materials, to form **sedimentary rocks**. These in turn were contorted into new mountains by collisions caused by the continual movements of the great plates of the earth's crust. The geology of the British Isles (3.5) and most of today's landscape have been greatly influenced by these massive upheavals.

Era	Geological period	Millions of years ago	Earth movements	Evolution of pl and animals
Ceno-zoic	Quaternary	2		People
Ceno-zoic	Tertiary	65	Alpine Skye volcanoes	Mammals Birds
Mesozoic	Cretaceous	140		Death of dinosa Flowering plants and Reptiles
Mesozoic	Jurassic	195		
Mesozoic	Triassic	230		Bony fish
Palaeozoic	Permian	280	Hercynian Variscan	Seed-bearing plants and
Palaeozoic	Carbon-iferous	345	Central Scotland volcanoes	Amphibians and insects
Palaeozoic	Devonian	395		Ferns and fish
Palaeozoic	Silurian	445	Caledonian	Coral and first land plants
Palaeozoic	Ordovician	510	Welsh volcanoes	Invertebrates
Palaeozoic	Cambrian	570		Trilobites, first shelly fossils
Protero-zoic	Pre-Cambrian	1000 to 3000	Moine thrust	Algae

3.2 The geological history of the British Isles

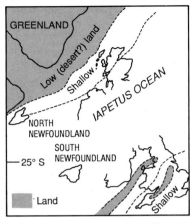

3.3 The Iapetus Ocean which finally closed about 400 million years ago during the Caledonian orogeny

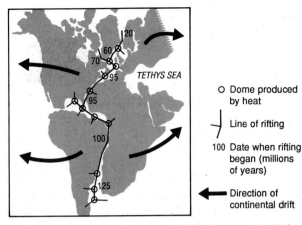

3.4 Pangaea: the Supercontinent as it appeared 200 million years ago just before the opening of the Atlantic Ocean

Conditions in the UK	Main rocks in the UK
Ice Age and warm periods	Recent deposits
Warm climatic conditions	Clays, sands, Skye basalts
Warm climate, seasonally wet, shallow seas, lagoons	Chalk (e.g. Chilterns, Downs, etc.)
Warm wet climate, shallow, tropical seas and swamps	Limestone (e.g. Cotswolds), sandstones
Desert conditions, flat landscapes, salt pans	Sandstones, gypsum, salt
Hot desert conditions, sand dunes, shallow seas	New red sandstones, limestones
Tropical climates, coastal swamps, coal forests, shallow warm seas	Coal, limestones (Pennines), sandstones
Warm desert coastline, hot climate, shallow seas	Old red sandstone, slates, marls
Warm dry shallow seas, coral reefs	Slates, shales, some limestones
Warm seas and deserts in north; cool seas and climate in south	Sandstones, slates, shales
Cold at times, widespread seas	Mudstones, slates, sandstones, gritstones
Great mixture over 2 billion years	Schists, quartzites, gneisses

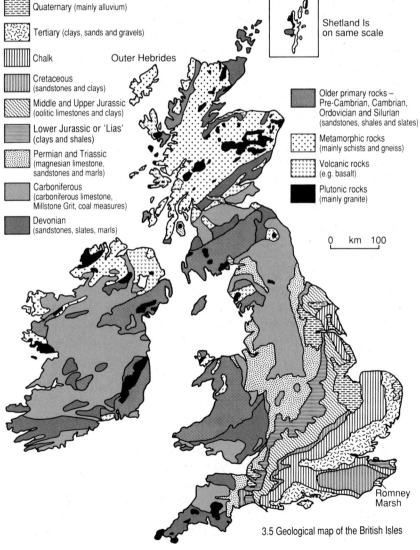

Legend:
- Quaternary (mainly alluvium)
- Tertiary (clays, sands and gravels)
- Chalk
- Cretaceous (sandstones and clays)
- Middle and Upper Jurassic (oolitic limestones and clays)
- Lower Jurassic or 'Lias' (clays and shales)
- Permian and Triassic (magnesian limestone, sandstones and marls)
- Carboniferous (carboniferous limestone, Millstone Grit, coal measures)
- Devonian (sandstones, slates, marls)
- Older primary rocks – Pre-Cambrian, Cambrian, Ordovician and Silurian (sandstones, shales and slates)
- Metamorphic rocks (mainly schists and gneiss)
- Volcanic rocks (e.g. basalt)
- Plutonic rocks (mainly granite)

Shetland Is on same scale

Outer Hebrides

Romney Marsh

3.5 Geological map of the British Isles

Landscapes

3.6 The Black Cuillins,Skye. A landscape of rugged volcanic mountains

Landscapes are a complex mixture of landforms of varying ages and origins. Stated simply, the landscape is the result of **agents of erosion** working on the **rocks** of the earth's surface over very long periods of time, at different scales.

Photo 3.6 shows part of the varied and beautiful landscape of the British Isles.There is a marked contrast between the rugged and sometimes spectacular mountainous areas of the north and west and the gently undulating lowlands of the south and east.

The British Isles are small but they have a very varied landscape of differing geological age and structure ranging from mountains, plateaux and hills to valleys and plains (3.7).

In the evolution of any landscape (3.8), the role of the geological structure is vitally important. The characteristics of the various rock types that underlie an area, the amount of tilting, folding and faulting, as well as the extent to which the rocks are buried, are all extremely important in shaping its landscape. The map of the British Isles (3.2) shows just how complex their geological structure is, with rocks ranging in age from the very young soft alluvium of the Romney Marsh deposited over the last 3000 years to the ancient and extremely hard gneisses of the

Outer Hebrides which originated over 2700 million years ago. With such a wide variety of rocks underlying the surface, it is not surprising that the landscapes of the British Isles are so varied.

But the fact that the geological structure of the British Isles is complex is not enough to create a varied landscape in itself. The agents of erosion – the wind, running water, ice and the sea – using the processes of erosion, transportation and deposition modify the landscape continuously, in different ways at different rates. Almost all the processes are dominated by gravity.

Material moves down a slope, either as a slowly creeping layer of soil, a bouncing boulder or a rapid landslide. Glaciers slide downhill and rivers flow down valleys. Debris is continually removed, carried downhill and deposited in valleys, lakes or the sea. In these ways, landscapes slowly evolve.

Thus, the creation of any landscape,for example, the Black Cuillin Hills of Skye, can be regarded on a variety of scales (3.9) from the creation of new land by volcanic eruptions caused by massive tectonic movements over millions of years, to the smaller-scale sculpting processes of weathering and human action over hundreds of years.

MacKinder's Tees–Exe line divides 'Highland Britain' from 'Lowland Britain'. The distribution of rocks older than 280 million years can be matched with the areas of strong relief: high mountains, plateaux and hills. The areas of low relief – valleys and low hills – can be matched with rocks younger than 280 million years old.

However, this division fails to explain entirely the great variation in the landscapes of the British Isles. The nature of the rock types, their properties, lines of weakness and the ways in which they are exploited by agents of erosion over time are vitally important in the evolution of different landscapes.

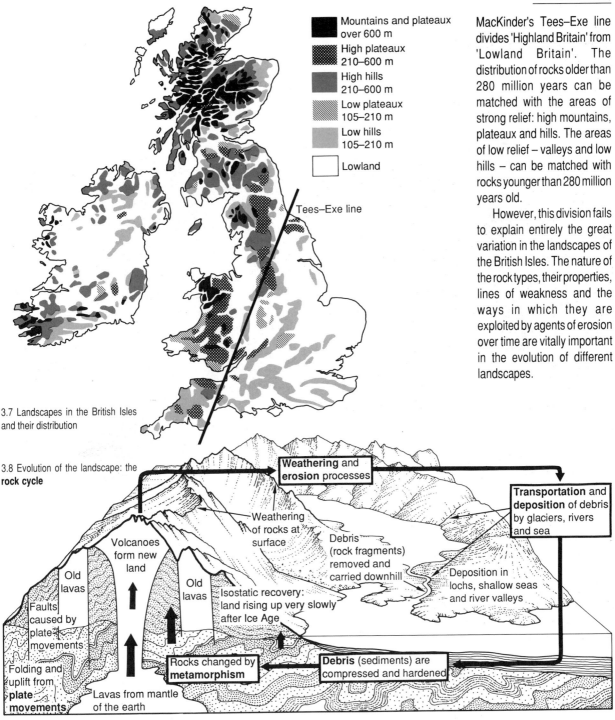

Mountains and plateaux over 600 m

High plateaux 210–600 m

High hills 210–600 m

Low plateaux 105–210 m

Low hills 105–210 m

Lowland

Tees–Exe line

3.7 Landscapes in the British Isles and their distribution

3.8 Evolution of the landscape: the **rock cycle**

Weathering and **erosion** processes

Transportation and **deposition** of debris by glaciers, rivers and sea

Weathering of rocks at surface

Debris (rock fragments) removed and carried downhill

Deposition in lochs, shallow seas and river valleys

Volcanoes form new land

Old lavas

Old lavas

Isostatic recovery: land rising up very slowly after Ice Age

Faults caused by plate movements

Folding and uplift from **plate movements**

Lavas from mantle of the earth

Rocks changed by metamorphism

Debris (sediments) are compressed and hardened

3.9 Scales in landscape processes

Creating processes Orogenies, intrusions, faulting	Readjustments Ice Ages, desert development	Modifications Glaciers, rivers, seas	Sculpting processes Weathering, slope processes, and people
Tens of millions of years	1–2 million years	Thousands of years	Hundreds of years

0 ——————————————— Time ——————————————— → Present

Ice Power

For three-quarters of the last 2.5 million years, the climate of the British Isles has been cold enough to support the spread of ice sheets. During this period, known as the **Pleistocene** or the Ice Age, there may have been as many as 20 different glaciations (3.10). The ice advanced in periods known as **glacials** and retreated in periods called **interglacials**.

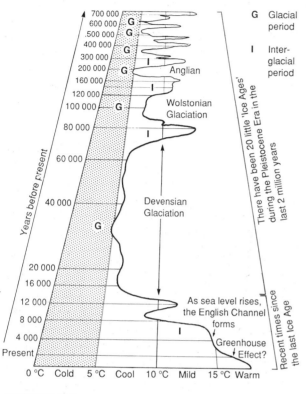

3.10 Little Ice Ages

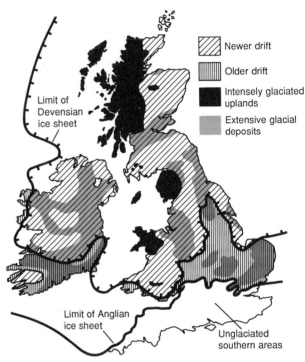

Key:
- Newer drift
- Older drift
- Intensely glaciated uplands
- Extensive glacial deposits

Limit of Devensian ice sheet

Limit of Anglian ice sheet

Unglaciated southern areas

3.11 The influence of glaciations in the British Isles

3.12 Glaciation in highland areas

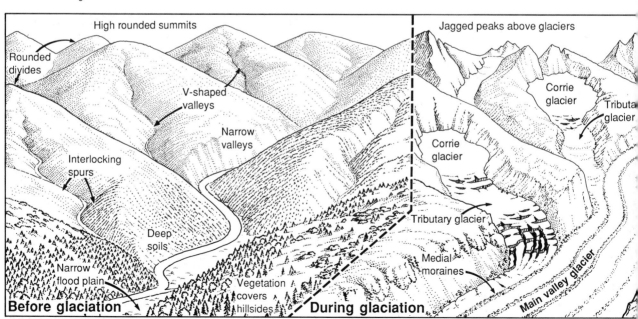

Before glaciation
- High rounded summits
- Rounded divides
- V-shaped valleys
- Narrow valleys
- Interlocking spurs
- Deep soils
- Narrow flood plain
- Vegetation covers hillsides

During glaciation
- Jagged peaks above glaciers
- Corrie glacier
- Tributary glacier
- Corrie glacier
- Tributary glacier
- Medial moraines
- Main valley glacier

The most extensive ice sheets are thought to have reached as far south as the Scilly Isles (3.11) and London during the oldest of the main glaciations, the Anglian, which occurred 270 000 years BP (before present). The limit of this glaciation defines the extent of glacial influence on the landscape of the British Isles. The Devensian glaciation (80 000 to 18 000 years BP) is also considered very important since its limit defines the boundary between the newer drift to the north and the older drift to the south. To the north of this line, there remains clearly preserved evidence of erosion and deposition by thick ice sheets.

By 18 000 BP the highland areas of the British Isles were covered in large domes of ice, extending down over lowlands to the south and east. A short-lived cold period from about 11 000 to 10 500 BP led to the Loch Lomond re-advance when ice returned to parts of the Scottish Highlands, the Lake District and North Wales.

Enormous quantities of snow and ice accumulated at the onset of each period of intense cold. The scenery of much of the British Isles probably resembled that of Antarctica today: huge expanses of glistening ice obliterating all but the tops of the highest mountains.

The majority of the British Isles lay beneath hundreds of metres of ice as recently as 18 000 years ago. Even the summit of Ben Nevis was then buried by over 350 metres of ice. Underneath the ice, the landscape was slowly modified as great valleys and massive hollows were gouged and scraped out of hard resistant rocks by the power of the ice (3.12). Ice is capable of widespread demolition of the landscape in upland areas, and extensive deposition in great valleys and lowland areas. But landscapes produced by ice are complicated since landforms created by one advance of the ice may be obliterated by the next (3.13).

Given Britain's icy history it is hardly surprising that much of the landscape of the British Isles has been shaped by ice sheets and glaciers. The degree of modification of the landscape by ice increases northwards. Intensely glaciated areas, such as the Cairngorm and North-West mountains, the Lake District and Snowdonia, are in great contrast to the southern areas which have never been glaciated. A drop in temperature of about 3 °C could see the return of glaciers in highland areas. It is thought that we are living through a short interglacial at present and that the ice will return in about 3000 years time.

3.13 A glaciated upland area

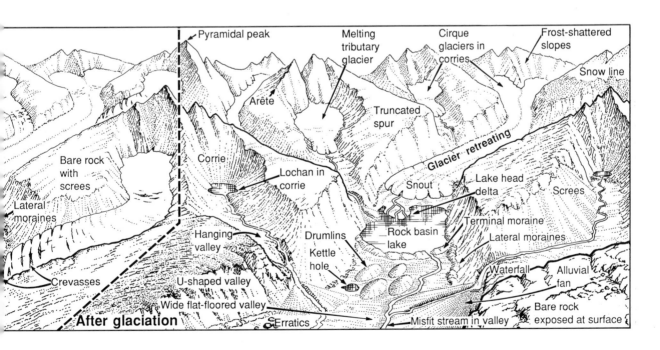

Glaciated Uplands

The areas of the British Isles which have been intensely glaciated are mainly uplands, including the Cairngorm mountains (3.14).

The present landscape of these mountains is the result of millions of years of uplift and erosion. The story begins 750 million years ago, when shales, sandstones and limestones were deposited on top of ancient crustal rocks. These sediments were then **metamorphosed** (changed into new rocks by heat or pressure) during the Caledonian orogeny about 500 million years BP. During this violent period, these rocks were heaved into huge overfolds, tens of kilometres across. They were upfolded high enough to form a range of mountains similar to the Alps today.

About 400 million years BP large masses of molten rock (magma) were pushed upwards into the roots of these mountains. The magma cooled to form a granite **batholith** beneath the peaks. In the years since then, all the overlying and much of the surrounding rocks (3.15) have been removed by erosion to reveal the present-day landscape. What we see today are not the ancient peaks but their worn down granite roots.

A large area of the Cairngorm mountains has the landscape of a dissected plateau (3.16): an area of high, relatively flat land cut by deep erosion. In great contrast to most of the south and east of the British Isles, the Cairngorms are a higher harsher landscape. The granite is a light pink colour with a high proportion of feldspar crystals. Where the granite lies exposed at the surface it is easily weathered. This produces a landscape of rounded summits, boulder-strewn slopes and occasional **tors** (3.17).

Many features of Cairngorm scenery are the result of the Ice Age. The high plateau is dissected by deep trenches such as Glen Einich (3.18) and Glen Avon which were gouged out by active glaciers during the last Ice Age. As the glaciers moved downhill, they eroded the landscape in two main ways. The underside of the ice froze onto jointed rocks and wrenching or **plucking** occurred as the ice tore away rock fragments while it moved downhill. With these rock fragments embedded in the base of the glacier, the ice scraped the land over which it moved. This process, known as **abrasion**, has produced hill slopes with a smooth general outline, but containing many rugged crags as a result of plucking. Rock fragments embedded in the sides and base of the glacier ice have also left scratches or **striations** on some otherwise smooth rock surfaces. These striations are clear evidence of the directions of ice movements. Corries (hollows or basins carved out at the source of the glacier) are common on north-facing slopes. They have steep craggy back walls and often contain corrie-lochs or lochans: Loch Etchachan is an example. Long narrow ribbon-lakes (e.g. Loch Avon) occupy the deep glaciated valleys, the sides of which show the scars of truncated spurs. These lakes gradually become shallower as sediments

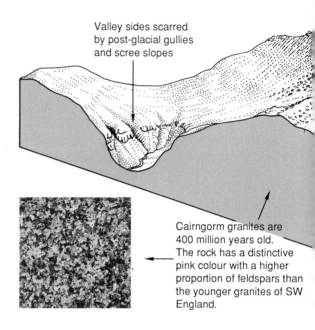

Valley sides scarred by post-glacial gullies and scree slopes

Cairngorm granites are 400 million years old. The rock has a distinctive pink colour with a higher proportion of feldspars than the younger granites of SW England.

3.14 Glaciated uplands: the Cairngorms, a gigantic granite batholith uplifted and eroded, forming Britain's highest mountain range

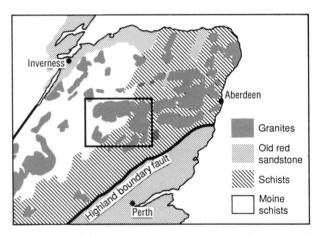

Inverness

Aberdeen

Granites

Old red sandstone

Schists

Moine schists

Highland Boundary fault

Perth

3.15 Location of the Cairngorm granites

are deposited by incoming streams. The valley floors are covered in different types of **moraine** (boulders and other debris deposited by the glacier), as well as post-glacial deposits of alluvial fans and screes. Intensive glaciation of the Cairngorms has left an inaccessible landscape with little soil cover.

Where the granite lies exposed for millions of years to the open air it weathers to form clays and sands. These in turn become the raw materials of new rocks and form other, younger landscapes in the British Isles.

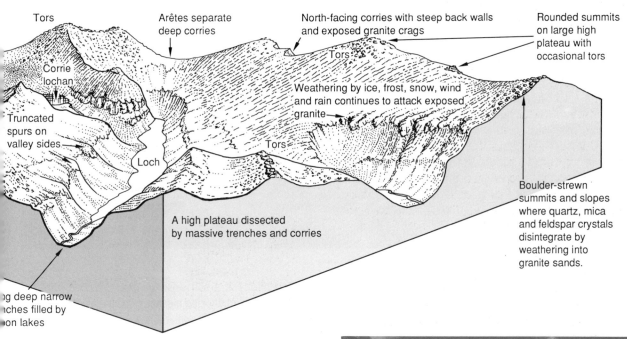

Tors

Arêtes separate
deep corries

North-facing corries with steep back walls
and exposed granite crags

Rounded summits
on large high
plateau with
occasional tors

Corrie
lochan

Tors

Truncated
spurs on
valley sides

Weathering by ice, frost, snow, wind
and rain continues to attack exposed
granite

Loch

Tors

A high plateau dissected
by massive trenches and corries

Boulder-strewn
summits and slopes
where quartz, mica
and feldspar crystals
disintegrate by
weathering into
granite sands.

g deep narrow
nches filled by
on lakes

3.16 The dissected Cairngorm Plateau

3.17 Cairn Lochan from Cairngorm summit

3.18 Glen Einich

Ribs and Gutters

Views such as the one in 3.19 show a very different landscape from those of the glaciated uplands composed of hard resistant granite. Such views are common in south-east England which is a landscape of **ribs** and **gutters**. The ribs are the long dry narrow uplands of the Chiltern and Cotswold Hills and the North and South Downs. The gutters, where the rivers flow, are the lower wetter vales of Oxford and Sussex. This a young landscape composed of relatively soft rocks such as sandstones, chalks and clays (3.20).

As igneous and metamorphic rocks are broken down by weathering and erosion, sediments – muds, silts, sands, etc. – are created. These, together with the bones and shells of dead sea creatures, form **sedimentary rocks** as they accumulate and become compressed in deserts, lakes, river beds, deltas and shallow seas. Several sedimentary rocks form the basis of south-east England. Chalks and clays cover the largest area.

Chalk (3.21) is a soft white limestone, formed from the protective shells of tiny sea creatures compressed on the sea floor in warm clear shallow water. Chalk is **permeable**, i.e. it has minute pore spaces or cracks through which water can pass slowly. It is a fine-grained rock, often containing hard **flints** (formed from the skeletal remains of sea-floor sponges).

Clay is an entirely different kind of rock. It is a finely grained softer rock, more easily eroded and able to hold moisture. It is an **impermeable** rock (water cannot flow through it) composed of fine rock fragments, such as weathered feldspar crystals from decaying granites, laid down in cool shallow seas.

3.21a Chalk

3.21b Clay

3.20 The geology of south-east England

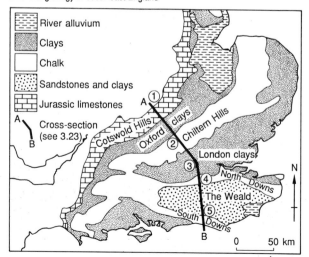

- River alluvium
- Clays
- Chalk
- Sandstones and clays
- Jurassic limestones

A — B Cross-section (see 3.23)

0   50 km

N

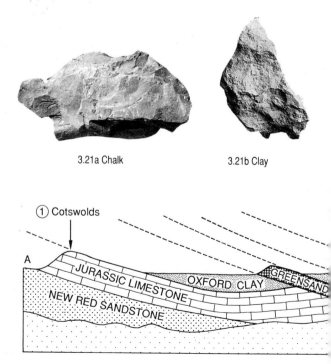

① Cotswolds

A — JURASSIC LIMESTONE — OXFORD CLAY — GREENSAND

NEW RED SANDSTONE

Other sedimentary rocks found in south-east England include limestones and sandstones.

The development of the landscape of this south-east corner of the British Isles is one in which deposition and crustal movements have been very important (3.22). The original land surface was a **peneplain** (the eroded base of a mountain range), tilted by the earth movements of the Hercynian orogeny. For over 200 million years a succession of sediments were laid down on top of this, and compressed to form the rocks found in the area today. Each had a different sedimentary environment: for example, new red sandstone was produced by wind action (aeolian); limestones and chalks formed from deposits on marine shelves; sandstones formed from lake (lacustrine) and deltaic deposits.

When the Alps and the Pyrenees were later thrust up during crustal upheavals 30 million years ago, the shockwaves rippled across these sedimentary rocks and lifted the chalks up from the floor of the sea. Anticlines such as the Wealden (3.23) were created, forming giant domes that covered south-east England.

But the bending and stretching of the earth movements weakened the rocks. Frost, ice, snow, rain, and rivers have since exploited these weaknesses and removed the centres of the great domes to expose the older sandstones of the Weald and limestones of the Cotswolds. The North and South Downs and Chilterns are all that is left of the rims of these great anticlines today (3.19).

3.22

Era	Period	Millions of years	Earth movements	Conditions	Rock types formed	SE England locations
Cenozoic	Quaternary	Less than 2		River deposits/ coastal deposits Erosion and weathering prevail	Alluvium/beach material/ river gaps/chalk cliffs	Romney Marshes, Adur Valley/Seven Sisters
	Tertiary	2–65	Alpine	Alpine Orogeny upfolds sediments	Synclines/anticlines	Scarp and vale landscapes
				Deep marine shelf, deposition of thick muds and organic debris	London Clay	
Mesozoic	Cretaceous (Latin for chalk)	65–140		Seas warm up again. Still, clear seas develop thick chalky muds; some skeletal remains of sponges	Chalks/flints	Chilterns/Downs
				Area floods and muds deposited	Gault clays	Maidstone/Ashford
				Deltaic deposition of sands and gravels	Greensands	Leith Hill
				Widespread erosion of uplands creates mudflats in deltas	Wealden clays	Vales of Sussex, Kent
				Wealden lake/swamp covers area Beds of mud and sands form	Weald sandstones	High Weald
	Jurassic	140–195		Cooler seas with rise in levels: fine rock fragments deposited	Oxford clays	Vale of Oxford
				Warm shallow seas flood area: small mudcoated shells and bones deposited on sea floor	Limestone (Oolitic: Jurassic)	Cotswolds
Palae-ozoic	Permian-Triassic	195–280		Arid desert, sand seas, wind-blown (**aeolian**) deposits develop	New red sandstones	Midland Plain (Leicester area)
	Permo-Carboniferous	280–300	Hercynian	Earthquakes and crust upheavals tilt land surface	Basement rocks of Peneplain	Ancient land surface (deeply buried)

3.23 Cross-section of south-east England

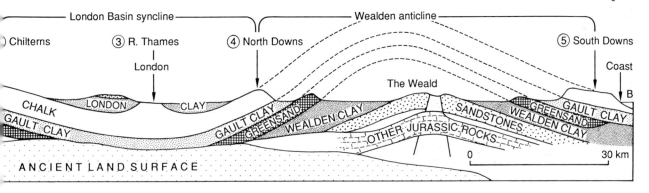

Scarpland

Where chalk and limestone ridges alternate with clay vales (3.24), the landscape is referred to as **scarpland**. Here, the ridges commonly have unequal slopes: a short steep **scarp** slope and a longer more gentle **dip** slope. Such ridges are called escarpments or **cuestas**: the North and South Downs are well-known examples.

The Wealden area is a scarpland which formed as different rock types became exposed at the surface. Where the chalk meets the coast, sea action produces white cliffs (3.25).

The structure and scenery of the landscape of south-east England (3.26) has evolved as a result of six main influences.

1. The ripple effect from the earth movement which built the Alps between 70 and 50 million years ago and which created the anticlines and synclines of south-east England (see page 85). The main structural divisions are the Weald and its surrounding eroded vales of Sussex and Kent. On 3.26 these are outlined by the inward-facing escarpments of the Downs.

2. The **differential erosion** of the rocks of the area. Chalks, sandstones and clays erode at different rates. The chalk generally forms the higher areas and sea cliffs. Some sandstones also produce bold escarpments, for example, the greensand which wraps itself around the Weald forms Leith Hill. The younger sands and clays are found in the broad lowlands of the vales of Sussex and Kent.

3. The processes of erosion and deposition. In this area these are mainly weathering, landslides and the action of running water. The chalk outcrops have little or no surface drainage with smooth scarp slopes and deep dry valleys. Greensand also has dry valleys and some marshy areas. The clays have an extensive drainage pattern with streams and wide flood plains, for example the Medway.

4. Changing climatic conditions since the Pleistocene glaciations. These have affected sea levels and altered the course of rivers such as the Stour. Meltwaters from the ice sheets of the nearby London area are thought to have been responsible for a great deal of the removal of the overlying sedimentary rocks to expose the High Weald (3.27).

5. The work of the sea. The main features of the geology of much of this area can be clearly seen in the changing nature of the coastline between Beachy Head and Dover. The sand dunes (Littlehampton), marshes (Romney), beaches, spits and bars are the result of longshore drift and deposition.

6. Human action. Vales have been drained to make productive farmland. The building of groynes at Hastings and Eastbourne to protect sandy beaches has caused as much erosion as it has prevented.

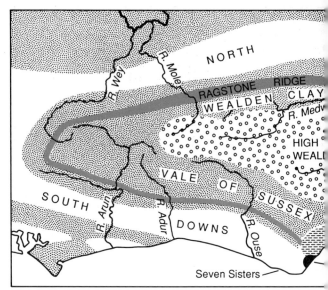

3.24 Geological map of south-east England

Chalk scarps

① Alpine folding and erosion reveal long chalk escarpments

② Eroded anticlines have steep faces known as **scarp** slopes

③ Longer, more gentle slopes are known as **dip** slopes

④ Short steep dry valleys in scarp slopes are known as **coombes**

⑤ Winter streams may flow in dry valleys. They are called **bournes**

⑥ **Outliers** are remnants of overlying chalks

⑦ Chalk uplands have little surface drainage

⑧ Famous 'White Cliffs' are formed by sea action where chalk meets sea

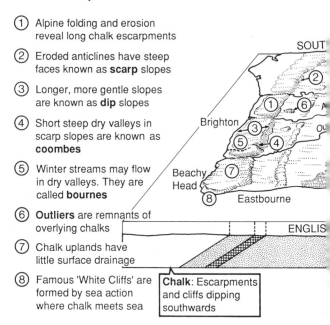

Chalk: Escarpments and cliffs dipping southwards

3.26 Structure and scenery of south-east England

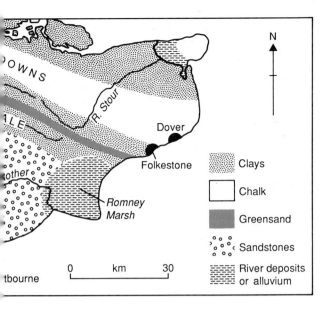

Legend:
- Clays
- Chalk
- Greensand
- Sandstones
- River deposits or alluvium

0   km   30

Dover
Folkestone
Romney Marsh
R. Stour
DOWNS
tbourne

N

3.25 The Seven Sisters: chalk meets sea

Clay vales

⑨ Eroded more easily than chalk, clays form low-lying areas

⑩ Clays are undulating lowlands or vales with much surface drainage

⑪ Vales saturate easily and are liable to flooding

⑫ Rivers meander across low land and have a tendency to flood, building up alluvial coatings.

⑬ In scarpland, clay vales provide easy routeways

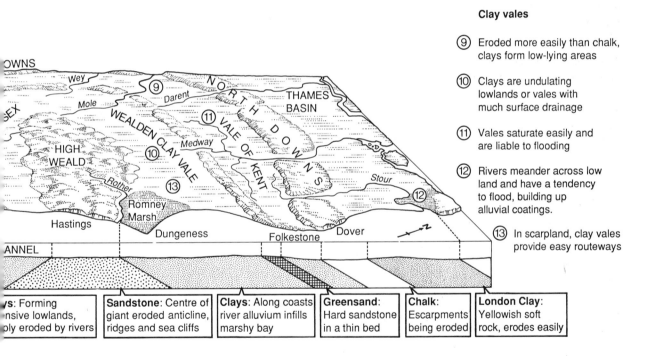

vs: Forming ensive lowlands, ly eroded by rivers

Sandstone: Centre of giant eroded anticline, ridges and sea cliffs

Clays: Along coasts river alluvium infills marshy bay

Greensand: Hard sandstone in a thin bed

Chalk: Escarpments being eroded

London Clay: Yellowish soft rock, erodes easily

3.27 Formation of the Weald

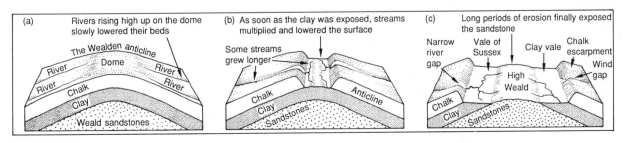

(a) Rivers rising high up on the dome slowly lowered their beds
- The Wealden anticline
- Dome
- River
- Chalk
- Clay
- Weald sandstones

(b) As soon as the clay was exposed, streams multiplied and lowered the surface
- Some streams grew longer
- Chalk
- Clay
- Sandstones
- Anticline

(c) Long periods of erosion finally exposed the sandstone
- Narrow river gap
- Vale of Sussex
- Clay vale
- Chalk escarpment
- High Weald
- Wind gap
- Chalk
- Clay
- Sandstones

Karst

3.28 Carboniferous limestone areas in the British Isles

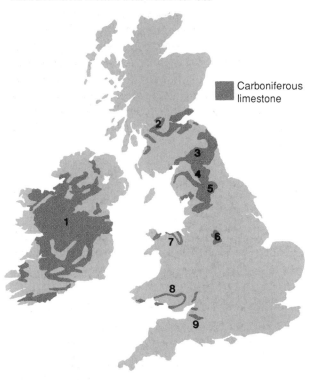

Carboniferous limestone

1 Central Plain	**4** Pennines	**7** North Wales
2 Lennox Hills	**5** Yorkshire Dales	**8** Brecon Beacons
3 Cheviot Hills	**6** Peak District	**9** Mendip Hills

3.29 Karst landscape of North Wales

All rocks influence the landscape of which they are the base but none form such distinctive landscapes as carboniferous limestone. The most extensive areas of carboniferous limestone in the British Isles are shown in 3.28. Many of these form well-known landscapes such as the Yorkshire Dales, Peak District and the Cheddar Gorge. The scenery that develops in such areas (3.29) is known as **karst**, named after an area of limestone in Yugoslavia.

Carboniferous limestone (3.30) is a hard grey sedimentary rock. It is entirely made of calcium carbonate ($CaCO_3$) and contains many fossilised remains. Limestone is **pervious**, i.e. water is able to pass through it by means of joints and bedding planes (though not pore spaces). It is the only common rock which is physically strong (hard) and yet will also dissolve slowly in rainwater. Consequently, the joints and bedding planes within the limestone (3.31) are gradually enlarged by underground water into wide channels and gaping chambers, which can absorb all surface drainage. The result is a 'gruyere' landscape – one that is full of holes!

3.30 Carboniferous limestone

The geological history of the limestone that forms the Yorkshire Dales begins in the Carboniferous period, named after the carbons found in the rocks which formed between 345 and 280 million years ago. Shallow tropical seas covered the area. Corals formed on the sea floor, where the skeletal remains of sea

creatures were also deposited. Over a period of 60 million years these were compressed into limestones as other sediments were overlain. Hercynian crustal movements then upfolded the entire area forming the giant anticline of the Pennine hills. As the younger sedimentary rocks have been eroded, the limestone has been exposed, forming high rugged uplands reaching to over 600 metres in parts of the North Pennines.

The main outcrops of carboniferous limestone in the Yorkshire Dales were first exposed about two million years ago. Since then the alternating climates of the Ice Ages have shaped the limestone by contrasting erosional processes (3.32).

The process of **solution** has been of major importance in shaping the limestone landscape. The rate that limestone dissolves depends on the amount of carbon dioxide present in the water

acting upon it. The availability of this gas in turn depends on the richness of the surface vegetation which, in turn, is determined by the climate. Thus during the interglacials water rich in CO_2 dissolved the limestone and eroded cave systems. This process continues in the present-day climate.

During glacial periods sub-surface systems were frozen and ice became the main agent of erosion but on the surface only. Large glaciers scoured the landscape; they deepened the dales, truncated many of the scars and scraped bare the plateau areas.

In periods when the ice cover was incomplete, powerful meltwater streams were released from the ice which carved deep gorges and enlarged the main dales. Geologists refer to the landscape which is the product of these alternations as **glaciokarst**.

3.31

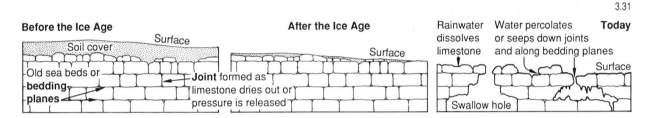

Before the Ice Age — Soil cover — Surface — Old sea beds or **bedding planes**

After the Ice Age — Surface — **Joint** formed as limestone dries out or pressure is released

Rainwater dissolves limestone — Water percolates or seeps down joints and along bedding planes — **Today** — Surface — Swallow hole

3.32 Karst scenery

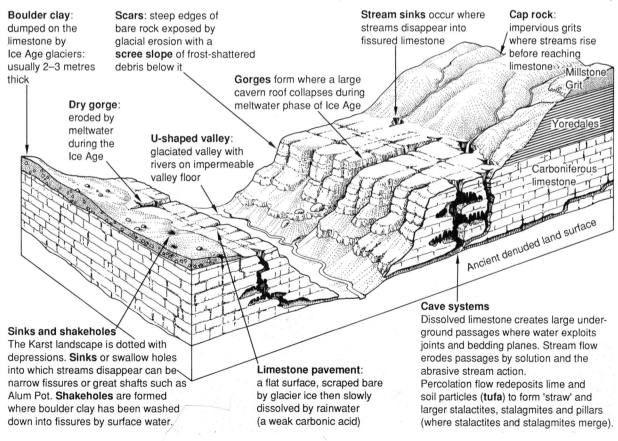

Boulder clay: dumped on the limestone by Ice Age glaciers: usually 2–3 metres thick

Scars: steep edges of bare rock exposed by glacial erosion with a **scree slope** of frost-shattered debris below it

Dry gorge: eroded by meltwater during the Ice Age

Gorges form where a large cavern roof collapses during meltwater phase of Ice Age

U-shaped valley: glaciated valley with rivers on impermeable valley floor

Stream sinks occur where streams disappear into fissured limestone

Cap rock: impervious grits where streams rise before reaching limestone

Millstone Grit

Yoredales

Carboniferous limestone

Ancient denuded land surface

Sinks and shakeholes The Karst landscape is dotted with depressions. **Sinks** or swallow holes into which streams disappear can be narrow fissures or great shafts such as Alum Pot. **Shakeholes** are formed where boulder clay has been washed down into fissures by surface water.

Limestone pavement: a flat surface, scraped bare by glacier ice then slowly dissolved by rainwater (a weak carbonic acid)

Cave systems Dissolved limestone creates large underground passages where water exploits joints and bedding planes. Stream flow erodes passages by solution and the abrasive stream action. Percolation flow redeposits lime and soil particles (**tufa**) to form 'straw' and larger stalactites, stalagmites and pillars (where stalactites and stalagmites merge).

Upland Limestone Landscapes

The carboniferous limestone of the Northern Pennines forms upland areas which are separated by flat-floored glaciated valleys or dales (3.33). The area lies within the Yorkshire Dales and features most of the scenery described on pages 88–9.

Within this area lies Malham: an area with a very special karst landscape. Few other areas of the British Isles posses rock formations on such an impressive scale (3.34). Crustal movements, sedimentation, glaciation and weathering have combined to create a landscape which includes deep gorges, scars, limestone pavements and dry valleys. These landforms can be studied both from the information on these two pages, and from the map extract of the Malham area on page 167.

Light grey limestone dominates the landscape of the Malham area, in the form of rolling plateaux. The limestone has no surface drainage but rivers occupy some of the very deep valleys, dissecting the uplands into blocks.

Geologists are certain that this area has been affected at least three times in the last million years by powerful ice flows. The legacy of these glaciations is still to be seen in the landscape of Malham. The rocks of the area were wrenched and twisted during the uplift of the Craven Fault (3.35) and then eroded during periods of intense glaciation. In some places the limestone was completely removed by ice erosion, exposing the older impermeable rocks which underly the Pennines. This explains why some of the deeper valleys contain rivers, and also explains the only expanse of water in the limestone landscape of the Yorkshire Dales: Malham Tarn. Glacial action scoured a hollow in the impermeable underlying slates (3.25) which was later filled with water, forming a lake.

Shallow dry valleys such as Watlowes (3.36) were created as abrasive meltwater streams scoured the frozen limestone towards the end of the last glacial period. The valley is dry today because surface water sinks into the limestone. Evidence of the power of the meltwater is also to be seen at the spectacular Malham Cove (3.37), first carved by grinding ice, and at Gordale Scar (3.38).

The last retreat of the ice 12 000 years ago left behind a barren landscape, scoured of its soil cover. The exposed limestone was then attacked by the weather. Rainwater began to dissolve the bare limestone, creating pavements (3.38). Frost-shattering attacked the limestone prising fragments of rock from scars and cliffs, forming **screes**.

The spectacular nature of the Malham landscape has attracted millions of visitors this century. The area now bares the new scars of eroded footpaths and large overcrowded car parks.

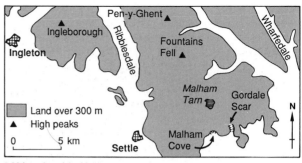

3.33 Location of the Malham area

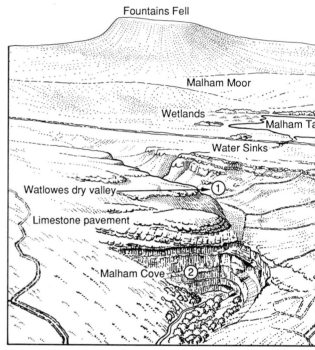

3.34 The Malham area. Valleys and gorges that were formed in glacials become dry when the climate changes and warms up. They are preserved because there is no surface water to erode them.

3.35 Geology of the Malham area

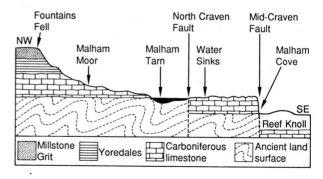

3.36 Watlowes dry valley, originally cut by icy meltwater above Malham Cove, now dry because water sinks into limestone

3.37 Malham Cove was created by ice and water erosion. This spectacular cliff of limestone, over 70 metres high, was first exposed by plucking. Then meltwater from Watlowes would have formed a giant waterfall over the cliff face. In post-glacial times, collapse of the weaker parts of the face has helped maintain its steepness.

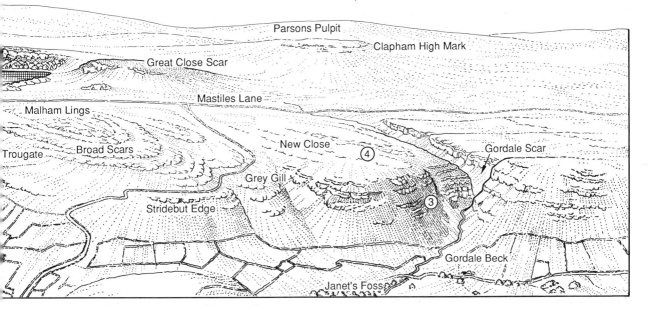

Parsons Pulpit
Clapham High Mark
Great Close Scar
Mastiles Lane
Malham Lings
Trougate
Broad Scars
New Close
④
Gordale Scar
Grey Gill
③
Stridebut Edge
Gordale Beck
Janet's Foss

3.38 Gordale Scar. Geologists differ over its development. Some believe that it was the site of a massive cavern whose roof collapsed under pressure from meltwater. Others suggest that the gorge was eroded by a very aggressive meltwater stream tumbling down the steep slopes at the end of the last Ice Age.

3.39 **Pavements** are areas of bare limestone, scraped clear of soil by glacial abrasion. Rainwater then dissolves the surface rock along the joints, enlarging these into deep gaps called **grykes** leaving raised blocks or **clints** of limestone inbetween. Some **bedding planes** (surfaces separating layers of sedimentary rock) are so opened up by solution that the clints wobble on top of the bedrock.

Q THE GEOLOGY OF THE BRITISH ISLES/ LANDSCAPES

1 (a) Explain the following terms: orogeny, anticline, sedimentary rock.

(b) Use an atlas to help you link each area listed on the left with the appropriate rock type on the right.

Chiltern Hills	Schists
Cairngorms	Cretaceous chalk
Pennines	Old red sandstone
NW Highlands	Granites
Exmoor	Carboniferous limestone

(c) What evidence is there of crustal activity in the British Isles?

(d) Explain how the closure of the ancient Iapetus Ocean brought together the different parts of the British Isles.

(e) Describe the effects of the three main orogenies on the structure and geology of the British Isles.

(f) What evidence is there of continental drift in the geology of the British Isles?

(g) Explain the terms (i) landforms, (ii) landscapes.

(h) Explain the importance of geological structure on the landscape.

(i) Design your own diagram to illustrate the rock cycle.

(j) On which different scales are landscapes created? Explain .

(k) What is the Tees–Exe line?

Q RIBS AND GUTTERS

Diagram 2

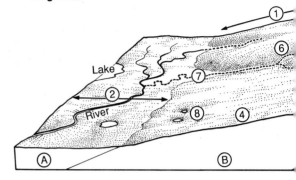

3 (a) In what way is south-east England a landscape of ribs and gutters?

(b) Explain the following in detail.

i. Chalk is a good example of a permeable porous rock.

ii. Clay is a good example of an impermeable impervious rock.

(c) Write brief notes on each of the following: flint, outliers, cuestas, vales, greensands.

(d) In which ways did the Alpine orogeny influence the structure of south-east England?

(e) Account for the formation of the scarplands of south-east England.

Q ICE POWER/GLACIATED UPLANDS

Diagram 1   Glaciated uplands

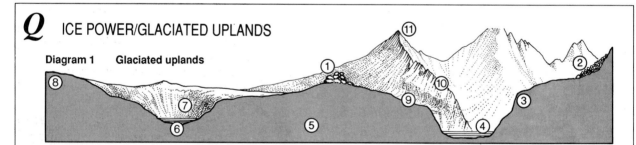

2 (a) Identify at least two large glaciated uplands in Britain.

(b) Define the terms Pleistocene, glacial and interglacial.

(c) Write brief notes to explain the following: truncated spur; arête; hanging valley; erratic; drumlin; terminal, lateral and medial moraines; pyramidal peak; corrie; lochan; alluvial fan.

(d) Classify the above features of glacial action into features of erosion or deposition.

(e) Draw a labelled field sketch of photograph 3.13.

(f) Describe the processes involved in the glaciation of an upland area such as the Cairngorms.

(g) Copy diagram 1. Complete the diagram by compiling a key for the numbers 1–10. Add any other landscape features you can think of to both the diagram and the key.

(h) Which factors affect the rate of glacial erosion?

(i) Explain the role of granite landscapes in the rock cycle.

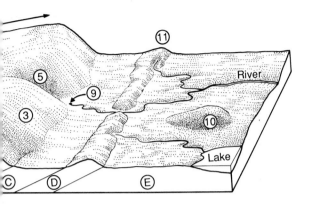

(f) South-east England displays a landscape created by **differential erosion**. Explain this process and its effect on the scenery of the area.

(g) Study diagram 2 carefully. Copy the diagram and complete it by identifying the main landscape features 1–11 of scarpland and the main underlying rocks A–E in a key.

(h) With the aid of diagram 2, describe and explain the influence of the landscape's structure on the drainage pattern and water availability.

(i) Write an essay entitled 'The main influences on the structure and scenery of south-east England'.

Q   KARST/ UPLAND LIMESTONE LANDSCAPES

4 (a) What is a karst landscape?

(b) Name five of the main areas of karst landscape in the British Isles.

(c) Describe the properties of carboniferous limestone.

(d) Explain each of the following in detail: solution, joints, bedding planes, cap rocks.

(e) What does the existence of carboniferous limestone indicate about the continental drift of the British Isles?

(f) List the main features of karst scenery.

(g) Annotate sketches of 3.29, 3.37 and 3.38 to describe the landscape shown in each.

(h) What evidence is there of glaciation in the Malham area?

Q   OS MAP EXTRACT (PAGE 167)

5 Use the (1: 25 000) map extract of the Malham area on page 167 and the text on pages 90–1 to answer the following questions on **karst** scenery.

(a) Re-order the items in the following three lists to match each grid reference with the correct landform and the correct description of the natural process which formed it.

Six-figure reference	Landform	Formation process
915641	Scar	Solution by rainwater.
901656	Spring	Layer of resistant rock hinders erosion.
903645	Waterfall	Eroded by meltwater/ cave roof collapse.
895674	Pavement	Boulder clay washed into fissure.
897641	Shakehole	Glacial erosion.
912634	Gorge	Re-emergence at surface along older, impermeable strata.

(b) Draw a very simple labelled sketch or diagram to show the structure, relief and drainage of the Malham area shown on the extract.

(c) Compare the relief and drainage of grid squares 8964 and 9163.

(d) Describe the land surface at (i) 903646 (ii) 916638 (iii) 884658.

(e) What map evidence is there to suggest that the Malham area has underground systems?

(f) Compare the distribution of scars and pavements with that of the shakeholes in the area of the map extract. Explain any differences noted.

(g) Draw a simple annotated cross-section of the area on the map extract from 893680 to 920640. Name the major landforms along the line of section and then describe the relief, geology and drainage along the line of section.

Research and Further Work

Compare the distribution, relief and drainage characteristics of scarpland and karst landscapes.
In which ways does each landscape limit its potential land uses?

Weathering: Small-scale Decay of the Landscape

The granite, clays and limestones that form the landscapes studied in the previous sections are found in entirely different environments today from those in which they originated.

They were formed at high temperature, or under pressure, in the absence of surface water or air. Millions of years later, they

have become surface rocks, exposed by a combination of crustal movements and subsequent large-scale erosion, and are now slowly undergoing small-scale decay. This process of **weathering** happens because the rocks are exposed to the earth's moist atmosphere, and temperatures which range from freezing point to 100 °C.

Weathering is the small-scale natural breakdown of rock. It is the result of the combined action of all the processes which cause rocks to disintegrate (break into fragments: 3.40) and decompose (rot through chemical reactions). The weathered material forms a layer which lies on top of the unaltered rock, and is known as the **regolith**. This, in turn, is acted upon further by the weather, by water moving through it, and by rotted plant matter and organisms to form soil.

Weathering is classified into three main types: physical,

3.40 Scree slopes at Wast Water, Cumbria

3.41 Small-scale decay of the landscape

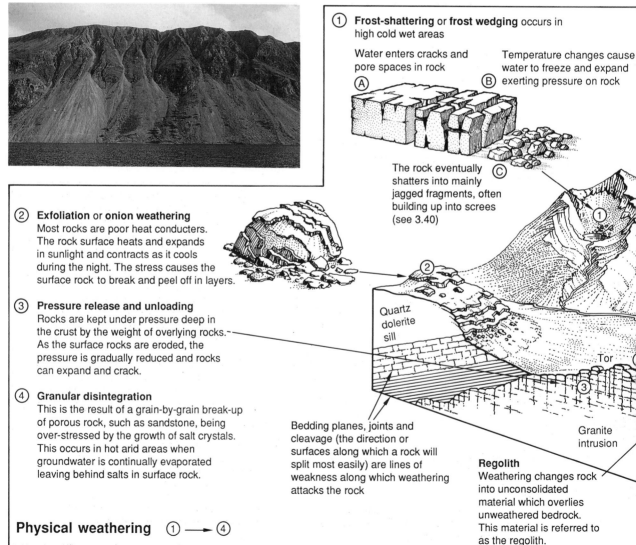

① Frost-shattering or **frost wedging** occurs in high cold wet areas

Water enters cracks and pore spaces in rock Ⓐ

Temperature changes cause water to freeze and expand Ⓑ exerting pressure on rock

The rock eventually Ⓒ shatters into mainly jagged fragments, often building up into screes (see 3.40)

② Exfoliation or **onion weathering**
Most rocks are poor heat conductors. The rock surface heats and expands in sunlight and contracts as it cools during the night. The stress causes the surface rock to break and peel off in layers.

③ Pressure release and unloading
Rocks are kept under pressure deep in the crust by the weight of overlying rocks. As the surface rocks are eroded, the pressure is gradually reduced and rocks can expand and crack.

④ Granular disintegration
This is the result of a grain-by-grain break-up of porous rock, such as sandstone, being over-stressed by the growth of salt crystals. This occurs in hot arid areas when groundwater is continually evaporated leaving behind salts in surface rock.

Quartz dolerite sill

Tor

Bedding planes, joints and cleavage (the direction or surfaces along which a rock will split most easily) are lines of weakness along which weathering attacks the rock

Granite intrusion

Regolith
Weathering changes rock into unconsolidated material which overlies unweathered bedrock. This material is referred to as the regolith.

Physical weathering ① ⟶ ④

chemical, and biotic weathering (3.41).

Physical weathering occurs where physical forces (mainly temperature changes) cause rock to disintegrate into smaller pieces. There is no change to the minerals within the rock. Physical weathering can be the result of frost-shattering. This happens when water enters cracks in rocks, then freezes and expands, forcing the cracks to open further, eventually causing pieces of rock to break off. Physical weathering can also be the result of rocks expanding when they are hot and then contracting when they are cool. If this happens repeatedly the stress can break a rock. Physical weathering tends to produce large rock fragments.

Anything smaller than a grain of sand is usually the result of **chemical weathering**. This occurs when there is a chemical reaction between water or a weak acid and rock, causing the minerals in the rock to alter. Rainwater is a weak carbonic acid. Water passing over decaying vegetation also produces acids. Both types of acid are capable of decomposing rocks (3.42). The new materials produced by chemical weathering are very small particles called **clays**.

Biotic weathering is a combination of physical and chemical weathering which is caused by plant and animal action.

Where there is a cover of vegetation, chemical weathering processes are more important than physical weathering.

Soils develop where chemical and biotic weathering are more dominant than physical weathering. People also influence the weathering processes, mainly by quarrying and industry which increases the acidity of rainwater.

Weathered material builds up where it is formed: no movement is involved except where the effects of gravity cause it to slip or fall downwards.

Chemical weathering ⑤ —→ ⑨

⑤ **Solution and carbonation** is the weathering process performed by rainwater on limestones. It is believed that, where a soil cover exists, this process of chemical weathering is more effective in creating pavements of clints and grykes.

⑥ Granite tors indicate that subsurface chemical weathering occurs before the rocks are exposed at the surface.

3.42 Tower karst scenery, South China

⑦ Limestone suffers rapid chemical weathering in tropical areas where carbonation is accelerated by heat. Monsoon rains in South China have created the 'tower karst' landscape of cone-shaped hills (3.42).

⑧ **Hydrolisis** is a chemical reaction between a mineral and water and is the most common chemical weathering process. Basalt rock is changed into bauxites or laterites. This process is responsible for rock weathering to great depth in warm moist climates.

⑨ In cooler climates acid water in soils reacts with feldspar. As granite contains much feldspar it is a rock steadily rotted by rain.

Gradual erosion of the landscape

Tropical sea

Biotic weathering

⑩ **Vegetation cover** shades soil surfaces. Plant roots expand as plants grow and can force rocks apart. This can set-off weathering by allowing water into rocks.

⑪ **Animals**: burrowing animals can expose rocks to weathering. Limpets secrete acids attacking coastal rocks.

⑫ **Industrialisation** by humans has increased the acidity of rainwater accelerating chemical weathering.

Mass Movements

3.43 Gravity is the main force affecting mass movements of weathered material and solid rock

Weathering may produce so much debris that it becomes unstable and moves downhill. The movement of this unconsolidated regolith or debris down a slope by the pull of gravity is known as **mass movement** or **wasting** (3.43). Such movements of rock waste may be very rapid or very slow and can be triggered off by an earthquake or torrential rain.

Gravity, rock type and structure, slope angle, vegetation cover and water content are the most important factors in determining the nature of mass movements on slopes.

On very steep slopes where soil or vegetation is lacking, the main slope processes are rapid physical ones. Rocks are prised away from bare slopes by frost-shattering or exfoliation. The result is **rockfalls** which accumulate at the foot of the slope in **talus** or **scree** slopes (3.44). Screes are not usually thick but they can protect slopes and prevent further physical weathering. Streams may wash the scree away from the foot of the slope. But, if this does not happen, screes will gradually rot where they are, to form a soil.

Landslides are rapid movements of soil or rock on less steep slopes. After heavy rain, water may build up in the soil and help lubricate the soil-subsoil layer. The increase in overlying weight causes rock or soil to slide downhill (3.45).

Slides affect both hard rocks and unconsolidated regolith. They happen when rocks or regoliths are not properly supported. Large-scale slides are frequent in Japan where torrential rainstorms add weight to rock or soil. Small-scale slides are common along embankments of railways or motorways, and can be very dangerous.

Mudflows and solifluction are rapid movements of saturated soil and water down hollows in a slope. Mudflows occur in areas with sparse vegetation which are subject to torrential downpours. They affect a greater depth than slides do, and resemble the flow of a stream. If the subsoil is impermeable, heavy rains may cause the topsoil to flow freely. Sandy soils, when saturated, often flow over impermeable subsoils (3.46).

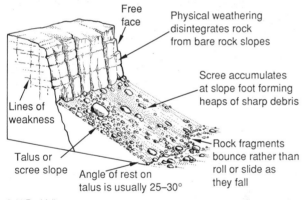

Free face

Physical weathering disintegrates rock from bare rock slopes

Scree accumulates at slope foot forming heaps of sharp debris

Lines of weakness

Rock fragments bounce rather than roll or slide as they fall

Talus or scree slope

Angle of rest on talus is usually 25–30°

3.44 Rockfalls

3.45 Slides

Large detached blocks of rock or soil break away

Impact point

Glide plane

Slides occur after torrential rain

Debris from last slide

3.46 Flows

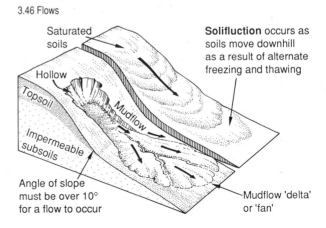

Saturated soils

Solifluction occurs as soils move downhill as a result of alternate freezing and thawing

Hollow

Topsoil

Mudflow

Impermeable subsoils

Angle of slope must be over 10° for a flow to occur

Mudflow 'delta' or 'fan'

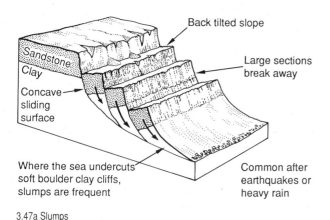

3.47a Slumps

3.47b Slumping along the Dorset coast

Slumping (3.47a) occurs in weaker rocks and involves a degree of rotational movement. Along parts of the Dorset coast, where clay underlies sandstone, slumping is very common, sometimes threatening lives (3.47b).

On more gentle slopes, slower mass movements take place. **Slopewash** occurs in places where rainfall exceeds the capacity of soil to absorb water. This can take various forms, including sheetwash (where excess surface water removes whole sheets of soil) and rillwash (where excess surface water concentrates into small channels: see 3.48). Where there is a lack of vegetation cover to hold the soil in place, slopewash can produce **gullying**.

Soil creep is an even slower process of mass movement. In this case, little or no movement takes place at the base of the soil. When rain falls on the soil and sinks in, the soil expands at right angles to the slope (3.49). When the soil dries out again it contracts in a vertical direction. The net result is a downward movement. The same effect can also be produced by freezing and thawing of water within soil particles. Soil creep is so slow that it is seldom actually witnessed.

Most slopes steeper than about 6° show signs of soil creep (see 3.49). Soil creep under turf or other vegetation only reaches speeds of about 1 cm a year. But removal of vegetation can accelerate soil movement. When the binding effects of plant roots are lost, a waterlogged soil can move downhill like a very viscous porridge.

Mass movements are also influenced by the actions of people. By deforesting slopes, removing grass or harvesting crops, by quarrying, road building or walking in large numbers on steep slopes, surface materials may be loosened and downward movements may be triggered.

3.48 Slopewash, Arizona, USA

3.49 Soil creep

Slopes

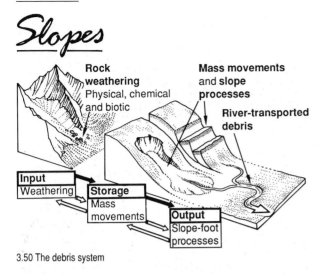

Rock weathering
Physical, chemical and biotic

Mass movements and slope processes

River-transported debris

Input		
Weathering	**Storage**	
	Mass movements	**Output**
		Slope-foot processes

3.50 The debris system

The slope processes examined on pages 96–7 can be thought of as part of a conveyor belt, transporting the products of weathering on the first part of the journey to the sea. We can think of the weathering as the **input** part of the **debris system** (3.50). Slope processes and mass movement form the next part of the system, and river transportation removes debris from the foot of the slope.

The relationship between the inputs and outputs on any slope determine whether the slope becomes steeper or more gentle.

A useful way to think of any hillslope (3.51a) is to imagine it as a jigsaw surface made of soil, vegetation, rock and water. Onto this mixture the atmosphere pours more water, then evaporates most of it, and heats then cools the surface. In this way the surface swells, shrinks, becomes wet or dries as the conditions change. The weathered materials from the rock slope are constantly pulled downhill by gravity, pushed into the ground by treading animals, the weight of plants and houses, or passing traffic. Usually the rate of movement in this system is very slow but the steeper the slope the more effective the force of gravity is. Rivers then erode the footslope; quarrying and drilling explosions shake it about; and water washes bits of debris away. If the weathered material is not removed from the foot of the slope, the debris accumulates and weathering slows down. A protective mantle of soil then builds up (3.51a).

The weight of rock on a hillside would lead to collapse if it were not for the strength of the underlying rock holding it up. Friction between rock surfaces may be responsible for preventing collapse. Soil moisture may make the soil cohesive (sticky) and stop downslope movement. These and other factors combine to produce various slope elements, including forms of debris accumulation (see 3.51b) and degrees of concavity or convexity. Weathering, mass movements and erosion are all components which combine to form valleys (3.51c) at the lower end of the conveyor belt.

3.51 Slope elements

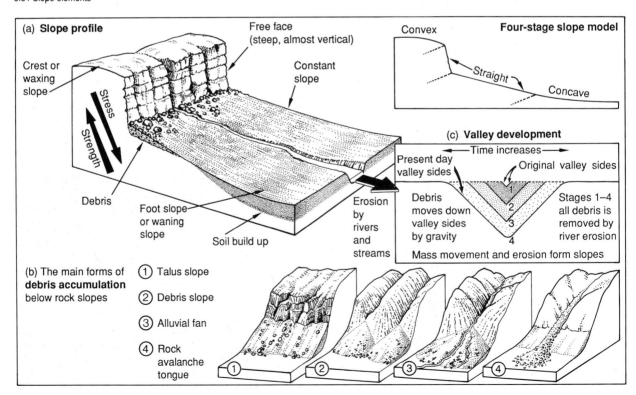

(a) **Slope profile**

Crest or waxing slope

Free face (steep, almost vertical)

Constant slope

Stress

Strength

Debris

Foot slope or waning slope

Soil build up

Erosion by rivers and streams

Four-stage slope model

Convex

Straight

Concave

(c) **Valley development**

←—Time increases—→

Present day valley sides

Original valley sides

Debris moves down valley sides by gravity

Stages 1–4 all debris is removed by river erosion

Mass movement and erosion form slopes

(b) The main forms of **debris accumulation** below rock slopes

① Talus slope

② Debris slope

③ Alluvial fan

④ Rock avalanche tongue

Slope evolution

The evolution of slopes is very important. It provides clues to how the landscape has developed. There are three main types of slope evolution: slope decline, slope retreat and slope replacement.

Slope decline. Slopes which evolve by slope decline (3.52) have slope angles which decrease in each phase of their development. The free face is gradually eliminated by the processes of falling and slumping (3.53, stages 1 to 3), so the slope eventually becomes more gentle (stages 4, 5). On this type of slope, weathering, debris removal and consequent ground-lowering increase in rate upslope. This inevitably leads to an overall decline of slope since the top is being removed more rapidly than the foot. Stage 4 shows the phase which is called a **graded slope**: one in which the inputs are in perfect balance with the outputs. Slope decline is most likely once a smooth graded profile has been established and is more likely to be found in the later phases of landscape development.

Slope retreat. In semi-arid areas (3.54) the free face seems to have much the same profile whether it is found on a cliff-line or small remnant of rock (butte). This suggests that all the upper slope units retreat by about the same amount so that the whole slope profile retains its original shape but moves backwards, leaving an extending concave footslope. Only this lower slope unit (pediment) tends to decrease in angle with time. The development of this slope sequence is controlled by the rate of retreat of the free face. The angle of the free face at the top of the slope is determined by the strength of the rock. A strong resistant rock will often form a vertical free face. In less resistant

3.52 Limestone free face in decline

3.53 Slope decline sequence of limestone slopes as shown in 3.52

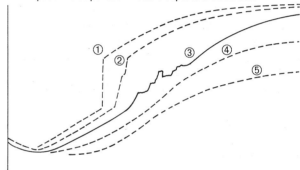

3.54 Slope retreat in a semi-arid area
(Monument Valley, USA)

rocks rapid weathering reduces the slope to a continuous debris-covered slope. All these slopes are thought to retain a constant angle throughout their development. The slope debris also maintains a constant thickness indicating that inputs and outputs are in balance. Slope retreat differs in these ways from the processes in slope decline.

Slope replacement. 3.55 shows a cliff undergoing slope replacement. The original cliff face is eventually replaced by a shorter free face and a lower-angle debris slope. The lower-angle debris slope or talus will itself ultimately be replaced by a still gentler slope. This is a process in which the transport of increasingly weathered material begins to extend a new depositional unit at the foot of the slope. In this theory of slope evolution, each slope unit is replaced by a lower angle unit growing up from below. In contrast to slope retreat, there is a change in the length of the segments as the slope develops. Some segments such as the free face may even be eliminated in time.

Although it is now possible to distinguish between various slope processes, it is important to note that, on any one slope, a combination of them can be operating to shape the landscape.

Slopes can be mapped in various ways but perhaps the most common approach is that of the **morphological map** (3.56). In this method of slope mapping, an area is divided into fairly distinct

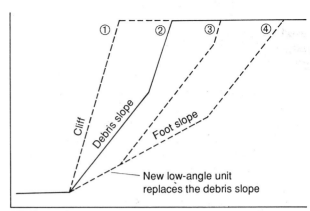

3.55 Slope replacement sequence

zones, each with its own slope angle and form (convex or concave). The boundaries between the zones on the map provide most of the information about form of slope. Symbols for other detail including other slope, channel and angle characteristics can be added to develop a description of the area under study. Additional information about the age and origin of the features within the study area can then build up a **geomorphological map**. Such maps contain much valuable information about the slope processes and land-use potential of areas under study.

3.56 Morphological mapping of slopes

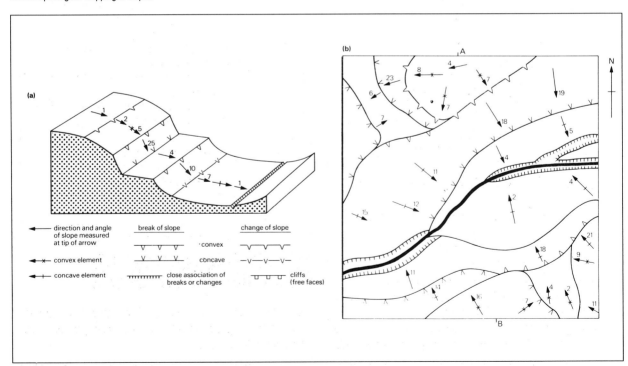

Q WEATHERING

1 (a) Describe and explain the contrast in the weathering processes that formed the landscapes in 3.40 and 3.42.

(b) Make an annotated sketch of photo 3.39. Explain the weathering processes involved.

(c) Name the type of weathering associated with each of the following: grykes, limpet acid, kaolin, screes, tors, tower karst, tree roots.

(d) Write brief notes to explain each of the following: frost shattering, exfoliation, regolith, granular disintegration and the role of vegetation cover.

(e) Which types of weathering are likely to be most effective in each of the following: deserts, north-west Highlands, tropical landscapes, and the chalk downlands of south-east England.

(f) Explain why the rate of chemical weathering in the British Isles is faster in summer than in winter.

(g) In which ways does industrial pollution increase the rate of weathering?

Q MASS MOVEMENTS

Graph 1

A classification of mass movements on slopes

2 (a) Identify the eight main types of mass movements which are classified on graph 1.

Choose from: landslide, soil creep, screes, solifluction, mudflow, slumping, rockfalls, slopewash.

(b) Contrast the differences in mass movements in photos 3.43, 3.47b and 3.48.

(c) With reference to 3.44–3.49, describe and explain any **two** of the following: scree slope formation, landslides, mudflows, slumping, and soil creep.

(d) Suggest factors which could cause an increase in the incidence of the two processes which you have selected.

Q SLOPES

3 (a) Make simple annotated sketches of photos 3.40, 3.47b, 3.52 and 3.54. For each, identify the main slope features and processes involved.

(b) Explain why the angle of view is important in determining slope features.

(c) Write brief notes to explain each of the following: the debris system, convex/concave slopes, slope decline, slope retreat, and slope replacement.

(d) Describe the ways in which weathering and rock type influence slope processes.

(e) Slopes determine many of the ways in which land is used. Study the land-use limitations listed in the table on the right. They do not match the slope angles correctly. Copy the information from the table but re-order the land-use limitations to match the correct slope angles.

Slope angle	Land-use limitation
0°	Mostly forestry and pasture land. Transport by special vehicle only, e.g. muskegs.
1°	Housing and road building difficult.
2°	Mountaineering, water catchment or scenic beauty are the only possible land uses.
4°	International airports, few problems except poor drainage and possible flooding.
5°	Limit for industrial and housing development.
8°	Main railways and juggernaut lorries are affected by slope. Flooding still a risk.
12°	Extreme limit for caterpillar vehicles. Agriculture and forestry very limited.
15°	Maximum for major roads and railways. Flood risk replaced by threats of soil erosion. Irrigation hindered.
25°	Road building difficult. Ploughing impossible.
35°	Maximum for railways and large industries. Contour farming advised.
55°	Problems for tractors and combines. Limit for large-scale site development.

Research and Further Work

Study the map extract on page 167. Draw a slope map of a small part of the map extract after carefully studying page 100. Produce a detailed key.

Q

1 (a) What is meant by 'landscape'? (3)
   (b) Look at map 1. Contrast the landscapes found to the north and west of the Tees–Exe line with those to the south and east of it. (6)

2 (a) Select any **one** of the following rock types: chalk/clay, granite, carboniferous limestone. With reference to a named area of the British Isles, show how a combination of rock type, structure, erosion and weathering has helped create the present landscape. (9)

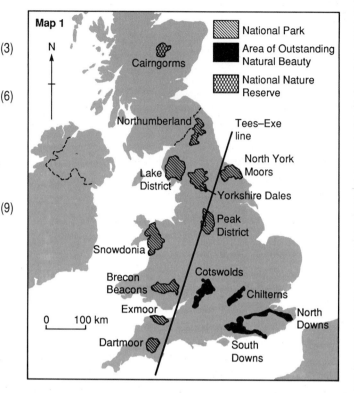

Map 1

Key:
- National Park
- Area of Outstanding Natural Beauty
- National Nature Reserve

Cairngorms
Northumberland
Tees–Exe line
North York Moors
Lake District
Yorkshire Dales
Peak District
Snowdonia
Brecon Beacons
Cotswolds
Chilterns
Exmoor
North Downs
Dartmoor
South Downs

0 100 km

Q

3 Study map 2 carefully.
   (a) What evidence would indicate that this upland area has been glaciated? (4)
   (b) Draw labelled cross sections of area A on map 2 before, during and after glaciation. (5)

4 (a) The glacier at B retreated about 10 500 years ago. Draw a simple sketch of what you would expect the valley to look like today. Annotate the likely glacial land forms. (6)
   Either
   (b) Describe the ways in which human factors have had an influence on how this and similar landscapes have evolved. (3)
   or
   (b) Discuss the statement that 'areas that were once glaciated provide a valuable resource', using named examples. (3)

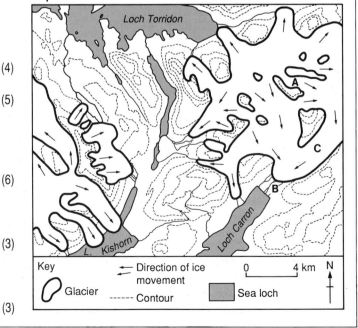

Map 2 Loch Lomond readvance around Loch Carron

Loch Torridon
A
C
B
L. Kishorn
Loch Carron

Key
- Direction of ice movement
- Glacier
- Contour
- Sea loch

0 4 km N

Q

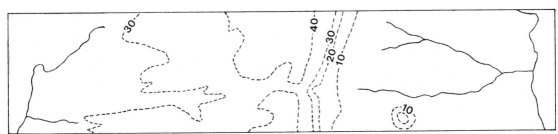

Map 3

5 Refer to map 3 above.
(a) Draw a labelled sketch or cross-section diagram to show the structure, relief and drainage of the scarp and vale landscape shown in map 3. (4)
(b) Write an explanatory account of the typical drainage pattern of a scarp and vale landscape. (4)

6 Compare and contrast the physical landscapes found in a chalk downland (e.g the South Downs) with that found in an area of carboniferous limestone (e.g the Yorkshire Dales). (9)

Q

7 (a) Explain the differences between the following rock types: permeable, impermeable, pervious. (3)
(b) Explain the formation of any **three** of the following features of carboniferous limestone scenery: pavements, scars, sink holes, collapsed caverns. (6)

8 (a) Describe and explain the physical characteristics of the karst landscape of the Yorkshire Dales. (6)
Either
(b) In which ways do people make use of karst landscapes? (3)
or
(b) In which ways do karst landscapes restrict people's use of them? (3)

Q

9 (a) Explain how the water content of a rock slope or regolith can influence mass movements. (3)
(b) Describe the processes operating on a free face which cause failure of the rock, and rockfalls. (3)
(c) Explain the main differences between any **two** of the following slope processes: decline, retreat and replacement. (3)

10 Look at the photograph on the right.
(a) Explain how the slow movement of soil down a slope takes place. (4)
(b) Suggest ways in which human activity can increase or decrease the rate at which this occurs. (5)

THE BIOSPHERE

Perfect Inventions: Ecosystems

Planet Earth is home to over 300 000 species of plants. Without this 'green mantle', animal life, including humans, would never have evolved. It was the development of plant life millions of years ago that boosted the proportion of oxygen in the atmosphere from a trace to one-fifth, and this fostered the development of animal life.

Plants are part of the earth's living organisms (**biosphere**) which form an interrelated system called an **ecosystem**. Ecosystems can exist at a variety of scales: from a single tree or group of trees; to a small hedgerow or patch of woodland; to the **bioclimatic** zone of tropical rainforests; to the whole of the earth. An ecosystem is the interaction of all living things (plants, animals, bacteria, etc.) with each other and with the non-living (chemical and physical) environment in which they live.

There are inputs, processes and outputs within any eco-system. 4.1–4.9 show some of the many different factors affecting an ecosystem. The driving force for the whole system is **solar energy** (see 4.2) which by photosynthesis is converted into other forms of energy, and flows throughout the ecosystem. Other inputs include air, water and nutrients.

Green algae, leafy plants and trees use the energy of light to produce food (carbohydrates) by means of photosynthesis. This energy is transferred to the herbivores (animals which feed on plants) and these in turn pass on the energy to the carnivores which eat other animals. The dead remains of these animals are then decomposed by fungi and bacteria, returning nutrients to the soil where they are used by trees and other plants.

Trees contribute in vital ways to the functioning of ecosystems. They give protection against erosion, and maintain soil fertility. Their canopies regulate evaporation from the soil. Trees play a fundamental role in the hydrological cycle, and also maintain the carbon cycle (4.5).

Ecosystems are the result of the interactions between various elements of the environment. Climatic conditions, soils, drainage and the amount of human interference vary, resulting in change in an ecosystem. The vegetation of any particular area on the earth can be thought of as a community of plants which gradually becomes more complex over time as environmental conditions change. This process of community change, called **plant succession**, influences in turn the development of the soil cover on which it thrives.

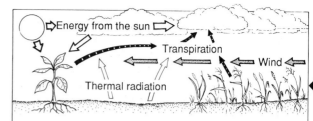

Energy. Various physical factors influence the total amount of energy that plants receive, and the temperatures that they attain. Plants convert one form of energy into another. They grow new tissue through the process of **photosynthesis** which uses light energy from the sun to harness nutrients from the air, water and soil. Direct heat from the sun and thermal radiation from the ground cause plants to **transpire** (wind also contributes by drying out leaf surfaces).

4.2
4.9

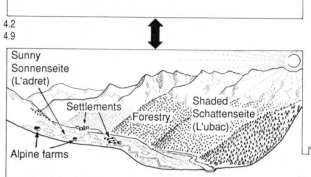

Light and shade. All plants need light to enable their green pigment (**chlorophyll**) to create new tissue. The amount and intensity of light varies with location and season, in relation to latitude, cloud cover, proximity of other plants, and relief. **Aspect** is an important environmental factor in determining available light. Shaded valley sides have less available light than sunnier, more open slopes and consequently support quite different plant communities.

4.8

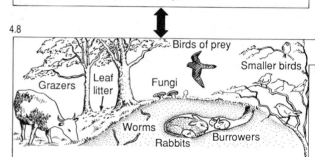

Biotic factors. The micro-organisms in the soil are among the least developed forms affecting plant life. Interactions between animals and plants have a direct influence on vegetation. For example, birds of prey and large animals keep down the numbers of smaller birds and animals which act as seed carriers or insect consumers influencing the growth of plants. Locust swarms, plagues of caterpillars, ever-increasing herds of cattle, and rabbits can all influence the vegetation of an area. Humans can also wreak havoc on natural vegetation by burning and clearing vegetation.

Temperature. Most plants are tolerant of a wide temperature range. The main growing temperatures lie between 6 °C and 35 °C with the optimum for growth around 25 °C. Stress levels on plants become intolerable if temperatures rise or fall outwith these thresholds. **Transpiration** is the efficient way that plants deal with high temperatures. Stomata on the surface of the leaves draw up large quantities of water from within the plant, and **evaporation** then cools the leaf. The combined process is known as **evapotranspiration** (evt).

4.3
4.1

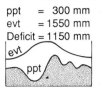

ppt = 300 mm
evt = 1550 mm
Deficit = 1150 mm

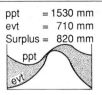

ppt = 1530 mm
evt = 710 mm
Surplus = 820 mm

Water. All plants depend on water for life. They play their part in the hydrological cycle, taking in water from **precipitation** (ppt) and releasing it as vapour through evapotranspiration. The water vapour forms clouds which return moisture to the earth as rain. The nature and amount of precipitation and its seasonal distribution are fundamental to plant growth. In areas of moisture surplus (where precipitation exceeds evapotranspiration) plants proliferate. In areas of moisture deficiency, the number and size of plants that can be supported decrease both in volume and range of species.

4.4
4.5

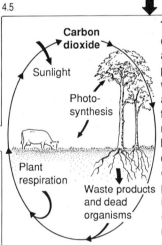

The carbon cycle. Plants take carbon dioxide (CO_2) from the air and, by means of photosynthesis, combine it with water to produce carbohydrates and oxygen. Plants and animals then reverse this process by means of **respiration**: they breathe in oxygen and breathe out CO_2 produced by the oxidisation of carbon compounds in the system. Burning of trees and **fossil fuels** (such as coal or oil) also return carbon dioxide to the atmosphere.

Carbon dioxide

Sunlight

Photo-synthesis

Plant respiration

Waste products and dead organisms

4.6

Canopy influences ground temperatures and soil humidity

Canopy provides shade

4.7

Humus content dependent on vegetation cover

Leaching influenced by vegetation cover

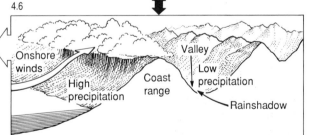

Onshore winds

High precipitation

Coast range

Valley

Low precipitation

Rainshadow

Soil (edaphic conditions). The relationship between plants and soils is a delicate one. Tree roots and leaf litter control soil erosion by reducing run-off. Dead organic matter helps maintain fertility. Moisture and chemical reactions within the soil provide plant food. The absence of nutrients such as calcium can influence surface vegetation.

Relief. Has many direct and indirect influences on plant life. The relief of an area can create conditions of increased or decreased moisture and temperature by acting as a barrier to onshore winds. Slopes influence the depth and texture of soils and drainage. Mass movements of surface materials may create a sequence of different soil types and affect further the pattern of natural vegetation. In areas of varied relief, aspect, exposure to strong winds, altitudinal differences, micro-climates and drainage patterns are all at work in influencing the types of plants and various forms of vegetation pattern.

The Primary Resource: Soil

All forms of life on land depend in one way or another on **soil**. This thin layer is the result of all the processes of physical and chemical weathering of the barren underlying rock of the earth. It can vary in depth from a few centimetres to many metres. Soil covers the planet's land surface, and is the biosphere's foundation and our primary resource.

The process of soil formation is slow. To form a soil the depth of this page could take as long as 10 000 years; a thickness of 1 centimetre would take 100–1000 years depending on a combination of soil inputs and outputs (4.10). A **soil profile** is a vertical section through the soil, down from the most recently deposited **topsoil** to the **parent material** (weathered bedrock,

not yet formed into soil). It reveals several layers or **horizons**. The dark A horizon is the topsoil (uppermost layer), containing decomposed dead organic matter (**humus**). Beneath this is the subsoil or B horizon in which minerals accumulate. The C horizon consists of the parent material and some weathered fragments of bedrock.

Soil is more than just layers of rock particles: it does not exist without life (4.11). Millions of small animals, fungi and microscopic bacteria live within it, breaking down dead and decaying plants and animals. These organisms help the decaying matter to go through the many complex processes which break it down into simple chemicals (nitrogen, phosphorous and sulphur) that enable plants to grow. Through this self-replenishing process the soil becomes enriched with dead organic matter, and remains fertile.

Not all the soil that covers the land surface is suitable for crops (4.12). Only about 11% of the total land area of 13 billion hectares is cultivated, although some scientists believe that 24% of the

4.10 What is soil?

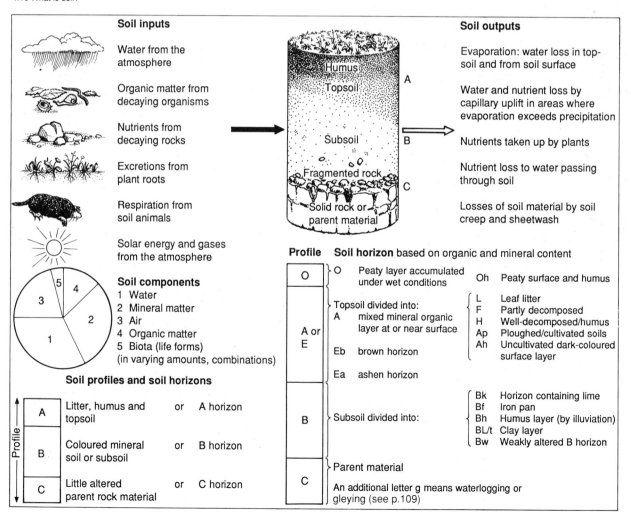

land area is fertile enough to grow crops. The rest presents too many limitations on agriculture: soils are either too dry or wet, too shallow or too cold. Europe (4.13) has a disproportionate amount of fertile soil relative to its land area, whereas Africa only cultivates 5% of its soil (although 16% of its land area is probably fertile enough to grow crops).

Most soils are a delicate and fragile living resource. Yet there is growing evidence which shows that this resource is being misused at an alarming rate, with resultant problems of erosion, famine, poverty and death.

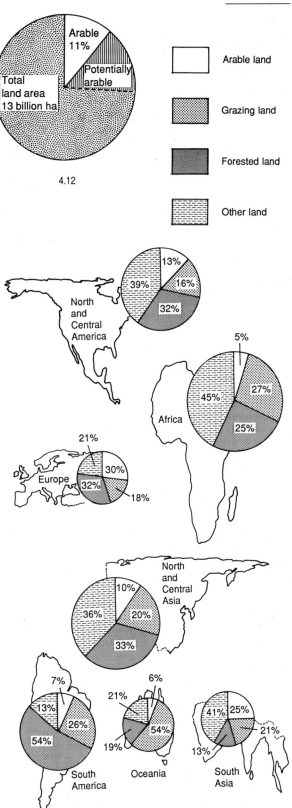

4.12

Arable land

Grazing land

Forested land

Other land

4.11 Soils: complex ecosystems

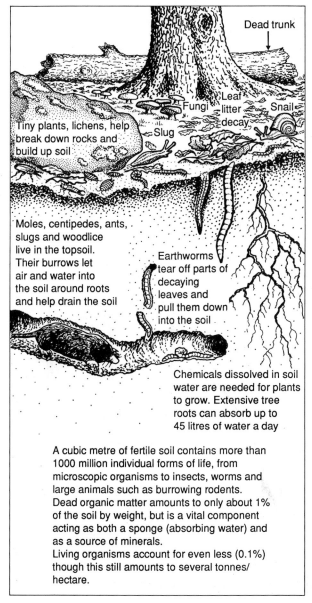

Dead trunk

Fungi · Leaf litter decay · Snail

Tiny plants, lichens, help break down rocks and build up soil

Slug

Moles, centipedes, ants, slugs and woodlice live in the topsoil. Their burrows let air and water into the soil around roots and help drain the soil

Earthworms tear off parts of decaying leaves and pull them down into the soil

Chemicals dissolved in soil water are needed for plants to grow. Extensive tree roots can absorb up to 45 litres of water a day

A cubic metre of fertile soil contains more than 1000 million individual forms of life, from microscopic organisms to insects, worms and large animals such as burrowing rodents.
Dead organic matter amounts to only about 1% of the soil by weight, but is a vital component acting as both a sponge (absorbing water) and as a source of minerals.
Living organisms account for even less (0.1%) though this still amounts to several tonnes/hectare.

4.13 Soils by continent.

Little by Little: Soil Formation

Pedology is the study of soils and their biological, chemical and physical properties. These properties are due to the integrated effect of **climate** and **living organisms** acting on the **parent material**, as conditioned by **relief**, over periods of **time**. These five major elements and other interrelated environmental factors in the formation of soils are shown in 4.14. The internal processes in soil development are controlled by these major factors which the soil scientist, H.Jenny, identified in the form of an equation:

$$s = f(Cl, O, R, P, T)$$

where s is the soil type which is dependent upon (or is the function of) the soil-forming factors: climate (Cl), organisms (O), relief (R), parent material (P) and time (T).

Climate is a very important factor in the development of soil. It controls the precipitation, soil moisture and range of temperatures. Water is essential to all the chemical and biological soil processes.

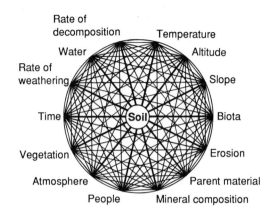

4.14 Interrelationship between soil and the environment

The moisture which eventually reaches the soil is less than the precipitation since some water is lost through evaporation above and on the surface, and plants intervene to soak up the excess (4.15). In semi-arid and continental areas of the world where there is more evaporation than precipitation, **pedocal** soils (rich

4.15

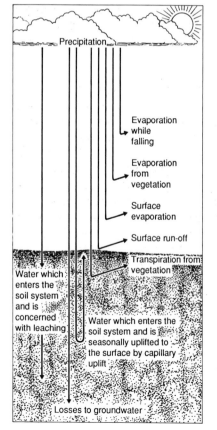

4.16 Development of pedocal soils

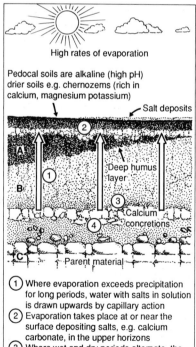

Pedocal soils are alkaline (high pH) drier soils e.g. chernozems (rich in calcium, magnesium potassium)

1. Where evaporation exceeds precipitation for long periods, water with salts in solution is drawn upwards by capillary action
2. Evaporation takes place at or near the surface depositing salts, e.g. calcium carbonate, in the upper horizons
3. Where wet and dry periods alternate, the salts may be taken down again and redeposited as calcium nodules
4. Under these conditions clay and humus are not washed down soil profile because of high pH. Humus is broken down and releases nutrients into this fertile soil

4.17 Development of pedalfer soils

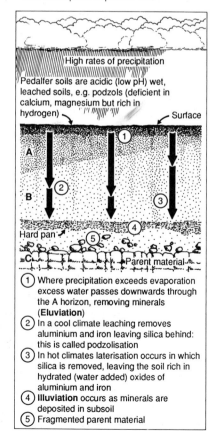

Pedalfer soils are acidic (low pH) wet, leached soils, e.g. podzols (deficient in calcium, magnesium but rich in hydrogen)

1. Where precipitation exceeds evaporation excess water passes downwards through the A horizon, removing minerals (**Eluviation**)
2. In a cool climate leaching removes aluminium and iron leaving silica behind: this is called podzolisation
3. In hot climates laterisation occurs in which silica is removed, leaving the soil rich in hydrated (water added) oxides of aluminium and iron
4. **Illuviation** occurs as minerals are deposited in subsoil
5. Fragmented parent material

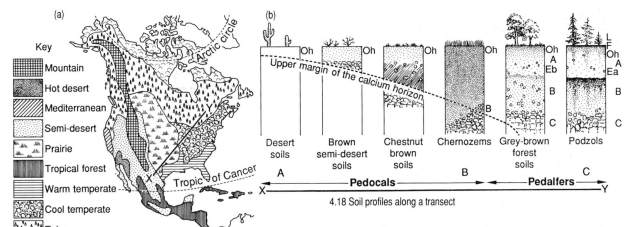

Key
- Mountain
- Hot desert
- Mediterranean
- Semi-desert
- Prairie
- Tropical forest
- Warm temperate
- Cool temperate
- Taiga
- Tundra

0   1250 km

4.18 Soil profiles along a transect

in calcium and other basic nutrients) develop (4.16). The movement of soil water by **capillary action** is principally upward and deposits of calcium are common features of these soils. By contrast, in areas where precipitation exceeds evaporation the water movement is principally downwards (4.17). In **pedalfer** soils (rich in hydrogen), water which percolates through the soil **leaches** minerals such as calcium, aluminium (Al) and iron (Fe) from the topsoil (**eluviation**) and deposits material in the subsoil (**illuviation**). The greater the precipitation, the further down the deposits of calcium are (4.18b) and generally the less fertile the soil. In areas of heavy rainfall or frequent snowmelt, the soil undergoes extreme leaching and becomes virtually sterile. The most fertile soils are chernozems: the least fertile are desert soils and podzols.

Temperature directly affects the rate of chemical and biological activity in the soil. In tropical climates, the rate of weathering is up to ten times that of Arctic areas and more than three times that of temperate areas. Often there are up to 50 metres of weathered regolith. Studies also show that the clay content increases with increasing temperatures. In tundra regions, the topsoil is frozen for most of the year and the subsoil is permanently below freezing point, so weathering and clay content are quite limited.

Organisms influence soil formation in a variety of ways. Soil bacteria play a vital role for they not only 'fix' nitrogen from the air in a form that plants can readily use but they also help the process of decay. Soil **biota** – the creatures that live in the soil – shift and aerate the soil. As they consume and excrete the soil they change its composition. Plants help stabilise the soil by reducing erosion and run-off. They are vital to the fertility of the soil since they concentrate organic matter and nutrients at the surface. Fine organic humus is provided by plants as they decay. Without life in the soil, there can be no proper soil formation.

Parent material can vary from solid rock to wind-blown sand. Most soils in the British Isles form on **unconsolidated** materials such as loess, boulder clays, gravels, and alluvium. In young soils, the type of parent material markedly influences the soil that forms above. The colour of the soil is often determined by the parent material. Ferrous oxide (found in podzols), for example, is black and adds a blue-grey colour to its soil. It is an iron compound reduced by lack of oxygen (as in waterlogged soils). Ferric oxide (rust, found in tropical soils) turns soils orangey-red. It is an oxidised iron compound. Soils more closely resemble their parent material in dry areas than in wetter areas as in dry areas the action of water in the soil development is minimal and organic influences are minor. Parent material is less significant in old soils since plants and climate have had a longer time to influence the nature of the soil.

Relief influences soil development through differences in drainage and debris accumulation rates. Soils are generally better drained on slopes than on flat areas where water cannot drain away and waterlogging or **gleying** occurs. Soils that are often waterlogged are deficient in oxygen and this prevents the build-up of soil organisms which promote organic matter decay. So the organic matter decays slowly, accumulating on the surface forming peat. Where a slope is over 25° degrees, material on the surface is unstable and moves downslope leaving bare rock or poor soil covering. Soil creep occurs on slopes of between 20° and 25° resulting in thin soil near the top and thick soil at the bottom of the slope. The downward movement is often interrupted by plants so that terracettes are formed on the slopes.

Time is also a vital component in soil formation. Most soils develop slowly. The processes of weathering, organic matter addition and water movements take hundreds of thousands of years to form soils. Young soils retain many of the features of the parent material but as they age they acquire new features including the addition of humus and the development of horizons. When soil reaches the point at which it is in equilibrium with its environment, it stabilises and does not change much after that.

Soil Classification

Soil classification has been carried out by soil scientists on a global scale and major soil groups can be classified into three different types:

- **zonal soils** which are associated with specific zones of climate and vegetation, e.g. taiga zone podzol soils, etc. (4.21 to 4.25);
- **intrazonal soils** which have been strongly influenced by parent material and can develop in more than one climate zone, e.g. rendzina soils (shallow and containing calcium carbonate);
- **azonal soils** which have developed only recently and show little horizon development. These include alluvial and volcanic soils which form independently of climate or vegetation.

The world map of the major zonal soil groups (4.19) is based on the prevailing environmental conditions which strongly reflect climate and vegetation. It shows the most probable areas of zonal soils but is very generalised. Such a map provides a useful basis from which to study the distribution of soil types given that it is inevitably an over-simplification and reflects generalised climatic and vegetational conditions. Experts have argued that local factors important in soil formation, such as the micro-climate, geology, drainage and relief, must also be taken into

Latitude zone	Major soil group	Bioclimatic zone
High latitudes (polar)	Tundra soils (Arctic browns, gleys)	Tundra, sub-arctic mountains
Middle latitudes (temperate)	Podzol soils	Taiga, heaths, cool temperate woodlands
	Brown earths	Cool/warm temperate deciduous woodlands
	Grey soils	Wooded temperatre grassland
	Chernozems	Temperate grasslands
	Chesnut soils	Semi-arid steppe/prairie
	Red/brown Mediterranean soils	Mixed moist evergreen woodlands
Low latitudes (tropical)	Red desert soils	Hot deserts
	Tropical ferruginous soils (red/yellow/black): rich in hydrated iron oxides	Areas with distinct wet and dry seasons (savanna)
	Tropical ferralitic soils (red/yellow): rich in oxidised iron and aluminium	Humid tropical areas, tropical rainforests

4.20 Zonal soils classification

4.19 Major zonal soil regions

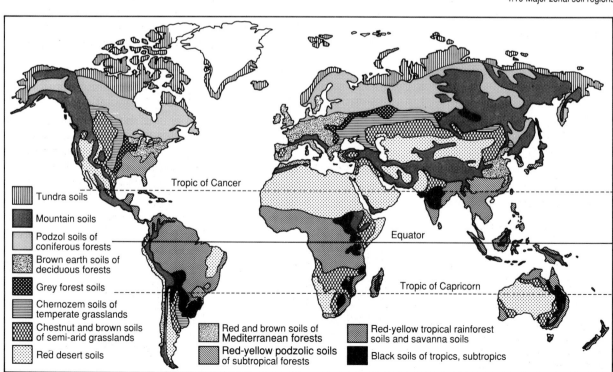

Tropic of Cancer

Equator

Tropic of Capricorn

- Tundra soils
- Mountain soils
- Podzol soils of coniferous forests
- Brown earth soils of deciduous forests
- Grey forest soils
- Chernozem soils of temperate grasslands
- Chestnut and brown soils of semi-arid grasslands
- Red desert soils
- Red and brown soils of Mediterranean forests
- Red-yellow podzolic soils of subtropical forests
- Red-yellow tropical rainforest soils and savanna soils
- Black soils of tropics, subtropics

account in addition to bioclimatic conditions. For example, in the British Isles most soils fall into two major soil groups: **podzols**, found in the north and west, and **brown earths**, found in the south and east. But within each of these major groups there is a wide variety of soils distinguished in terms of colour, texture and parent material. These sub-groups are often given a reference name from the local area of origin. Nevertheless, since climate is one of the most important influences on soil formation, the following discussion of zonal soils is based on a broad bioclimatic scheme (4.20).

Zonal soils

Tundra soils (see Fig. 1, page 170) are found in areas where the subsoil remains permanently frozen (**permafrost**) and tundra vegetation grows in the topsoil during the brief summer. When the frozen topsoil thaws at the end of the winter, the ground becomes waterlogged since drainage is prevented by the permafrost layer. In these waterlogged or **gley** soils (deficient in oxygen), bacterial action is restricted and, beneath the low vegetation of lichens, mosses and shrubs, lies a black mass of very slowly decaying plant matter with much acid humus (rich in hydrogen, deficient in nutrients, low pH). The continual seasonal freezing and thawing produces expansions and contractions which lead to vertical mixing within the tundra soil. This prevents the development of clearly defined horizons but weathered fragments of parent material are often obvious within the blue-grey and peaty clays of the B horizon. The potential for use of tundra soils is severely limited by the dominant conditions of the Arctic climate.

Podzol soils (see Fig.2, page 170) are found along the wide belt of the northern hemisphere associated with coniferous forests. The extensive areas of conifers take few minerals from the soil and the falling cones and needles form a very acidic humus. The annual precipitation is low but spring snowmelt releases water which causes very heavy leaching. This enables the organic acids to remove iron and aluminium oxides from the topsoil leaving behind a high silica content. Illuviation of the oxides in the subsoil or B horizon deposits an **iron** (or **hard**) **pan** which can impede drainage and cause waterlogging in the topsoil. Soil horizons are more clearly defined in a podzol as the cold climate restricts the actions of soil biota and little mixing occurs. Podzols are of limited agricultural potential but they can be improved by artificial drainage and considerable liming. Only the hardiest of crops can be cultivated in improved podzols. These include oats, potatoes and hay.

Grey-brown forest soils (see Fig.3, page 170) are found further south than podzols and are associated with deciduous forests. The thick leaf debris returns many of the nutrients removed by the deciduous trees. The milder climate encourages more rapid decomposition and the resulting humus is mild and more alkaline. Earthworms, insects and rodents mix debris through the layers and the roots of trees penetrate deep into the soil absorbing nutrients. Grey-brown forest soils are pedalfers: precipitation exceeds evaporation and gradual leaching occurs. Iron pans can develop where leaching is more active. These soils have a greater agricultural potential than tundra or podzol soils and can produce a wide range of cereals including oats, barley and wheat as well as good grazing for beef cattle. Where iron pans develop, **gleying** or waterlogging of the topsoil can cause problems.

4.21

4.22

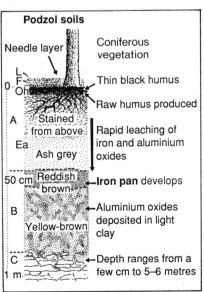

4.23

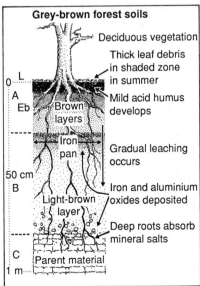

Chernozem soils (see Fig.4, page 170) are associated with temperate grassland vegetation. The climate here is generally warmer and drier than in forested areas though, in continental interiors, winters can be very cold with much snow and frost. During the spring snowmelt, water leaches the soil removing salts such as calcium carbonates to the subsoil. Throughout the hot dry summer, when evaporation exceeds precipitation, capillary action carries the salts upwards through the chernozem. The upper layers of the soil are often very dark in colour and are referred to as 'black earths'. They tend to have a loose and crumbly structure and are among the most fertile and productive of soils, because they contain large amounts of basic nutrients (calcium, magnesium) in the deep topsoil. They have a very high agricultural potential, and by far the most important use is for cereal crops including wheat and maize in the prairies of North America and steppes of the USSR. They are, however, delicate soils and must be cultivated with great care.

Latosols or tropical red soils (see Fig. 5, page 170) develop under tropical rainforests where drainage is good. These are old and deep soils with a browny-red colour and crumbly texture. These **ferralitic** (iron-rich) soils form under conditions of constant high temperatures and moisture surplus, so decomposition and leaching are dominant soil processes. Because of the high temperatures, decomposition of leaf litter is rapid. The A horizon is usually a light brown colour because soluble silica (sand) is leached away by the heavy rainfall. The climate causes rapid chemical weathering resulting in deposits of reddish layers of iron and aluminium (called **sesquioxides**) in the B horizon. These can be concentrated into a hard crust or **laterite** which may be found at the surface or in the subsoil. As the parent rock disintegrates rapidly, tropical red soils may become deep if they are formed on level surfaces. On any other surface they are easily eroded particularly when the vegetation is cleared away.

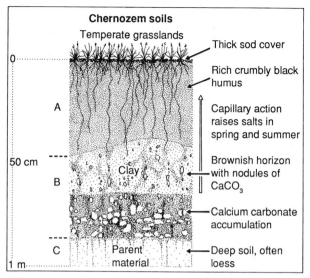

4.24

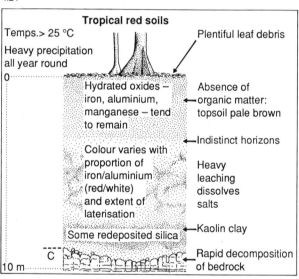

4.25

Intrazonal soils

As their name suggests, these soils are not confined to any particular bioclimatic zone. They owe their characteristics to conditions common to different parts of the world such as evaporation, aridity, waterlogging, parent material or relief. For example, alkaline **rendzina soils** (see Fig. 7, page 170) occur in limestone areas and are rich in calcium carbonate. Rendzina is a dark-coloured soil, fairly rich in humus, that develops in sub-humid climates on softer limestones such as chalk. There is usually a sharp transition between the soil and the calcium-rich bedrock marked by a thin layer of fragmented limestones. Rendzina is sometimes called an A–C soil because of the absence of a B horizon in which leached materials accumulate. This is because there is little leaching of the A horizon. Other types of intrazonal soils include **gleys** which occur where soils are waterlogged, and **terra rossa** (see Fig. 8, page 170), a red thin clay loam soil, rich in iron.

Azonal soils

These have usually been formed fairly recently and can be found within any of the zonal soil distributions. These soils lack well-defined profiles since they have not time to develop fully. Some are thin, such as those found on hill slopes. Others are deep, and of various textures, such as sand, silt, clay, alluvium, glacial drifts and resorted outwash sands and gravels. Recent volcanic and loess soils are also azonal.

Soils in Dartmoor: a case study

Dartmoor is the largest and highest upland area in southern Britain (4.26). It is the eroded remains of a giant granite intrusion (4.27). The area is exposed to strong winds and high precipitation and has a cool climate.

The soils have formed on a parent material of mainly granite with some slates, and are generally acidic. They include brown earths, peaty gleys and blanket bog soils (4.27). They are the results of a combination of factors operating on the Dartmoor landscape. Relief and drainage have had a strong influence on the soil development. The high average altitude of over 300 metres creates cool wet exposed climatic conditions. The giant dome shape of Dartmoor leads to a radial drainage pattern. Soils on slopes are generally well drained but, on the flat divides, on valley floors and on open moors, water cannot drain away quickly and waterlogging occurs. This restricts the entry of oxygen into the soil and leads to the process of **gleying** in which red (ferric) iron oxides are reduced to blue-grey (ferrous) iron compounds. Scattered red patches (mottles) occur where there are local patches of air, and oxidisation occurs. Because soil organisms do not thrive in stagnant conditions, organic matter tends to decay slowly, accumulating on the surface, and blanket bogs form. Diagram 4.28 shows a typical soil sequence for a Dartmoor valley. The three different soils have formed from the same parent materials but vary according to differences in climate, slope, drainage and vegetation. Such a soil sequence is known as a **soil catena**.

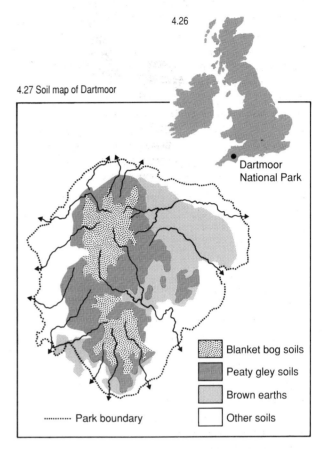

4.26

4.27 Soil map of Dartmoor

Dartmoor National Park

Blanket bog soils

Peaty gley soils

Brown earths

Other soils

.... Park boundary

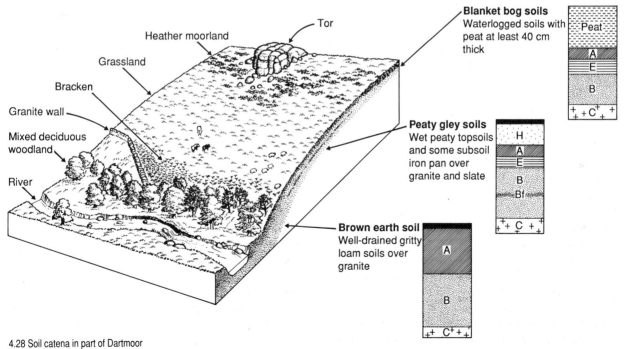

Heather moorland
Tor
Grassland
Bracken
Granite wall
Mixed deciduous woodland
River

Blanket bog soils
Waterlogged soils with peat at least 40 cm thick

Peat
A
E
B
+ + C + +

Peaty gley soils
Wet peaty topsoils and some subsoil iron pan over granite and slate

H
A
E
B
Bf
+ + C + +

Brown earth soil
Well-drained gritty loam soils over granite

A
B
+ + C + +

4.28 Soil catena in part of Dartmoor

Questions

Q PERFECT INVENTIONS: ECOSYSTEMS

1 (a) Define the term 'ecosystem'.
(b) What is the driving force for the ecosystem?
(c) Argue the case that ecosystems are perfect inventions.
(d) Design a simple diagram to show the interrelationships within an ecosystem.
(e) How can ecosystems be changed?

Q THE PRIMARY RESOURCE: SOIL

2 (a) Why is soil referred to as the primary resource?
(b) Design your own diagram to show soils as a system of inputs >> processes >> outputs.
(c) Explain the differences between: profiles and horizons; soil and regolith.
(d) Define fully the following: humus, parent material, biota, topsoil and subsoil.
(e) Explain why each of the following is found in greater proportion near the soil surface: plant remains, worms.
(f) Construct a version of map 4.13 showing soils and their uses by continent on an outline map of the world.
(g) Identify areas in which the soil is under the greatest pressure from over-use. Give reasons to explain this.

Q LITTLE BY LITTLE: SOIL FORMATION

3 (a) Which factors contribute to the development of soil profiles?
(b) Why does the proportion of unweathered rock within the soil increase with depth?
(c) Explain each of the following soil processes: leaching, eluviation, illuviation, capillary action, gleying, decomposition.
(d) Explain the terms 'pedocal' and 'pedalfer' soil types.
(e) Describe how and explain why the colour, humus content and direction of water movement within soils vary so greatly between different soil types.
(f) Using diagram 4.18, explain the relationship between precipitation and the depth of calcium horizons.

Q SOIL CLASSIFICATION

4 (a) What is a zonal soil?
(b) How do intrazonal soils differ from azonal soil types?
(c) Explain the effects of climate and vegetation on the development of the soil profiles of chernozems, podzols and latosols.
(d) Explain the term 'soil catena' with the aid of a suitable diagram.
(e) Study map 1 below carefully. Name a zonal soil found in each of areas 1–4. Compare the agricultural potential of each of soil types 1–4.
(f) Compile a table to classify zonal soils according to climatic influence and vegetation.

Map 1. North America: vegetation regions

Research and Further Work

(a) Describe and account for the changes in soils from northern to southern USSR.
(b) Identify soil profile 6, page 170. Include a sketch profile and details of colour, texture, and potential for use, in your answer.
(c) Investigate the soils of your local area. Describe their agricultural potential.

114

Biomes: World Ecosystems 1

A **biome** is an ecological community of plants and animals extending over a large natural area. Ten major biomes are shown on map 4.29, but of course human activity has destroyed part or tonnes. Of this amount, well over half (or about one-third of all biomass) is contained in tropical forests, even though they cover only 8% of the land surface. In contrast to the abundance of phytomass in the Tropics, hot desert and tundra regions contain only 2% even although they cover one-quarter of the land surface. Human croplands account for only a meagre 0.5% though they cover more land than tropical forests.

Rate of plant growth or 'primary productivity' ranges from virtually zero at the poles to vast amounts in the tropical forests.

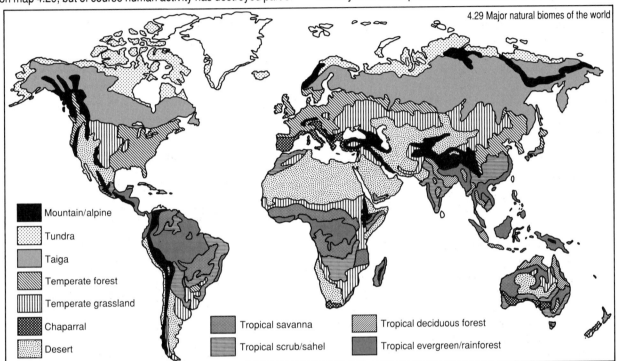

4.29 Major natural biomes of the world

- Mountain/alpine
- Tundra
- Taiga
- Temperate forest
- Temperate grassland
- Chaparral
- Desert
- Tropical savanna
- Tropical scrub/sahel
- Tropical deciduous forest
- Tropical evergreen/rainforest

all of the natural biomes in many of these areas. **Tundra** is a cold treeless desert, frozen in winter and marshy in summer; **taiga** comprises coniferous forest. **Temperate forest** is a mixture of evergreen and deciduous trees; **temperate grasslands** include prairies and steppes. **Chaparral** is short shrubby 'Mediterranean-type' vegetation (see 4.33). **Hot desert** has little vegetation; **tropical savanna** comprises grassland with scattered trees; **tropical scrub** has 'open canopy' stands of trees. **Tropical deciduous forest** is a 'closed canopy' community; while **tropical evergreen rainforest** represents one of the most diverse and productive plant biomes in the world.

During the twentieth century scientists have attempted to quantify the amounts of living tissue or **biomass** for each biome (4.30). Biomass is expressed as a dry weight of **phytomass** (plant material) and **zoomass** (animal matter). 99% of all the biomass on earth is plant material.

Our planet's land surface is covered in about one million million (10^{12}) tonnes of living phytomass. Not surprisingly, forests contain more than 75% of all phytomass: in fact about 950 million

In general, the amount of new phytomass produced each year in the humid parts of the world doubles with the move from polar to temperate areas and more than doubles again from temperate to tropical areas.

4.30 Biomass by biome: percentage share of the world's phytomass for each biome compared with its percentage share of the world's land area

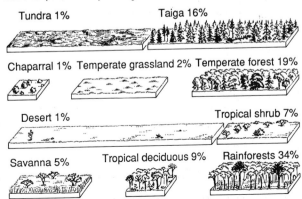

Tundra 1%   Taiga 16%

Chaparral 1%   Temperate grassland 2%   Temperate forest 19%

Desert 1%   Tropical shrub 7%

Savanna 5%   Tropical deciduous 9%   Rainforests 34%

Biomes: World Ecosystems 2

Any journey from the equator to the poles reveals the variation of biomes on the planet. Each biome is primarily recognised by the characteristics of its 'natural' vegetation, such as a savanna grassland or chaparral (4.31).

Climate exercises a major control over the distribution of biomes, and climate and natural vegetation strongly influence the formation of soils. These interrelationships generate broadly similar patterns for zones of climate, 'natural' vegetation and soils, which combine to determine the distribution of the world's biomes (4.32).

Temperature and precipitation are the most important climatic factors influencing the character of biomes (4.33). Increasing distance from the equator or sea level *reduces* average temperatures, while increasing distance from the moderating influence of the sea *increases* the annual range of temperature. Both journeys influence significantly the precipitation distribution and levels to such an extent that biomes display gradients of change with increasing aridity (4.34).

Each biome has its own particular constraints; the tropical evergreen forest, for example, is found in regions with a wide range of precipitation conditions (above 1500 mm annual rainfall) but does not occur where low temperatures are found; grassland biomes tolerate a wide variety of temperatures but less variation in conditions of precipitation.

Temperature is a more significant controlling factor than precipitation in most world ecosystems or biomes. This reflects the strong relationship between temperature and energy within an ecosystem. Most biome patterns broadly parallel changes in latitude, with the complexity of plant life increasing from simple plant communities in the tundras to the diverse and abundant plant communities at the equator.

People have also been a major factor in influencing the distribution and character of biomes, because they have been burning and clearing vast tracks of vegetation for centuries. Only small remnants of many natural biomes survive today. It is, however, important to identify broad biome patterns since they provide a reference point to study the impact of people on the natural ecosystems of the planet.

4.31 Chaparral vegetation

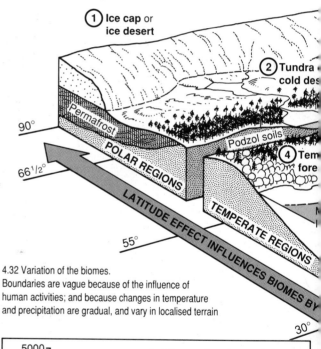

4.32 Variation of the biomes.
Boundaries are vague because of the influence of human activities; and because changes in temperature and precipitation are gradual, and vary in localised terrain

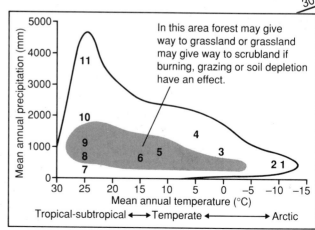

In this area forest may give way to grassland or grassland may give way to scrubland if burning, grazing or soil depletion have an effect.

Mean annual precipitation (mm)

Mean annual temperature (°C)

Tropical-subtropical ⟷ Temperate ⟷ Arctic

4.33 How the 'natural' biomes (1–11 on 4.32) relate to variation in temperature and precipitation

	Wet (favourable) environment	Increasing aridity →	Dry (extreme) environment
Productivity	**High** (2000 dry g/m² year)		**Low** (5 dry g/m² yr)
Community size	**Large** (trees > 40 m high)		**Small** (plants < 1 m high)
Biomass	**Large** (> 40 kg/m²)		**Small** (< 1 kg/m²)
Plant coverage	**Complete** (> 100%)		**Partial** (< 10%)
Community structure	**Complex** (many species)		**Simple** (few separate plants)

4.34 How precipitation affects the nature of biomes

Biomes seasonally deficient in heat and/or water

3 Taiga
4 Temperate forest
5 Temperate grassland
6 Chaparral
8 Tropical scrub/Sahel
9 Savanna
10 Tropical deciduous forest

Biomes permanently deficient in heat and/or water

2 Tundra
7 Hot deserts
12 Mountain or Alpine

Biomes promoting growth all year round

11 Tropical evergreen rainforest

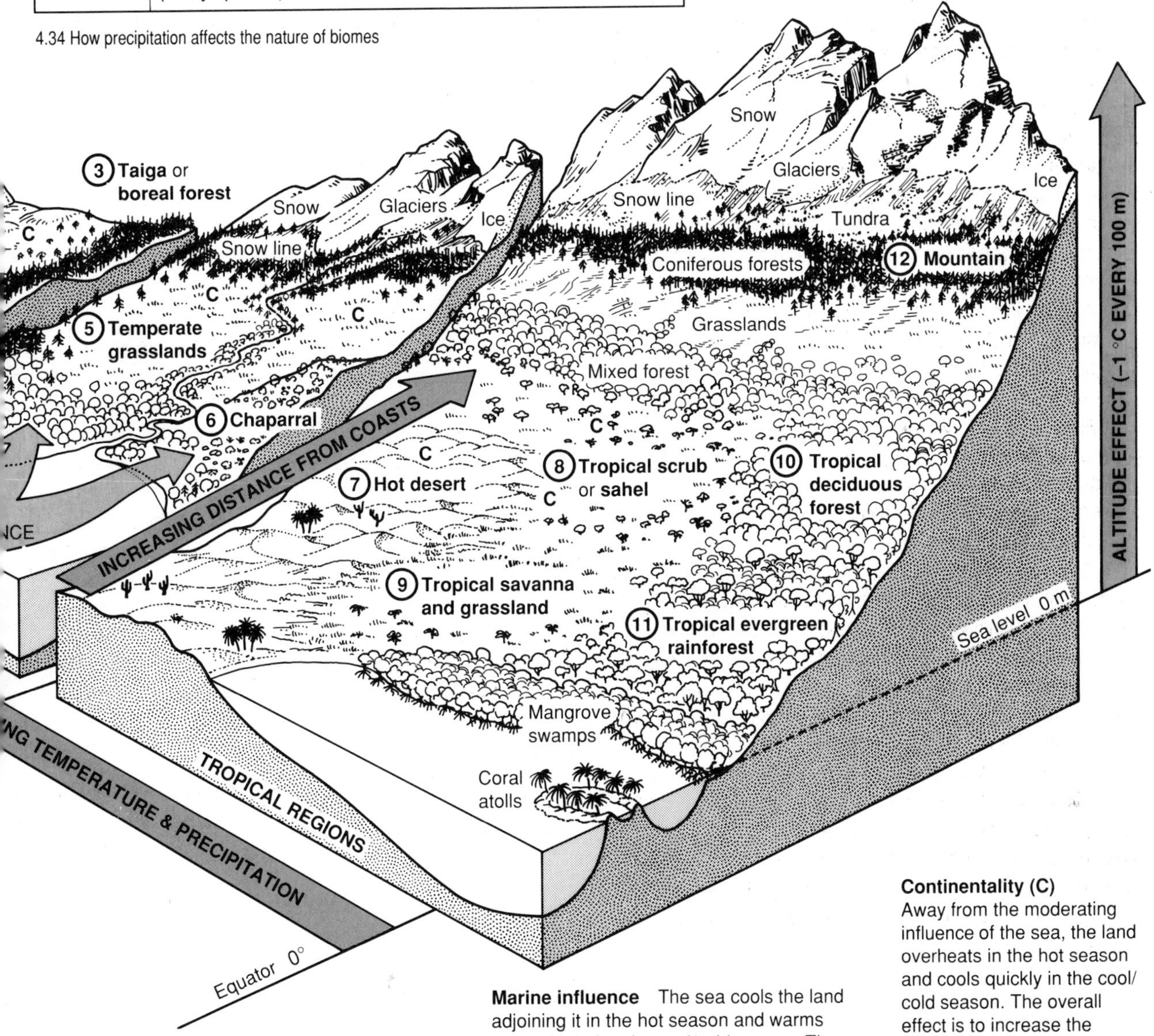

Marine influence The sea cools the land adjoining it in the hot season and warms it slightly during the cool/cold season. The overall effect is to reduce the annual range of temperature and increase the annual total precipitation

Continentality (C) Away from the moderating influence of the sea, the land overheats in the hot season and cools quickly in the cool/cold season. The overall effect is to increase the range of temperature and decrease the total annual precipitation.

CHAPTER 4

Towards Climax

Biomes (world ecosystems) represent plant and animal communities living together in association with their physical habitat (4.35). Habitats can change through time and the plants can change with them. Plant **succession** occurs when altered environmental conditions begin to favour certain species of plants. These species can compete more successfully for available nutrients, light and space. Well-adapted species then replace earlier ones which are now less well equipped to compete.

During succession, the ecosystem goes through a series of stages. Each stage is called a **seral** stage and the complete series of plant communities resulting from the process of succession is called a **sere**. There are various types of seres (4.36), each taking its name from the type of environment in which it develops.

Primary successions or **priseres** are those which develop on new, biologically unaltered sites. Any succession which takes place on a site which was formerly vegetated is called a secondary succession or **subsere**.

Pioneer stage

The process of succession may start with bare ground. This might be a mudflat, a sand dune behind a beach, new river deposits, or volcanic ash. Over time, such priseres become colonised by plants which then slowly alter the environmental conditions. For example on fresh layers of volcanic lava there is little loose surface material or available water. The first plants to colonise the new surface are called **pioneers**. They consist of a few species of lichens and mosses. These plants will eventually form a deeper and richer soil by weathering the surface, releasing nutrients, adding humus and retaining water around their roots. These changing conditions will eventually encourage insects to live in the soil. Gradually, the environmental conditions will become favourable for other species to move in. Succession has then begun.

During succession

The pioneers are then displaced by other plants species and these new arrivals may be larger plants which shade the ground, altering the micro-climate. Evaporation within the soil is thus reduced producing favourable conditions for different plants. During succession, the plants compete for available nutrients, water and space. The most successful survive at the expense of others. The diversity of plants is increased initially as many new species move in to take advantage of the altered site. As the ecosystem reaches stability, a few species begin to dominate

4.35 Tropical grassland biome

and the diversity of plants is slightly reduced. Succession can be classified as either autogenic or allogenic. **Autogenic succession** is when plants themselves alter their environment which, in turn, results in further changes in the plant community. **Allogenic succession** is the result of changes caused by some external factor such as a volcanic eruption depositing layers of lava and ash on the landscape.

Climax

Eventually, in the mature stage of the succession process, the ecosystem becomes stable and relatively unchanging. This stage is referred to as the **climax**. The climax community is in a state of dynamic equilibrium, that is it maintains overall stability despite continuous small changes. The climax is the stage at which the plant community reaches the maximum possible development under the prevailing environmental conditions. This means the maximum biomass, productivity, structural complexity and species diversity. This state of equilibrium will exist as long as the environmental conditions persist. When the climax lasts for hundreds or thousands of years and is seen to be dependent principally on climate, it is sometimes called the **climatic climax** (or natural vegetation). Sometimes a climax can be determined by other factors, such as soil (edaphic climax) or human influence (plagioclimax).

4.36 Types of seres. (Many successions eventually converge)

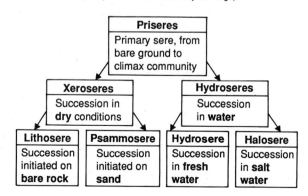

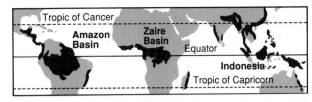

4.37 Location of tropical rainforests

Forests and the Biosphere

Tropical rainforests

The tropical rainforest is the climatic climax vegetation of the humid tropics. These forests are the richest and densest of all the forests, with luxuriant growth and great diversity of species. Tropical rainforests form a green band around the equator extending roughly 10 degrees north and south (4.37). They account for only a small proportion, about 8%, of the earth's land surface. Yet they comprise almost half of all the growing wood and at least two-fifths of the plant and animal species on the planet (4.38).

An area of 1.5 hectares of forest may hold over 200 different trees. They grow in a multi-layered arrangement (4.39) where tall **emergents** pierce the dense **canopy**; lianas, stranglers and tree creepers colonise the buttressed roots of the giant trees; lichens, mosses and algae grow on every surface, and the forest floor and tree bark are covered in all types of fungi. Almost every branch is hung with **epiphytic** (non-parasitic) plants such as ferns and orchids, while smaller trees and shrubs compete for light and space in the **understorey** below. This intricate plant life supports an even greater diversity of insect and animal life with life cycles linked to certain plants.

Yet the abundance of plant life masks the fact that, without the protective canopy above, the soils of the rainforest would be infertile and incapable of supporting it. The overwhelming proportion of the nutrients necessary to maintain the rainforest ecosystem are held in the vegetation itself. Dead leaves drop to

4.38 Tropical rainforest

the forest floor almost continuously where they decompose rapidly, forming humus. All rainforest trees spread roots laterally (sideways) just below the soil surface. The roots form a net to catch the nutrients released before they are leached by the percolating rainfall. The plants then take up the nutrients in a almost continuous growth cycle. The rainforest therefore exists only by maintaining its supply of nutrients to the soil.

4.39 Section through rainforest

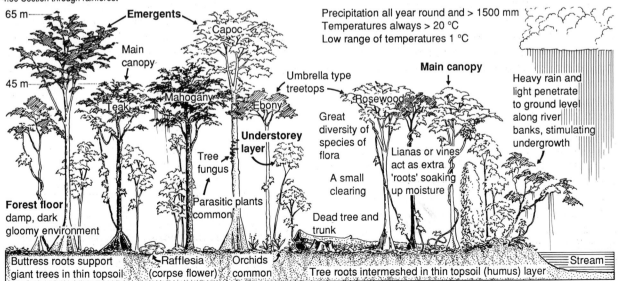

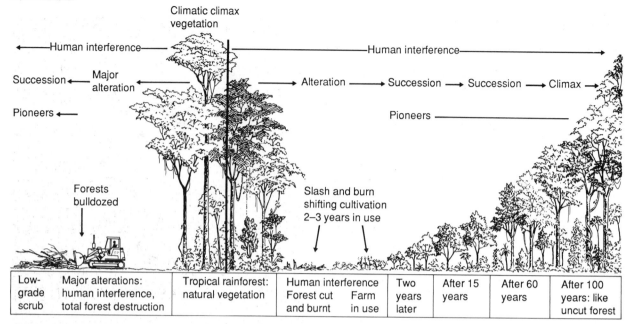

Low-grade scrub	Major alterations: human interference, total forest destruction	Tropical rainforest: natural vegetation	Human interference Forest cut and burnt	Farm in use	Two years later	After 15 years	After 60 years	After 100 years: like uncut forest

4.40 Intervention in rainforest biome

Sometimes the stability of the rainforest biome can be disrupted naturally. When a large tree dies, it topples over and brings down others around it. Sunlight immediately floods the clearing and soon seeds begin to sprout and flourish. Within a matter of weeks the forest floor is a mass of herbs, small shrubs and grasses all fighting for light and space. They rise in a continuous cover up to 3 metres high but they do not survive for long. Tree saplings soon outgrow them and within two to three years they provide a higher protective cover, shading out the lower layers which then die out. These new trees form a secondary forest of fast growing softwoods. However, they too have a limited life span and die out after 30 years leaving the slower growing but taller hardwoods to form a new canopy. This succession of trees, each giving way to another until a final and stable climax vegetation has reformed, may take hundreds of years, so rainforest is not easy to replace.

But the stability of the rainforest is also disrupted deliberately by people in various ways (4.40). When people create large gaps in the forest canopy such as those caused by **shifting cultivation** (slash and burn), industrial clearance (for minerals such as bauxite, oil and gas), large-scale cattle ranches or new communication links, the micro-climate of the mature rainforest disappears. Over large areas, the forest floor becomes exposed to direct sunlight. The air and soil become dry. Tropical storms can cause severe erosion of topsoil. In areas where the forest has been cleared by slash and burn (4.41) the poverty of the soil limits agricultural use to 2–3 years. The ash from the burning of the rainforest is a valuable fertiliser but the new environmental conditions combine to limit the usefulness of newly cleared areas. However, pioneer plants can take advantage in this situation and the processes of succession may still be set in motion enabling the eventual return of the mature phase of the vegetation. Therefore, small-scale shifting cultivation does not completely destroy the rainforest biome and the forest can recover to something like its original climax. However, bulldozing huge areas can have very serious repercussions. The soils may become destroyed. In the end, all that may replace what was once mature rainforest may be scrappy, low-grade scrub.

4.41 Effects of slash and burn on rainforests

Temperate deciduous forest

4.42 Location of temperate deciduous forests

4.43 Temperate deciduous forest

The temperate deciduous forests are mainly distributed in a zone including much of the eastern area of the USA, Western Europe and eastern Asia (4.42). Temperate deciduous forests are distinguished by the annual fall or shedding of leaves at the end of the summer season (4.43). Tree species are limited and can be readily listed: oak, beech, lime, chestnut, maple, hickory, alder, hazel, birch, yew, poplar and tulip tree. Even these few species rarely occur together. they are more commonly found growing in groups or **stands** of two or three species which dominate a forest for large distances.

At least 5000 years of human interference have left very little of the natural vegetation intact. The best surviving examples are to be found in the southern Appalachian mountains of eastern USA. Even where the initial clearings were made, **plagioseral** succession (natural regrowth altered by human interference) has been able to proceed and in other areas almost complete climatic climax vegetation still exists in small patches.

The typical temperate deciduous forest has a four-layer structure (4.44). The tallest trees have their crowns 20–50 metres above ground. There is a sparse understorey, often of birch and holly, as light is limited by the dense canopy above. Beneath this is a shrub layer, sometimes containing evergreens reaching 2 metres in height. At ground level there is a deep carpet of dead organic matter and the plants have one of two **adaptations**

(induced changes). There is the group that flower in spring and seed before the canopy closes over them (e.g. primrose, anemone and bluebell); and the group that are shade tolerant (e.g. ivy and arum lily). Lichens and mosses are also found on rotting wood or on patches of bare soil. The soils of the temperate deciduous forest areas are naturally fertile brown earths. The spread of developments in agriculture, lumbering, communication and settlement have meant the almost total alteration of this biome especially in Western Europe.

4.44 Section through temperate deciduous forest

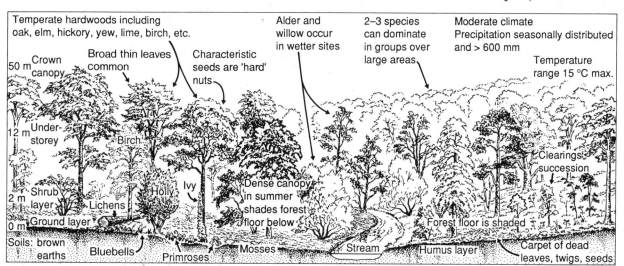

Temperate hardwoods including oak, elm, hickory, yew, lime, birch, etc.

Broad thin leaves common

Characteristic seeds are 'hard' nuts

Alder and willow occur in wetter sites

2–3 species can dominate in groups over large areas

Moderate climate
Precipitation seasonally distributed and > 600 mm

Temperature range 15 °C max.

50 m Crown canopy

12 m Under-storey

Birch

2 m Shrub layer

Holly Ivy

Lichens

0 m Ground layer

Dense canopy in summer shades forest floor below

Clearings succession

Forest floor is shaded

Soils: brown earths

Bluebells

Primroses

Mosses

Stream

Humus layer

Carpet of dead leaves, twigs, seeds

Coniferous forests

4.45 Location of coniferous forests

Taiga or coniferous forest is the climatic climax vegetation of the high latitudes and is distributed across a broad band which includes northern Canada, Scandinavia and Asia (4.45). Coniferous forest is characterised by few species of tree: pine, fir and spruce are dominant (4.46). These trees occur in massive stands covering hundreds of kilometres of taiga. Conifers (cone bearing trees) tend to be shallow rooted in order to obtain surface nutrients and keep above the permafrost that underlies much of the area. Extreme gleying is also a major problem in this area where soils are podzoloic and generally infertile for most plants.

In their natural state coniferous trees are quite widely spaced and light reaches the forest floor allowing a carpet of heather, bilberry, mosses and lichens to flourish (4.47). Conifers are adapted in several ways to the low temperatures, insolation and high snowfall. Being mostly evergreen species, they are able to make maximum use (by photosynthesis) of the low-angled sunlight throughout the year. Their needles resist transpiration while their shape and downward sloping branches help shed snow and prevent branches breaking.

The coniferous forest displays a three-tier structure where the tallest trees reach 15 to 35 metres. Below this lies a shrub layer of up to 3 metres with the ground level plants rarely reaching over 1 metre. In wetter areas spruce predominates whereas on drier

4.46 Coniferous forest

slopes and glacial sands and gravels, pine and fir are to be found. Needles are renewed only once in several years and their decomposition on the forest floor is very slow. This prevents the formation of humus, and the release of meltwater from the substantial snowfalls leaches a high proportion of minerals from the topsoil. The coniferous forests are for the most part found in isolated areas and therefore little affected as yet by human interference. In more accessible areas, such as southern Canada, Scandinavia and Siberia, the taiga provides valuable timber supplies for the pulp and paper industry. Mineral excavation, limited agricultural and recreational developments (the latter leading to serious fires) have caused great damage to the climax vegetation of the coniferous forest zone.

4.47 Section through coniferous forest

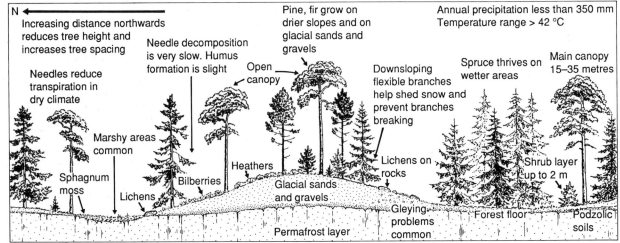

Q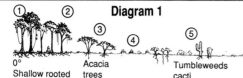

Diagram 1

0°
Shallow rooted

Acacia trees

Tumbleweeds cacti

Long prairie

Chaparral

Mixed forests

Shallow roots

60°

BIOMES: WORLD ECOSYSTEMS 1

1 (a) Copy and complete diagram 1 by identifying biomes 1–8 and 10–11.
(b) Explain, using a diagram, what is meant by ecosystem.
(c) Write brief notes on each of the following: biome, biomass, chaparral, taiga and tundra.
(d) Using 4.30 draw a pie chart to show biomass by biome (assume 5% for other producers).

Q BIOMES: WORLD ECOSYSTEMS 2

2 (a) Write brief notes on each of the following influences on biomes: latitude, altitude, continentality and the sea.
(b) Describe the effects of increasing aridity on biomes.
(c) For any two biomes, describe the main influences on their distribution.
(d) Classify the biomes in a table according to heat and water sufficiency.

Q TOWARDS CLIMAX

3 (a) Write a brief account of each of the following giving at least two examples of each: plant succession, climatic climax vegetation, prisere.
(b) Explain the difference between allogenic and autogenic succession.
(c) Why is it rare to find examples of true climatic climax vegetation?

Research and Further Work

(a) Ecosystems are modified by people. For any three areas, describe the effects of human intervention on the nature and diversity of plant species.

Q FORESTS AND THE BIOSPHERE

4 (a) Discuss the various factors which have influenced the distribution of the rainforest biome.
(b) Describe using an annotated diagram the tropical rainforest biome.
(c) Explain why it is considered to be a fragile ecosystem.
(d) Describe the temperate deciduous forest biome.
(e) Map 2 shows the climax vegetation for Britain. Describe and explain the distribution of three types of vegetation.
(f) Which soil-forming processes are at work in this biome?
(g) Explain the distribution and structure of the coniferous forest biome.
(h) Compare and contrast the main forest biomes in terms of their distribution, species diversity, structure and main influences.

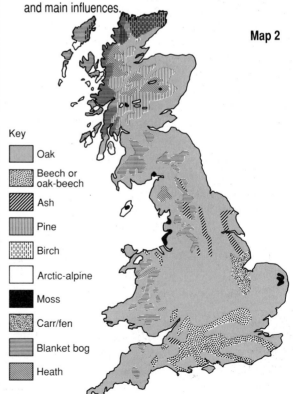

Map 2

Key
- Oak
- Beech or oak-beech
- Ash
- Pine
- Birch
- Arctic-alpine
- Moss
- Carr/fen
- Blanket bog
- Heath

Dune Belts

4.48 Sand dunes: fragile ecosystems

In all ecosystems, whatever their size or distribution, the climax vegetation is eventually reached through the processes of colonisation, competition, succession and stabilisation. In this way ecosystems develop from simple to diverse plant communities. These processes are to be found at work in all corners of the planet, from the complex and majestic tropical rainforests to some of newest ecosystems: those found along the land–sea boundary. It is in these sandy environments that **psammoseres** develop.

Some 6000 years ago when the present sea level was attained, sediments deposited along the sea shore at the end of the last glaciation began to be blown inland. These formed the basis of our present-day **dune** systems (4.48). Most of these consist of a series of dry sandy ridges interspersed with flat plains or wetter hollows known as **slacks**. The main areas of dunes occur in the Western Isles and north-east Scotland, in Cardigan Bay and north Norfolk (4.49).

Plant life is essential for the development and stabilisation of coastal dunes in the British Isles. Succession and eventual climax are based on the fact that the oldest dunes lie farthest from the sea.

Behind the strand line (see 4.50), sea couch grass and sea-rocket often form the first barrier to wind-blown sand: the **embryo dune**. The accumulation of sand accelerates as marram grass quickly becomes the main stabilising agent. At this stage the dunes are known as **yellow dunes** because of the amount of bare sand in evidence.

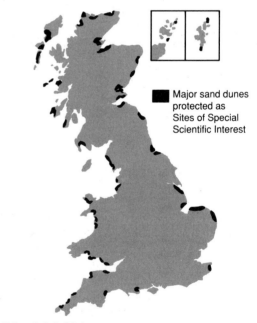

Major sand dunes protected as Sites of Special Scientific Interest

4.49 Dune belts in Britain

In these early stages, the dunes are deficient in water and nutrients, and are unstable. Only a few plants in addition to marram grass can survive in this environment (4.51). These include sand sedge, sea-holly and dune fescue. As the dune develops in height over 10 metres, shelter behind it reduces the supply of fresh sand and the marram grass dies out. As it decays on the sand, humus forms and a soil begins to develop. Other plants are then able to succeed the marram grass including

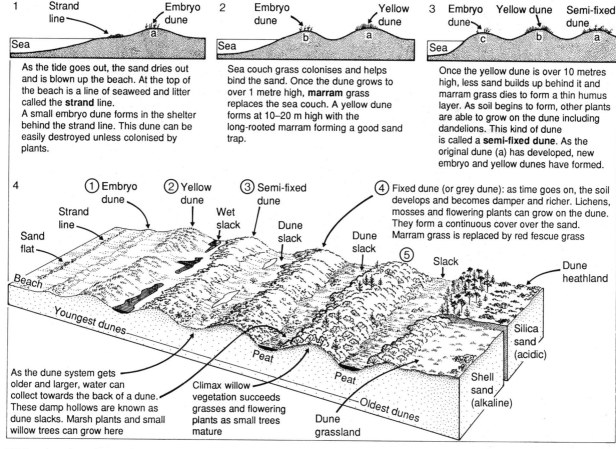

1 Strand line — Embryo dune — a — Sea

As the tide goes out, the sand dries out and is blown up the beach. At the top of the beach is a line of seaweed and litter called the **strand line**.
A small embryo dune forms in the shelter behind the strand line. This dune can be easily destroyed unless colonised by plants.

2 Embryo dune — Yellow dune — b — a — Sea

Sea couch grass colonises and helps bind the sand. Once the dune grows to over 1 metre high, **marram** grass replaces the sea couch. A yellow dune forms at 10–20 m high with the long-rooted marram forming a good sand trap.

3 Embryo dune — Yellow dune — Semi-fixed dune — c — b — a — Sea

Once the yellow dune is over 10 metres high, less sand builds up behind it and marram grass dies to form a thin humus layer. As soil begins to form, other plants are able to grow on the dune including dandelions. This kind of dune is called a **semi-fixed dune**. As the original dune (a) has developed, new embryo and yellow dunes have formed.

4
① Embryo dune
② Yellow dune
③ Semi-fixed dune
④ Fixed dune (or grey dune): as time goes on, the soil develops and becomes damper and richer. Lichens, mosses and flowering plants can grow on the dune. They form a continuous cover over the sand. Marram grass is replaced by red fescue grass
⑤ Slack
Strand line
Sand flat
Beach
Youngest dunes
Wet slack
Dune slack
Dune slack
Dune heathland
Silica sand (acidic)
Shell sand (alkaline)
Peat
Peat
Oldest dunes
Dune grassland

As the dune system gets older and larger, water can collect towards the back of a dune. These damp hollows are known as dune slacks. Marsh plants and small willow trees can grow here

Climax willow vegetation succeeds grasses and flowering plants as small trees mature

4.50 Dune formation and succession

dandelions and rest-harrow. This type of dune is called a **semi-fixed dune**. As the soil develops it becomes wetter and richer in nutrients and many more plants can be found such as lichens, mosses, and beautiful plants like bird'sfoot trefoil. The plants continuously cover the soil forming a **fixed dune**. Water collects in the sheltered hollows or slacks between the dunes, and marsh plants and small willows flourish. As a dune matures and becomes more isolated from the sea, new embryo dunes form.

The mature vegetation which then develops on the older dunes can take many forms, from pines to oaks, from heathland with heathers to grassland with creeping willow.

The major difference in vegetation types depends on the amount of calcium carbonate present in the dune system. Where sand grains contain a high proportion of shell fragments, rich grassland flourishes. By contrast, on dunes built up from silica sand or on very old dunes where the lime has been leached out, an acidic soil develops. Acid-tolerant heathland plants become dominant including heathers and ling. In both these dune types, the influence of the sea on the plant species becomes progressively less important, as aquatic vegetation gives way to land plants.

4.51 Major plants on sand dunes: numbers indicate dune type (see 4.50) on which the plant is found

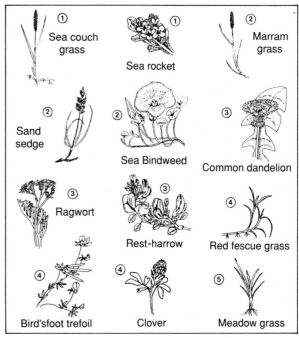

① Sea couch grass
① Sea rocket
② Marram grass
② Sand sedge
② Sea Bindweed
③ Common dandelion
③ Ragwort
③ Rest-harrow
④ Red fescue grass
④ Bird'sfoot trefoil
④ Clover
⑤ Meadow grass

Heather Moorland and Bog

Large areas of the north and west of Britain are dominated by **moorland** vegetation. Moorland consists of both heathland and peat bogs.

The chief characteristic of heather moorland is one of uniformity: there are few predominant plants with ling, bell heather and gorse being most common (4.52). All three of these plants are able to grow because they transpire very little. Otherwise they would have difficulty in obtaining sufficient water for their needs. The porous freely drained sand or gravel soils hold little water. In places, however, leaching may produce a hard pan which restricts drainage and results in **wet heather moorland**. All heather species are acid tolerant. Distributed among the larger plants may be many small less obvious species such as lousewort and heath milkwort. The distribution and density of plant populations are heavily influenced by two main factors: the intermittent availability of moisture, and a shortage of mineral nutrients, especially nitrates.

Succession on moorland areas (4.53) can be studied in relation to slopes and hollows where a wide diversity of ecosystems occur. Variations in relief and drainage patterns, the erosion of surface soil by wind and rain, and the accumulation of decaying plants, result in a spatial differentiation between three or four ecosystems, including raised bog, lowland bog, upland (or blanket) bog, and heather moorland. 4.54 is a generalisation of the stages in the formation of heaths and bogs.

In contrast with the vegetation on drier moorland, the constant waterlogging of hollows and basins encourages the development of peat bogs (4.53). In particular, because of the British climate,

4.52 Windswept heather moorland with few trees. Ling is the dominant plant with rushes on wet sites in the foreground.

a special type of peatland called **blanket bog** has developed. Caithness and Sutherland (4.55) have one of the largest and most intact areas of blanket bogs in the world. The cool wet climate and the low rolling moorlands produce the waterlogged conditions necessary to form peat (4.56). Fen (water-loving) vegetation thrives in conditions of constant flooding, and as it decays it accumulates as peat. Subsequent decomposition of the dead vegetation is prevented because this process requires oxygen, which is deficient in waterlogged soil. Consequently, the peat becomes thick, binding most of the available nutrients into this layer. For this reason, the only source of minerals available for plant growth are those dissolved in rainfall. For peat formation, there must be a healthy actively growing bog plant community. In this **hydrosere** (a succession from water to land environment) few plants can survive the extreme conditions without special

4.53 Spatial variation in plant communities on heather moorland and bog

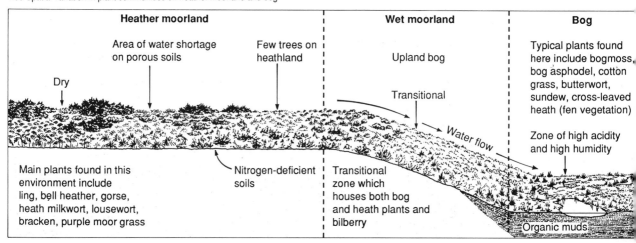

Heather moorland	Wet moorland	Bog
Area of water shortage on porous soils / Few trees on heathland / Dry	Upland bog / Transitional / Water flow	Typical plants found here include bogmoss, bog asphodel, cotton grass, butterwort, sundew, cross-leaved heath (fen vegetation) / Zone of high acidity and high humidity
Main plants found in this environment include ling, bell heather, gorse, heath milkwort, lousewort, bracken, purple moor grass / Nitrogen-deficient soils	Transitional zone which houses both bog and heath plants and bilberry	Organic muds

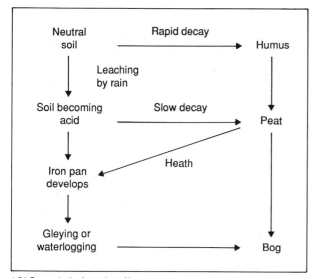

4.54 Stages in the formation of bogs

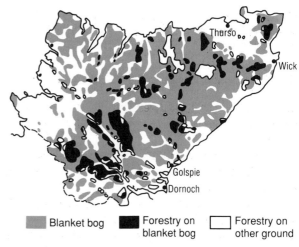

4.55 Extent of blanket bog in Caithness and Sutherland with areas of forestry established on peatland and elsewhere

means of obtaining nutrients. Some, such as sundews and bladderworts, obtain nutrients by trapping insects but the powerhouse of the bog is the sphagnum moss which absorbs water through holes in the cell walls of its leaves. It is so successful that carpets of bog moss expand and begin to replace the fen vegetation, transforming fen into true bog. They even keep the surface moist in periods of severe drought and their acids prevent the decay of plant remains.

An increasing thickness of sphagnum peat slowly accumulates and the surface of the bog begins to rise above the level of the surrounding land. The gradually swelling bog can reach over 10 metres in height after 7000 to 8000 years of growth. On the flattest areas of peat there may be many pools in a variety of intricate patterns. Patterned bog and broad low hills form much of the typical moorland of the north and west of Britain.

4.56 The dubh lochans (black lochans) stained dark with peat. They form pool systems where water has collected on the highest and flattest parts of the bog surface

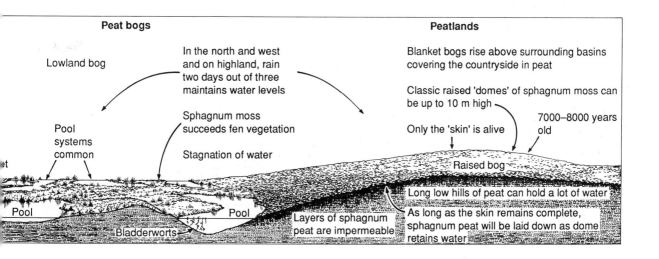

Walls and Waste Land

Walls

Walls either form parts of buildings or act as boundaries to fields and gardens. The plant communities which colonise walls are influenced by three main factors.

1. The **age** of the wall: as the wall weathers and deteriorates, many small crevices develop where moisture and humus can accumulate. The older the wall, the more plants colonise it.

2. The **fabric** of the wall (the type of rock, and mineral content) determines the nature of the habitats it provides. It determines the accumulation of humus and eroded rock as well as the **pH** of the water. This in turn determines whether the physical conditions are suitable for **calcicole** (alkaline tolerant) or **calcifuge** (acid tolerant) plant species. For example, on limestone walls with a pH of 8.5 (alkaline), there can be extensive colonisation of walls by the wall-pepper or *Sedum acre* (4.57). In contrast, on old brick walls in similar areas where the pH is much lower, white stonecrop or *Sedum album* is the dominant species.

3. The **aspect** of the wall affects the most important factor influencing the nature of plant communities: a continuous supply of water. North-facing sides of walls tend to retain water and are therefore more heavily populated than their south-facing sides which are more exposed to the effects of sunshine.

Plant succession on walls not only depends on the physical environment but also on the existence of pioneer vegetation. 4.58 shows a possible succession. However, owing to fluctuating conditions and human interference, the environment of walls seldom remains stable for long.

4.57 Wall-pepper on an old limestone wall

Waste land includes rubbish tips, slag heaps, derelict building sites and demolition areas. Such sites have several common characteristics no matter where they are: they are only temporary (limited to a few years or less); their plant communities seldom develop beyond the pioneer stage; on each site there is a wide variety of physical conditions such as light and humidity.

All pioneer plant species of waste land must be able to survive in adverse soil (edaphic) conditions, especially those of drought, and be able to reproduce themselves at a very high rate. Common pioneer species include hairy bitter cress, pineapple weed, groundsel and couch grass, elder, silverweed and creeping cinquefoil.

In the peculiar conditions of derelict areas, successional stages occur rapidly. 4.59 shows a derelict area three years after demolition. The fast-colonising weed, rosebay willowherb (*Epilobium angustifolium*) indicates dry conditions; it finds rooting possible in the cracks of concrete pavements and roadways.

4.59 Derelict building site three years after demolition

4.58 Theoretical succession on walls

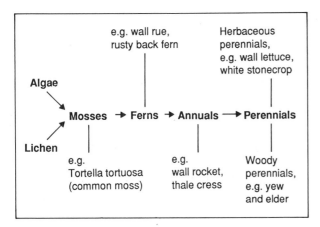

Q DUNE BELTS

1 (a) Describe the environment of a psammosere.
(b) Make an enlarged copy of diagram 1 and complete it by writing the appropriate labels in the seven boxes shown. Choose from: woodland, scrub, marsh, semi-fixed dune, fixed dune, slack, dune heathland.
(c) Describe the sequence of plant succession on sand dunes.
(d) Complete a larger copy of the table below by listing the field evidence of plants found in a typical dune area.

Dune type	Field evidence
Embryo	
Yellow	
Semi-fixed	
Fixed	
Slack	
Old	

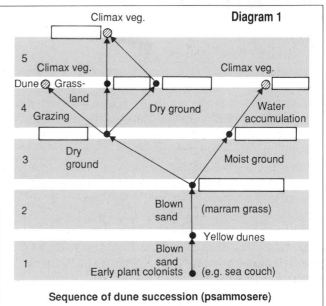

Diagram 1

Sequence of dune succession (psammosere)

Q MOORLAND AND BOG

2 (a) Draw a diagram to describe the spatial variation in plant communities from bog to heathland.
(b) Write brief notes to explain each of the following: heath, wet heath, bog, peatland, hydrosere.
(c) Describe the stages in the formation of heather moorland and bogs.
(d) Which plant species would you look for to distinguish wet heath from bog?
(e) Draw simple annotated field sketches of 4.52 and 4.56 labelling the main plant environments.
(f) Study diagram 2 carefully. Name the soil type and describe its formation.

Diagram 2 Soil profile

Heath vegetation
Peat
Bleached layer
Cemented layer
Mottling
Transition to parent material

Rainfall + Evaporation

High rainfall, lower temperatures and acid vegetation litter = limited bacterial decay. Peat accumulation

Leaching

Gleying

Iron pan: iron redeposited, the cause of gleying, surface waterlogging and peat development.

Gleying

Q WALLS AND WASTE LAND

3 (a) Which factors influence plant colonisation on walls?
(b) If you found plant species, *Sedum acre* and *Sedum album* on a field study what would this tell you?
(c) Describe a possible succession on a wall and explain why a complete sequence is seldom achieved.
(d) Compare the colonisation of a wall by plants on its north-facing and south-facing aspects.

(e) Which factors influence plant succession on waste land?
(f) Annotate a field sketch of 4.59 indicating both its physical conditions and typical plants.
(g) Compare the main ways in which bogland plants obtain nutrients.
(h) In any area of waste land, what is the evidence of plant succession?

The Living Earth

How close is our relationship with this planet we call home? And to what extent are the immediate problems facing the earth problems for us also? There is life on earth only because conditions happen to be right for it. We hardly need reminding of the environmental dangers now facing the earth, dangers which, if left unchecked, will jeopardise these essentials for life.

The living world or biosphere occupies a thin layer on the surface of the planet (4.60). 30 kilometres above this, the air is too thin and cold for survival. 100 kilometres below this, the globe is white hot at 3000 °C.

In between, the tropical forests and shallow sunlit seas and reefs are home for much of the earth's living wealth of flora and fauna. Indeed the planet's green mantle is itself necessary for other forms of life. Plants alone, through photosynthesis, convert the energy in sunlight to the chemical energy (food) that animals need for survival. It was the emergence of photosynthesising algae in the oceans over two billion years ago which first released oxygen into the atmosphere and at the same time began to absorb the high levels of carbon dioxide. These algae still supply over 70% of our oxygen and this in turn maintains the protective layer of ozone in the upper atmosphere. Plants and the oceans act as sinks for carbon dioxide from the air.

Plant cover provides the basis of all food chains; it contributes to water cycles and stabilises micro-climates as well as protecting the living soil. Billions of micro-organisms and microbes in the shallow muds of the sea floor and swamps, and in all soils, convert decaying matter into mineral nutrients and thus complete nutrient cycles. Without the systems that collectively interact, the earth would be another lifeless planet. If this spark of life was extinguished, conditions on the earth would change very rapidly to that of a blistering desert with temperatures 2 to 3 times that of boiling water, and a choking oxygenless atmosphere composed of 98% carbon dioxide.

The idea of the earth as a living interacting system has been called the Gaia hypothesis. Dr James Lovelock, a NASA scientist, took the name, Gaia, from the greek word for mother earth. He proposed that, far from being an inanimate object, our planet can be regarded as a living organism. The Gaia theory utilises his work for NASA in which the planets of the Solar System have been tested for their ability to support life. Unlike our neighbouring planets, the earth's results do not compute. It has been calculated that our atmosphere should contain mostly carbon dioxide with a very small trace of argon whereas in reality the air we breathe contains about 0.03% CO_2 with 79% nitrogen and 21% oxygen. Also the average temperature of the surface should be 300 °C whereas it is only 13 °C in reality. These figures prompted Lovelock to suggest that the earth itself had by some means created the ideal conditions for life. It is known that some living things remove CO_2 from the atmosphere. Carbon is locked in the soil in the tissue of plants and on the ocean floor as skeletons of plankton. Tropical forests and shallow continental shelves are important since both environments store CO_2 at a very high rate. Increased biological activity results in a lowered carbon dioxide content in the atmosphere and the subsequent lowering of temperature produces Ice Ages. Some Gaia scientists believe that cool glacial periods are our planet's preferred stable state, and that recent increases in the temperature of the planet may be an indication that Gaia is failing to cope with changing conditions in the atmosphere. Some think that the 'Little Ice Age' of the sixteenth.century was the start of the return of the great ice sheets. But the increase in carbon dioxide from people's burning of fossil fuels is thought to have forestalled the onset of the next glacial period.

The earth should perhaps be called Ocean since over 70% of its surface is covered in water. The very presence of the oceans is a result of the life process on the earth. The breakdown of CO_2 by plants and animals, and the storage of carbon, releases oxygen which combines with hydrogen to produce water which is in turn recycled across the planet.

The earth has for the last two million years tolerated the presence of the parasite 'people'. It is clear that it is in the parasite's interest to maintain its host, the earth, in the best possible health. But the human race seems recklessly determined to drain the host of its life force, with what Gaia scientists warn will be grave consequences. The greenhouse effect, the ozone hole, the destruction of the tropical forests, the over-exploitation of minerals and the sea, and the pollution of the continental shelves are already well established. Has the parasite become too great a burden for the host? If so, the host may well take steps to do all it can to rid itself of the parasite. People must learn this lesson quickly.

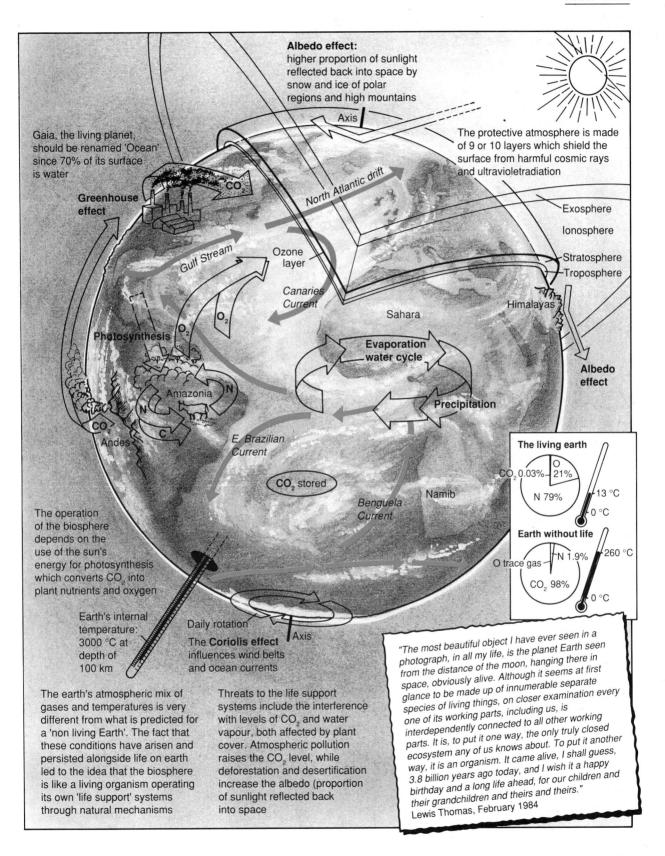

Albedo effect:
higher proportion of sunlight reflected back into space by snow and ice of polar regions and high mountains

Gaia, the living planet, should be renamed 'Ocean' since 70% of its surface is water

Greenhouse effect

CO_2

North Atlantic drift

Axis

The protective atmosphere is made of 9 or 10 layers which shield the surface from harmful cosmic rays and ultravioletradiation

Exosphere
Ionosphere
Stratosphere
Troposphere

Gulf Stream

Ozone layer

Canaries Current

Sahara

Himalayas

Albedo effect

O_2

Photosynthesis

O_2

Evaporation water cycle

Amazonia

N

N

N

C

Precipitation

CO_2

Andes

E. Brazilian Current

CO_2 stored

Namib

The operation of the biosphere depends on the use of the sun's energy for photosynthesis which converts CO_2 into plant nutrients and oxygen

Benguela Current

The living earth

CO_2 0.03% — O 21%
N 79%

13 °C
0 °C

Earth without life

O trace gas — N 1.9%
CO_2 98%

260 °C
0 °C

Earth's internal temperature: 3000 °C at depth of 100 km

Daily rotation

Axis

The Coriolis effect influences wind belts and ocean currents

The earth's atmospheric mix of gases and temperatures is very different from what is predicted for a 'non living Earth'. The fact that these conditions have arisen and persisted alongside life on earth led to the idea that the biosphere is like a living organism operating its own 'life support' systems through natural mechanisms

Threats to the life support systems include the interference with levels of CO_2 and water vapour, both affected by plant cover. Atmospheric pollution raises the CO_2 level, while deforestation and desertification increase the albedo (proportion of sunlight reflected back into space

"The most beautiful object I have ever seen in a photograph, in all my life, is the planet Earth seen from the distance of the moon, hanging there in space, obviously alive. Although it seems at first glance to be made up of innumerable separate species of living things, on closer examination every one of its working parts, including us, is interdependently connected to all other working parts. It is, to put it one way, the only truly closed ecosystem any of us knows about. To put it another way, it is an organism. It came alive, I shall guess, 3.8 billion years ago today, and I wish it a happy birthday and a long life ahead, for our children and their grandchildren and theirs and theirs."
Lewis Thomas, February 1984

Q

1 Study diagram 1.
(a) Water balance is vitally important to the development of soils. Explain any three of the soil processes shown in diagram 1. (6)
(b) For either temperate forests or coniferous forests, describe and explain the role of these processes in the formation of the soil profile. (3)

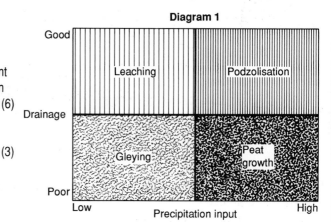

Diagram 1

Q

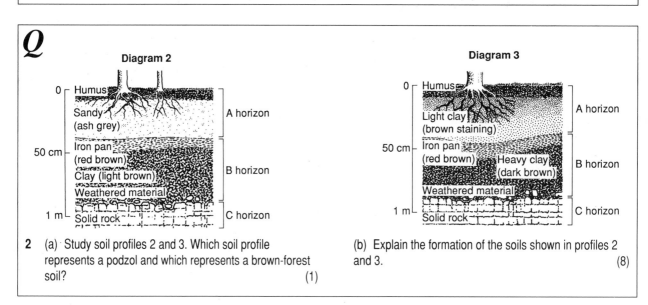

2 (a) Study soil profiles 2 and 3. Which soil profile represents a podzol and which represents a brown-forest soil? (1)

(b) Explain the formation of the soils shown in profiles 2 and 3. (8)

Q

3 Study diagrams 4a–d carefully. Explain the relationships between the climate and the vegetation along any three of transect lines A–B. (9)

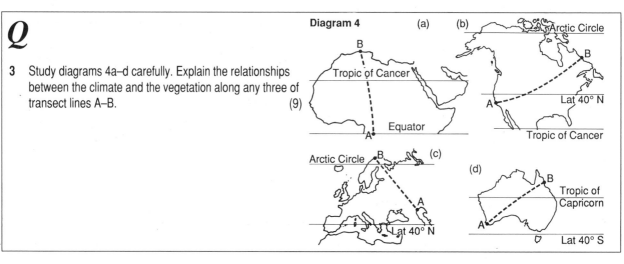

Diagram 4

ANSWER EITHER QUESTION 4 OR QUESTION 5.

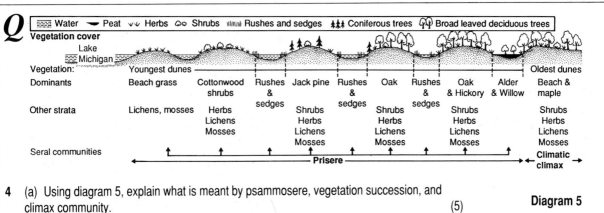

Q

4 (a) Using diagram 5, explain what is meant by psammosere, vegetation succession, and
climax community. (5)
(b) The path towards a climax community is seldom without interruption. Describe the field
evidence for plant disturbance in a psammosere and discuss possible causes. (4)

Diagram 5

Q

Diagram 6

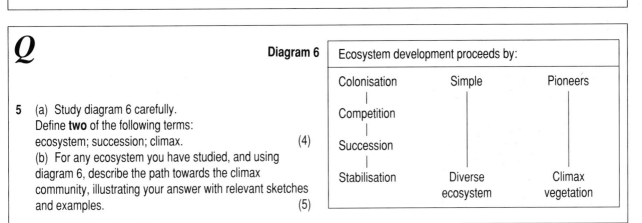

5 (a) Study diagram 6 carefully.
Define **two** of the following terms:
ecosystem; succession; climax. (4)
(b) For any ecosystem you have studied, and using
diagram 6, describe the path towards the climax
community, illustrating your answer with relevant sketches
and examples. (5)

Q

6 Study diagram 7 which shows the changes in a plant
community over time.
(a) Under what conditions do the following types of
vegetation thrive: sphagnum moss; heaths; reeds? (3)
(b) What effects do relief and drainage have on the types
of vegetation shown in the diagram? (2)
(c) Describe the stages of colonisation and succession
shown in the diagram. (3)
(d) Which type of succession is displayed in the diagram:
allogenic or autogenic? (1)

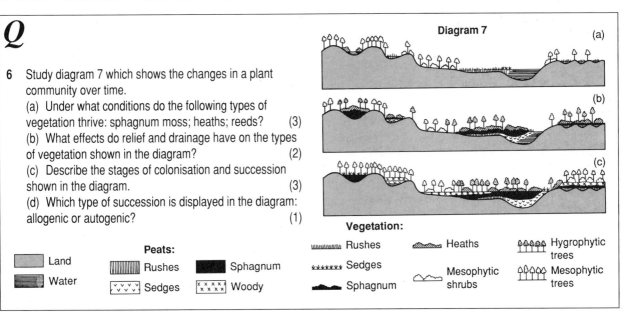

Diagram 7

RURAL LAND RESOURCES

Cherished Land?

5.1 Limestone quarrying in the Peak District has long been a controversial issue

The United Kingdom has a population of 56 million in an area of 240 000 km², making it one of the world's most densely populated countries. The population is not distributed evenly, however, and there are many isolated or scenic areas with low population densities. Many of these scenic areas, such as the Peak District (5.1), are now suffering severe pressure on the landscape from the increase in the number of visitors, and the development of various industries including quarrying and forestry.

This pressure on Britain's most beautiful and least populated areas has been a growing problem since the Industrial Revolution. In the last 200 years, there have been many social trends which have contributed to the increase in demand for land for various purposes. The population of the United Kingdom has steadily grown from about 10 million in 1800 to 56 million in the 1990s. During this time, more and more land has been taken over for urban and industrial purposes. At the same time, more and more people have been visiting Britain's scenic areas for leisure purposes. This is because there has been a 'leisure revolution' as the number of hours in the working week has steadily been reduced. Today at least a third of our lives is leisure time. Several factors have contributed to this, including a rise in standard of living, an increase in personal mobility, improvements in the motorway and rail networks across Britain, and an increasing interest in outdoor recreation.

Since the 1940s, various measures have been adopted to protect the shrinking area of 'cherished land' within the United Kingdom. The government set up the **Countryside Commission** in 1968 as the official agency with overall responsibility for conserving the rural land resources in the United Kingdom. The Countryside Commission (CC) aim to 'conserve and enhance the natural beauty of the countryside and to encourage the provision and improvement of countryside facilities for open-air recreation by the public'. This has proved to be a difficult task as the rural land resources of the United Kingdom have never been under greater user pressure. Making decisions about the use of countryside areas is complex and greatly influenced by the various other official and non-official agencies and interested bodies. The Countryside Commission recommend to the government and local authorities areas of natural beauty which they think should be **designated** for conservation. These include many different types (see 5.2 and 5.3).

The work of the official bodies is complemented by the efforts of various non-official or voluntary bodies such as the National Trust, the Royal Society for the Protection of Birds, and the Council for the Protection of Rural England (CPRE).

Perhaps the best known designated areas are the National Parks (5.4). Each has its own characteristic landscape and provides varying economic and social opportunities including agriculture, forestry, rural industry, recreation, and tourism. The interrelated nature of these opportunities is considered in the rest of this chapter, which is a case study of the Lake District.

5.2 Designated areas: explanation of terms

National Parks (11)	Large protected areas of spectacular scenery in England & Wales
National Park Direction Areas (5)	Large areas of beautiful scenery in Scotland
National Scenic Areas (40)	Areas of beautiful scenery in Scotland, smaller than NPDAs
Areas of Outstanding Natural Beauty (33)	Similar to, but smaller than, National Parks; designated by CC, but run by local authorities
National Nature Reserves (11)	Areas of important flora, fauna, geology; selected by the Nature Conservancy Council (NCC)
Sites of Special Scientific Interest (3800) SSSIs	Areas containing rare flora, fauna or geology; introduced in 1981, run by NCC in conjunction with landowner
Environmentally Sensitive Areas (over 40)	Similar to, but smaller than, SSSIs, and run on a voluntary basis
Heritage Coasts (33)	Areas of spectacular coastline in England & Wales
Green belts	Protected countryside around major urban areas
National trails (12)	Officially recognised beautiful footpaths

National Parks (England and Wales)

1 Lake District
2 Yorkshire Dales
3 Peak District
4 Northumberland
5 Exmoor
6 Norfolk Broads
7 Pembrokeshire Coast
8 North York Moors
9 Snowdonia
10 Breacon Beacons
11 Dartmoor

National Park Direction Areas (Scotland)

12 Lochs Torridon, Maree, Little Loch Broom
13 Glens Affric, Cannich, Strathfarrar
14 Cairngorms
15 Ben Nevis, Glen Coe, Black Mount
16 Loch Lomond and the Trossachs

▼ **National Nature Reserve**
e.g. Strathy Bog, Caithness

Areas of Outstanding Natural Beauty
(AONB) (England & Wales)

1 Antrim Coast
2 Sperrin
3 Strangford Lough
4 Mourne
5 North Pennines
6 Bowland
7 Northumberland Coast
8 Anglesey
9 Clwyd
10 Lincoln Wolds
11 Lleyn Peninsula
12 Shropshire Hills
13 Norfolk Coast
14 Suffolk Coast
15 Gower
16 Wye Valley
17 Cotswolds
18 Chilterns
19 Wessex Downs
20 Mendips
21 North Devon
22 Bodmin
23 Cornwall
24 South Devon
25 Dorset
26 Wiltshire Downs
27 Isle of Wight
28 South Downs
29 Weald
30 North Downs

National trails

a Speyside Way
b West Highland Way
c Southern Upland Way
d Pennine Way
e Cleveland Way
f Wolds Way
g Offa's Dyke Way
h Ridgeway
i Pembroke Coastal Path
j North Downs Way
k South Downs Way
l South West Coastal Path

○ Forest Parks

• Country Parks

◇ Environmentally Sensitive Areas (ESA) (England & Wales)

Heritage Coasts (England & Wales)

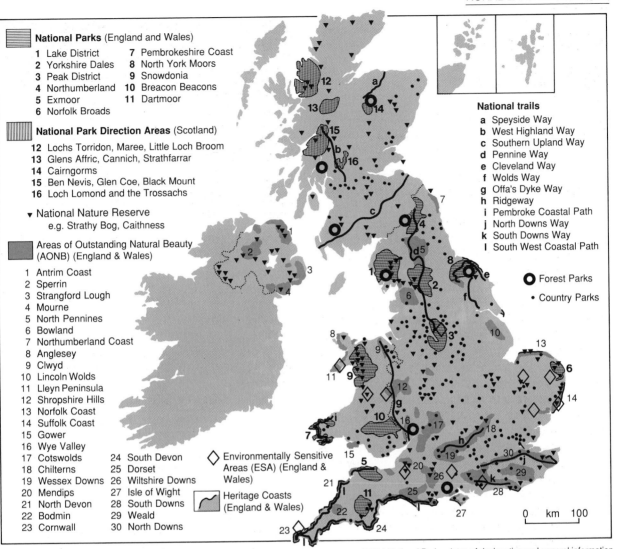

▲ 5.3 Location of areas of protected land in the United Kingdom

▼ 5.4 National Parks: dates of designation and general information

 Peak District (1949). Landscapes of moors, limestone and millstone grit. Covers 1400 km² and forms the southernmost part of the Pennines.

Lake District (1951). Largest National Park, covering 2240 km². Landscape of glaciated upland scenery including England's highest mountain, and largest lake.

 Yorkshire Dales (1954). Covers an area of 1760 km² and forms the central Pennines. A karst landscape of high moorland, bare limestone scenery and wide valleys.

Snowdonia (1951). Covers over 2170 km². Spectacular glaciated mountain scenery with 14 peaks over 900 m, and many lakes. Large areas now forested.

 Dartmoor (1952). Landscape of high moorland, granite tors and incised valleys. Covers almost 1000 km².

Pembrokeshire Coast (1952). The smallest National Park covering just 270 km². Landscape of spectacular cliffs and deep rias. Competition for land from industry and army.

 North York Moors (1952). Covers 1430 km² with high moorland, beautiful valleys and spectacular coasts. Contains the largest heather moorland of any Park.

 Exmoor (1955). Has a magnificent coastline and large heather moorlands. Covers 700 km² but reclamation and enclosure of moorland have increased farmland.

 Brecon Beacons (1957). Limestone landscape covering 1340 km² with high sandstone moorlands: a virtually unspoilt area.

Northumberland (1956). The most northerly National Park, covering over 1000 km² in the Cheviot and Simonside Hills. Landscape of moor and forest encompassing Hadrian's Wall and the extensive Keilder Forest.

 Norfolk Broads (1989). A water park with the same status as a National Park. An entirely artificial landscape of old peat workings which were flooded by the sea in 1287. There are 41 lakes in an area of over 20 km².

The Lake District : Rock Structure

The Lake District displays a wide variety of landscape for a small area of the British Isles (5.5). This is partly due to the rocks of the area, which are among the oldest exposed in England. Most are between 400 and 570 million years old and none, except glacial and alluvial deposits, are younger than 200 million years old.

The four main rock groups run from north-east to south-west across the area. Their formation (5.6) is the result of a complex history of geological events. The oldest rocks are the Skiddaw slates which make up the northern part of the Lake District (5.7). The slates are composed of ancient muds and sandstones laid down as sediments in cool seas in the Cambrian Period. Towards the end of this period, volcanic eruptions threw up lavas and **tuffs** (volcanic ash) to form the central core of the Lake District: the Borrowdale volcanic group. The Silurian rocks of the Windermere group form much of the south of the Lake District. These rocks consist of soft, muddy and gritty sediments of shales and sandstones. They were laid down when this area became submerged beneath a warm tropical sea about 430 million years ago. Layers of carboniferous limestone, coal measures and red sandstone built up on top of the existing rocks. Plate tectonic movements during the Caledonian orogeny, and later during the Alpine orogeny, combined to fold the area into a giant dome. The overlying layers of sediments were then eroded, exposing the older rocks at the centre of the area. Associated with the formation of the Lake District dome were intrusions of magma which cooled to form granite now exposed along the eastern edge of the area.

Each rock type has contributed to its own characteristic scenery (5.8). The Skiddaw slates are composed of conical, smooth-sided mountains (e.g. Skiddaw 931 m). The Borrowdale volcanics form the highest area within the Lake District as they are very resistant igneous rocks. They give rise to dramatic, craggy and jagged peaks such as the Langdale Pikes, Great Gable and Scafell Pike (978 m). The lower undulating plateau and valley landscape of the Windermere area is associated with the softer Silurian sedimentary rocks such as shale and sandstone.

Since its formation the Lake District dome has been repeatedly glaciated. This has contributed to the removal of thousands of metres of the original rock surface and the development of a **radial drainage** pattern. The evidence of glacial and post-glacial action remains today.

5.5 The spectacular glaciated landscape in the Lake District

© Crown copyright 1991/MOD reproduced with the permission of the Controller of HMSO.

5.6 Evolution of the Lake District

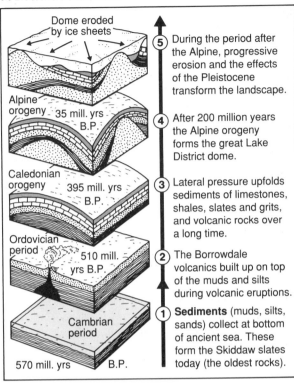

Dome eroded by ice sheets

Alpine orogeny 35 mill. yrs B.P.

Caledonian orogeny 395 mill. yrs B.P.

Ordovician period 510 mill. yrs B.P.

Cambrian period

570 mill. yrs B.P.

(5) During the period after the Alpine, progressive erosion and the effects of the Pleistocene transform the landscape.

(4) After 200 million years the Alpine orogeny forms the great Lake District dome.

(3) Lateral pressure upfolds sediments of limestones, shales, slates and grits, and volcanic rocks over a long time.

(2) The Borrowdale volcanics built up on top of the muds and silts during volcanic eruptions.

(1) **Sediments** (muds, silts, sands) collect at bottom of ancient sea. These form the Skiddaw slates today (the oldest rocks).

5.7 Geological map of the Lake District

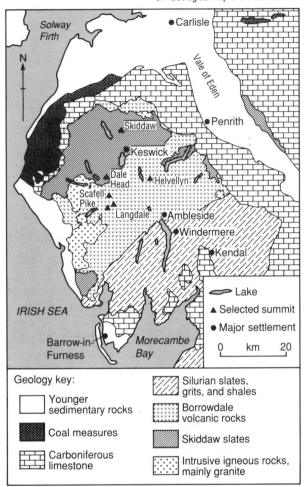

Geology key:

☐ Younger sedimentary rocks

▓ Coal measures

▦ Carboniferous limestone

▧ Silurian slates, grits, and shales

▿ Borrowdale volcanic rocks

▨ Skiddaw slates

⸬ Intrusive igneous rocks, mainly granite

〰 Lake
▲ Selected summit
● Major settlement

0   km   20

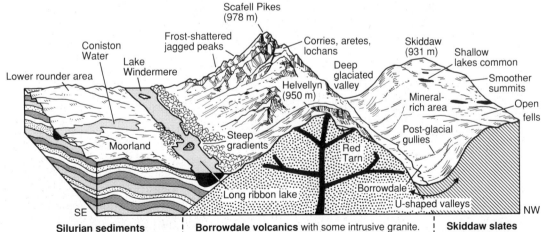

5.8 Lake District: simplified structure and landscape. This is diagrammatic only, and is not correct in terms of scale

Silurian sediments
Softer bands of sediments of shales, sandstones and grits have been folded and then completely overrun by ice. The result is a lowered landscape of rounded smoothed hills, gentle slopes and shallow lakes.

Borrowdale volcanics with some intrusive granite. A series of toughened lava layers interspersed with softer fine-grained **tuffs** (ashes). These indicate varying eruptions 500 million years ago.

In this area, the classic, rugged, frost-shattered summits are to be found. Differential erosion mainly by Pleistocene ice has sculpted famous glaciated features. Valley systems are linked by steep passes. Deep ribbon lakes are also common on fringes.

Skiddaw slates
Hard ancient metamorphic muds, veins of minerals (copper, lead)

Mountain and Lake

Many of the varied features in the Lake District landscape of rugged mountains, moorland and long finger lakes are the result of glaciation. There are sixteen lakes which radiate from an elongated dome, running from Scafell in the south-west to Helvellyn in the north-east (5.9). They have formed in long deep U-shaped valleys which were widened, deepened and straightened during the Ice Age which ended some 15 000 years ago. As glaciers moved downhill, they eroded the landscape in two main ways. Plucking occurred where the underside of the ice froze onto jointed rocks and wrenched or plucked away rock fragments as it moved downhill. Abrasion then occurred as the fragments embedded in the glacier ice scraped or abraded the land which it moved over. This action produced a generally smooth landscape but with many rugged crags as a result of plucking.

Roches moutonnees (5.10) are the combined result of both plucking and abrasion on the valley floor. Partly embedded rock fragments in the sides and base of the glacier ice also left scratches or **striations** on smooth rock surfaces. As the snow continued to accumulate, the glaciers thickened, forming a huge dome of ice over the Lake District mountains. The ice moved outwards in all directions, concentrating its erosive power in valleys, gouging and deepening long troughs.

Although erosion has been the main effect of glacier ice there are also traces of glacial deposition. There are examples of **terminal moraines** (5.11) to be found in Borrowdale. These hummocky ridges mark the positions of the snouts of glaciers at their furthest extent. Along the sides of Borrowdale and Thirlmere, there are areas of hummocky **lateral moraine**. In many valley bottoms, the land is very flat. This is in great contrast to the high

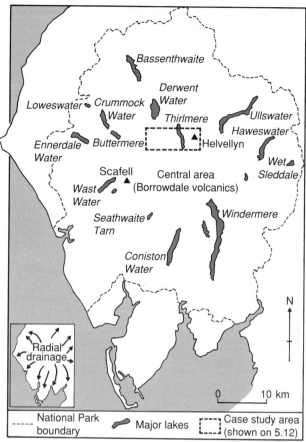

5.9 Radial drainage in the Lake District

and jagged peaks such as Scafell and Langdale Pikes. These flat stretches were formerly lakes dammed by moraines after the ice had disappeared. The rivers flowing out of these lakes have since cut down into the moraine and drained the lakes. The flat valley floors of lake floor deposits are the most fertile areas.

5.10 Roches moutonnées

5.11 Terminal moraine

The central area around Helvellyn and Borrowdale (5.12 – 5.14) displays most of the characteristics of the glaciated scenery of the Lake District. Since the end of the Pleistocene era, the effects of post-glacial action (screes, gullies, alluvial fans and lake head deltas) as well as the influence of people in the last 7000 years (spoil heaps from mining, the scars of artillery ranges and the erosion of popular footpaths) contribute to the varied nature of the scenery.

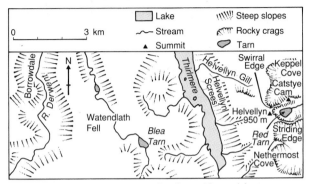

5.12 Location map of case study area: Hevellyn and Borrowdale

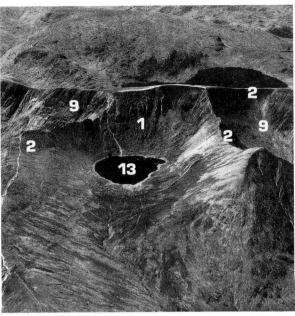

5.13 Helvellyn and Red Tarn (numbers refer to features listed in 5.14)

5.14 Relief and drainage of the Helvellyn and Borrowdale area

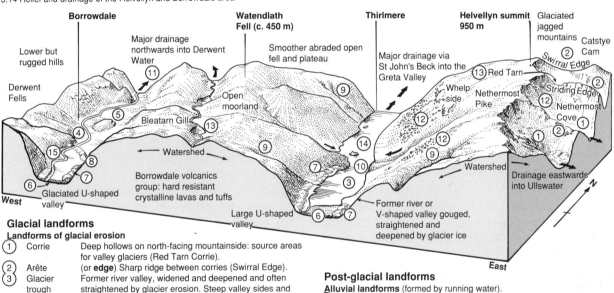

Glacial landforms

Landforms of glacial erosion

1. **Corrie** — Deep hollows on north-facing mountainside: source areas for valley glaciers (Red Tarn Corrie).
2. **Arête** — (or **edge**) Sharp ridge between corries (Swirral Edge).
3. **Glacier trough** — Former river valley, widened and deepened and often straightened by glacier erosion. Steep valley sides and U-shaped cross-section (Thirlmere).
4. **Rock basin** — Formed by irregular erosion on valley floor (Borrowdale).
5. **Roche moutonnée** — Small knoll of solid bedrock, found on valley floor smoothed by abrasion on the upstream side and craggy on the downstream side as a result of plucking (5.10)

Landforms of glacial deposition

6. **Ground moraine** — Unsorted deposits laid down by glacier on valley floor (Borrowdale/Thirlmere).
7. **Lateral moraine** — Mounds of loose unsorted material deposited on the valley side at the edge of the glacier (Thirlmere).
8. **Terminal moraine** — (or end moraine) Low ridge of loose deposits marking extent of glacier in retreat (5.11).

Post-glacial landforms

Alluvial landforms (formed by running water).

9. **Post-glacial gullies** — Small V-shaped valleys formed since glaciers retreated.
10. **Alluvial fan** — Cone-shaped deposit at mouth of gully.
11. **Lake head delta** — Flat alluvial land found where deposition occurs at head of lake (Derwent Water).
12. **Screes** — Frost-shattered, jagged rocks and boulders (Helvellyn screes).

Water features

13. **Tarn** — Corrie lake or Lochan (Red Tarn)
14. **Rock basin lake** — Found in glacier trough (Thirlmere)
15. **Misfit stream** — Stream draining glaciated valley. Too small to have eroded valley by itself (River Derwent).

Stewards of the Landscape

The Lake District is the largest of the eleven National Parks in England and Wales. It is run by the Lake District Special Planning Board, often referred to unofficially as the Lake District National Park Authority or LDNPA. The LDNPA is the local government body established to ensure that the aims described by the National Parks Act (1949) are achieved. These are defined as 'preserving and enhancing the great natural beauty of the area' and 'encouraging public enjoyment of the scenery by giving opportunity for open-air recreation'.

The diverse and spectacular upland scenery (see page 136) of the Lake District provides opportunities for public enjoyment of a wide range of recreational activities such as walking, sailing, horse riding and fishing. But there are problems inherent in the basic aims of the LDNPA. The preservation of the great natural beauty of the 'fells' seems at odds with increasing demands for land for different purposes, such as reservoirs, forests, caravan and camping sites, urban expansion and improved communication links. In addition, the Lake District has a local resident population of almost 41 000 who are dependent on primary (farming, forestry and mining) and tertiary (tourist-related) forms of employment. The LDNPA strives to carry out its main functions (5.15) of protecting the environment and enabling visitors to enjoy its recreational opportunities while also protecting the social and economic well-being of the local community. This is a very complex task and one which is hampered by the fact that the Lake District is not owned by the nation. There are a number of public and independent organisations which own land within the park (5.16). The Lake District is mainly in private ownership but, in consultation with the LDNPA, (restricted) public access is encouraged to footpaths, bridleways, open fells and mountains. The exceptions are the military training areas and grouse moors.

		%
Total Area of National Park	227 920 ha	100
LDNPA	8 660 ha	3.8
National Trust	56 655 ha	24.8
Forestry Commission	12 734 ha	5.6
North West Water (NWWA)	15 560 ha	6.8
Ministry of Defence	461 ha	0.2
Total owned by organisations	94 070 ha	41.3

5.16 Major landowners in the Lake District National Park

In recent years the opening of the M6 motorway and the A66 dual carriageway have made the park much more accessible to tourists. Using the motorway makes a daytrip to the Lake District possible for people living in south Lancashire, the North Midlands and the north-east. People from the south and east of England and Wales also have much easier access to the Lake District as it lies within a day's travelling distance. This means that more and more people are visiting the park, especially the more accessible areas around Ullswater, Windermere, Langdale and Coniston.

The development of the Lake District as one of the most popular tourist destinations in Britain can be viewed as a mixed blessing for the park area. Although increasing tourist-related developments are generating wealth within the Lake District there are serious problems facing the LDNPA in its stewardship of the environment. It must mediate and reconcile the conflicts arising from conservation of the environment, the needs of the local community and the ever-increasing demands from developers for the park area. The case study of the Hartsop Valley (5.17 to 5.19) provides a typical example of the varied pressures on small areas within the Lake District National Park.

The Lake District was traditionally maintained by its farmers. As the demands of tourism take an increasing toll on the landscape, and employment in farming declines, it becomes more difficult to pay for conservation of the environment. It the traditional economy is no longer profitable enough, should farmers be specially paid to be stewards of the landscape? Or if tourism is replacing farming as the principal income earner, should this new industry, and visitors, pay to maintain the quality and beauty of the landscape?

National Park Officer			
Land Use and Planning	Administration	Park Management	Visitor Services
Development Control	Administration	Practical Conservation	External Relations
National Park Plan	Clerical	including:	Information Service
Local Plans	Legal	Upland Management	Visitor Centres
Land Agent		Estate Work	Youth and Schools Service
Ecologist		National Park Rangers	Residential Centres
Landscape Architect		Anti-litter team	Caravan Site(s)
		Toilet cleaners	Boating Centre
			Car Parks

5.15 Structure and functions of a National Park Authority Board or Committee

Changing Hartsop?

The Lake District has a romantic heritage, much celebrated in art and literature.
'People are seen as a minor influence set against the natural landscape'

William Wordsworth

People have traditionally based their livelihood on the fell landscape: rearing sheep in this harsh environment.

Hartsop Valley south of Ullswater is an open upland landscape, greatly affected by recent changes.

5.17 Location of the Hartsop Valley

The main features of the valley reflect the dominant activity within it: hill sheep farming. But changes in the fortunes of farmers eventually work their way through into changes in the valley landscape.

Village of Hartsop built in seventeenth century by local farmers using blue slate. Now facing invasion by wealthy owners of second (holiday) homes, and retired people.

Hill sheep farmers are viewed by the National Trust as stewards of the landscape, caring for the land, maintaining walls, clearing ditches, etc.

Income of traditional hill sheep farmers supplemented by small amount of income from campers and bed and breakfast fees.

The Lake District climate is a mild wet one with precipitation falling as snow on mountains in winter. The cloudiness and altitude make sheep rearing and growing of fodder the most economically viable agriculture.

The uncertain economics of hill sheep farming in the Lake District is evident in the deterioration of traditional features of the landscape:
* collapse of dry-stone walls
* derelict barns and hog houses
* fewer sheep, leading to an increase in hillside bracken

Increasing accessibility has led to influx of thousands of visitors. Development of modern purpose-built camp sites has concentrated tourism in a few selected areas, depriving farmers of extra income.

Many farmers are now applying for the 'set aside' scheme, financed by the European Community. In this scheme farmers are given an annual payment to leave parts of their cropland unused for five years (paid by the hectare).

Traditional rural employment in hill farming, slate mining, wall building are now being replaced by tourist-related employment (recreation, camp sites, hotels, guides, tours, etc.), much of which can lead to deterioration of the landscape.

5.18

5.19 Hartsop Valley today

Land Use in the Lake District

For a small area of British Isles, the Lake District encompasses a wide variety of land uses (see 5.20), many of which have had a major impact on the landscape. For the past decade, experts have suggested that there is an imbalance in the way the countryside of the Lake District is used. There is growing pressure from various land uses, including farming, forestry, military and quarrying, as well as tourism.

The Lake District was traditionally an area whose land resource base mainly provided opportunities for rural primary industry: hill sheep farming, quarrying for limestone and slate, and forestry. There was a small proportion of secondary and tertiary employment in the few main settlements such as Keswick and Windermere.

The seeds of significant change were planted in 1847 when the railway first reached Windermere. Since then, with the increase in leisure time and subsequent further improvements to the communications networks in northern England, tourism has developed into the area's most important industry, and many traditional rural industries have declined.

In areas such as the Lake District there are often disagreements over how the land should be developed and used (5.20). There can be opposition to major schemes for tourist-related development, large areas of forest plantations, water use, and military training. Some people believe that it is best to develop some tourist honeypots (such as Tarn Hows: 5.21) to which visitors are deliberately directed and attracted, thereby protecting other more sensitive sites. Others think that all of the Lake District should be preserved from too many visitors and that the introduction of a 'tourist tax' payable on entry to the Lake District would help reduce visitor pressure. Locals and large private land owners complain that this sort of scheme would rob the area of its livelihood.

5.21 Tarn Hows 'honeypot'

5.20 Selected land uses in the Lake District

Tourism. The Lake District receives over 12 million visitors annually, 78% of whom travel by car. This is vital to the local economy, creating over 20 000 full-time and part-time jobs associated with tourism. However, tourism puts massive pressures on local resources and the environment. The majority of visitors engage in passive leisure activities such as touring by car, picnicking, sunbathing, relaxing. Fewer visitors take advantage of more active leisure opportunities such as hill walking, climbing, boating.

Water supplies. Increasing demands are being placed on water supplies, mainly by the Greater Manchester conurbation (water is taken from Thirlmere, Haweswater, Ullswater and Windermere). Cumbrian coastal industries (paper and chemical) also use water. Conflicts often arise over new plans: e.g. in 1978 it was proposed to increase water levels in Ennerdale and increase water supplies to British Nuclear Fuels Ltd from Wast Water from 4 to 11 million gallons a day.

Afforestation schemes.
11% of the LDNP is forested. The Forestry Commission own only 6%, the rest is in private ownership. Major controversies arise over planting and felling schemes. In 1935, 3000 hectares of conifers were planted in Ennerdale, against public opinion. There are now agreements *not* to plant in the central Lake District and to plant deciduous species wherever possible in the outer areas.

Beauty spots. These are so over-visited that they are now omitted from tourist guides. The LDNP is often forced to close (especially on bank holidays) because of long traffic jams. Three beauty spots in the Lake District –Tarn Hows, Hawkshead and Sawrey – have been identified as being in danger of becoming a wasteland for conservation because of their popularity.

COC

Slate quarrying
Honister is one of only two quarries s... working, but the sc... of many abandone... quarries also rema...

Key

▨	National Trust land (56 665 ha or 25%)
▨	Forested land (24 451 ha or 11%)
▨	North West Water land (15 560 ha or 7%)
▨	LDNPA (8660 ha or 4%)
☐	Land over 200 m
🗻	Lake ⌇ River

0   km   10

LDNP

▤ Major town
▬ Motorway
▬ Main road
- - - - Minor road

Car parking for:
● over 150 vehicles
● 149–100 vehicles
● 99–50 vehicles
• up to 49 vehicles

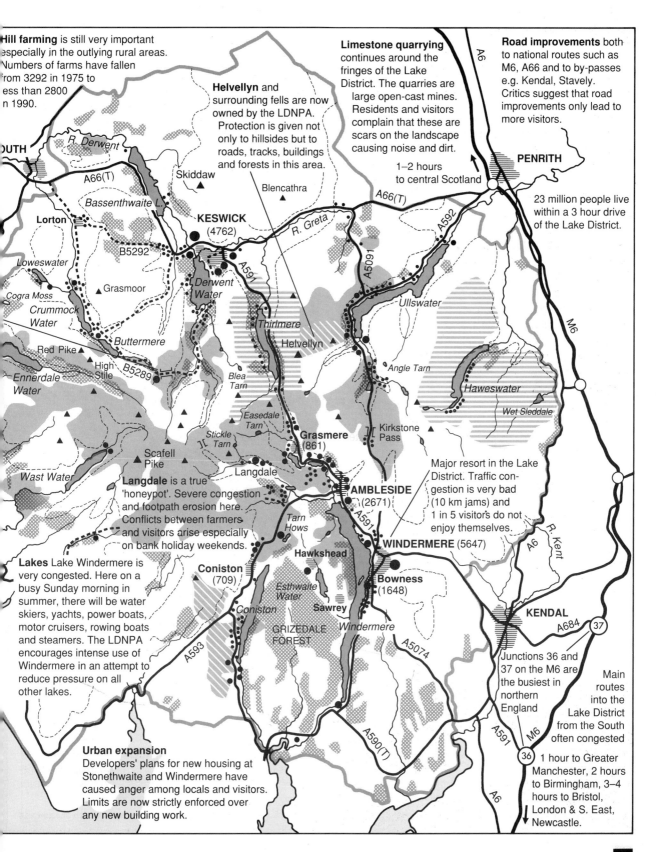

Hill farming is still very important especially in the outlying rural areas. Numbers of farms have fallen from 3292 in 1975 to less than 2800 in 1990.

Helvellyn and surrounding fells are now owned by the LDNPA. Protection is given not only to hillsides but to roads, tracks, buildings and forests in this area.

Limestone quarrying continues around the fringes of the Lake District. The quarries are large open-cast mines. Residents and visitors complain that these are scars on the landscape causing noise and dirt.

1–2 hours to central Scotland

Road improvements both to national routes such as M6, A66 and to by-passes e.g. Kendal, Stavely. Critics suggest that road improvements only lead to more visitors.

23 million people live within a 3 hour drive of the Lake District.

Langdale is a true 'honeypot'. Severe congestion and footpath erosion here. Conflicts between farmers and visitors arise especially on bank holiday weekends.

Lakes Lake Windermere is very congested. Here on a busy Sunday morning in summer, there will be water skiers, yachts, power boats, motor cruisers, rowing boats and steamers. The LDNPA encourages intense use of Windermere in an attempt to reduce pressure on all other lakes.

Major resort in the Lake District. Traffic congestion is very bad (10 km jams) and 1 in 5 visitors do not enjoy themselves.

Junctions 36 and 37 on the M6 are the busiest in northern England

Main routes into the Lake District from the South often congested

1 hour to Greater Manchester, 2 hours to Birmingham, 3–4 hours to Bristol, London & S. East, Newcastle.

Urban expansion
Developers' plans for new housing at Stonethwaite and Windermere have caused anger among locals and visitors. Limits are now strictly enforced over any new building work.

Map labels: R. Derwent, SOUTH, A66(T), Skiddaw ▲, Blencathra ▲, A6, PENRITH, Bassenthwaite L., Lorton, B5292, KESWICK (4762), R. Greta, A591, A592, A5091, Loweswater, Grasmoor ▲, Derwent Water, Cogra Moss, Crummock Water, Red Pike ▲, Buttermere, High Stile ▲, B5289, Thirlmere, Helvellyn, Ullswater, Angle Tarn, M6, Ennerdale Water, Blea Tarn, Haweswater, Wet Sleddale, Easedale Tarn, Stickle Tarn ▲, Grasmere (861), Kirkstone Pass, Scafell Pike ▲, Langdale, Wast Water, Tarn Hows, AMBLESIDE (2671), A591, R. Kent, A6, WINDERMERE (5647), Hawkshead, Coniston (709), Esthwaite Water, Sawrey, Bowness (1648), KENDAL, A684, 37, Grizedale Forest, Coniston, Windermere, A5074, A593, A590(T), A591, M6, 36, A6

Lakeland Conflicts

The forests and woodlands make a major contribution to the environment of the Lake District. Plantations and woodlands cover over 24 400 hectares (about 11%) of the National Park area. The Forestry Commission own only 5.6% of the land but there is much private forestry. (The North West Water Authority is a significant forest owner.) Forestry is not subject to planning control but the Forestry Commission has an obligation to consult the LDNPA and the Countryside Commission before giving planting grants. Where grants are not requested there is no control over the spread of forestry developments. This situation has been a recipe for conflict. For example, as long ago as 1935 a major controversy occurred in the Ennerdale Valley (5.22, 5.23) when 3500 hectares of conifers were planted against public

5.22 Blanket conifer plantation in Ennerdale

opinion. There are always conflicting views over the large-scale use of National Park land for forestry. 5.24 shows some of the arguments on both sides. You may be able to think of others.

5.23 Ennerdale: forested glaciated valley

Ennerdale Valley

① Ennerdale is an intensely glaciated valley.
② Pillar and Steeple are peaks of Borrowdale volcanic rocks: craggy and frost-shattered.
③ The ridge from High Stile to Great Borne consists of granite: smooth scree-covered south-facing slopes.
④ Ennerdale Water is contained in a U-shaped valley by a low mound of terminal moraine.
⑤ Lake head delta of the River Liza.
⑥ Upland glaciated landforms include ice-plucked slopes, truncated spurs, corries, arêtes, etc.

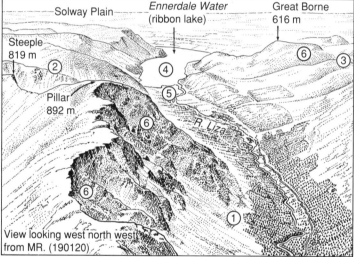

Solway Plain — Ennerdale Water (ribbon lake) — Great Borne 616 m
Steeple 819 m
Pillar 892 m
R. Liza
View looking west north west from MR. (190120)

Ennerdale forest

• Over 3500 hectares of coniferous woodland are planted in Ennerdale.
• Plantations are on drier slopes above damper areas of lake-flats and valley bottoms.
• Rectangular forest boundaries are common, as trees have been planted in angular 'blocks'.
• Species are mainly Sitka Spruce, Norwegian Spruce and European Larch. Few deciduous species.
• In the 1970s facilities for recreation were developed, including forest walks, picnic sites and nature trails.

5.24 Arguments for and against forestry development

In favour of forestry developments
• The beauty of areas such as Ennerdale is enhanced.
• Jobs in rural areas can be created and maintained.
• Britain's increasing demands for timber can be met.
• Tourism is encouraged by giving access to woodlands and creating picnic sites, walks and nature trails.
• Trees stabilise soils and reduce soil erosion on steep slopes.
• Trees reduce rapid run-off and reduce flooding problems.
• Wildlife in upland areas is preserved and encouraged.
• Coniferous species are more profitable than other traditional land uses on steep glaciated slopes.
• Coniferous species are well suited to the mild wet climate.

Against forestry developments
• Coniferous plantations 'sterilise' the natural varied landscape into rows of uniform species.
• Forests increase the risk of fires.
• Clothing the landscape in rectilinear blocks spoils the natural beauty of scenic areas.
• Forests use land previously suited to sheep, grouse and walking.
• Few rural jobs are maintained.
• Access to fells is limited by forest (esp. private forests) land.
• Very slow return for the high investment. Takes 50 years for reasonable profits to accrue.
• Coniferous forests block light and discourage flora and fauna.

Windermere

Visitors to the Lake District tend to cluster in the more attractive and accessible places. The Lake District's major honeypot is Lake Windermere. It is accessible from the M6 and lies within 3 hours travelling distance for 23 million people. On busy bank holidays and at weekends, the population of Windermere can swell from 5647 to well over 20 000. The resulting congestion of cars and people can be a major problem on roads and the lake itself (5.25) and in settlements such as Bowness (5.26) and Ambleside. Tourist facilities can hardly cope with the influx of visitors who pursue both active (sailing, walking, etc.) and passive (coach tours, picnics, etc.) leisure pursuits in the area.

Map 5.27 shows some of the main land uses competing for space along the edges of the lake. Critics of the honeypot strategy for Lake Windermere say that the whole landscape is under threat from visitor pressure. Others support the strategy saying that it brings wealth and employment to Windermere and helps protect other less accessible parts of the Lake District.

5.25 Congestion on Lake Windermere

5.26 Congestion in Bowness-on-Windermere

5.27 Simplified land use map of area around Lake Windermere

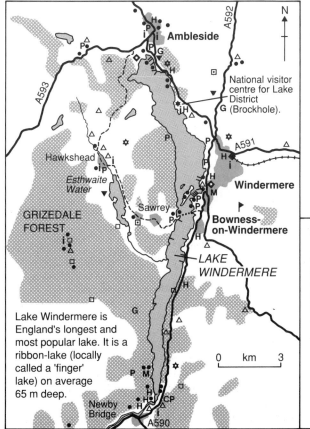

Lake Windermere is England's longest and most popular lake. It is a ribbon-lake (locally called a 'finger' lake) on average 65 m deep.

National visitor centre for Lake District (Brockhole).

0   km   3

Key

Lake with boat launch/hire	**CP** Country Park
Major settlement	▣ Country house or mansion
Forested area	**G** Gardens open to visitors
┼┼┼┼■ Railway station/line	▶ Golf course
—— Main road	◆ Outdoor pursuits centre
P Car park	△ Camping/caravan site
✿ Viewpoint	▼ Youth hostel
▫ Picnic site	**H** Hotel
i Tourist information centre	**M** Museum
	• Other tourist facilities

Landscapes of Tomorrow?

The beautiful landscapes of the Lake District National Park attract over 12 million visitors each year. Some of the best loved features of the scenery are the glaciated mountains and lake-filled valleys clothed by the seemingly endless network of dry-

stone walls and scattered hog houses. The walls enclose a patchwork of meadow and pastureland. Together with pockets of woodland, open fellsides and stone-built villages these features comprise one of the finest upland landscapes in the British Isles.

Unlike National Parks in many other areas of the world the Lake District is not a true wildscape. The present landscape (5.28) reflects the influence of human activities over many centuries. The countryside has been changed drastically from the primaeval forests of 8000 years ago. It is still being changed today by landowners, farmers and tourists. Although change to

5.28

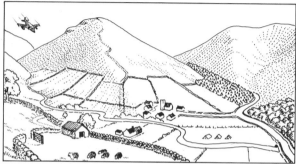

Present landscape. Many of the local community earn their living from farming or tourism. Farm incomes are supported by government subsidies intended to maintain and supplement production. Meadows are used to produce hay or are used for intensive silage. Most hog houses and walls are well maintained but some are being replaced by fences and modern sheds. Overgrazing by sheep and beef cattle mean broad-leaved woodland and heather moorland are gradually disappearing.

5.29

Abandoned landscape. If subsidies were withdrawn, fell farmers would have to compete with more profitable lowland farmers. The few remaining fell farmers would keep flocks on the better land but outlying meadows and moorland would be abandoned to scrub and thistles. Some farmers would turn to farm-based tourism or forestry to survive. Barns and dry-stone walls would become derelict as there would not be enough money to maintain them.

5.32

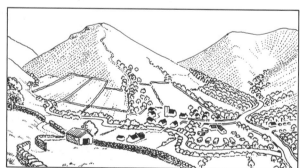

Enhanced landscape. By taking advantage of limited conservation grants or by using their own finances, fell farmers could enhance the best of the traditional farmscape features. Any sites of dereliction could be tidied up. The few remaining walls and hog houses would be well maintained. There would be more hay meadows and the heather moorland would be managed for sheep, grouse and other wildlife. Mixed forest could be planted with deciduous trees along all water courses and footpaths. Planned tourist facilities such as visitor centres and camp sites could be built.

5.33

Hay meadow

Hay meadows with flowers

Conserved landscape. This future view depends on limited amounts of public money available to those fell farmers who continue to produce livestock and show they are maintaining the landscape at the same time. Conservationists could help provide a pool of volunteer labour. Farm-based tourism could supplement farm income. Hog houses and walls would be well maintained as would old broad-leaved woodlands and new ones would be planted. There would be many more hay meadows and heather moors than today.

the landscape is gradual, it affects almost all of the Lake District. Even land over 800 metres, once thought to be the only true wildscape, is changing with the pressure of numbers of walkers who are now said to be destroying the very landscape they come to see!

It is the job of the LDNPA to direct the changes which are occurring so that 'the natural beauty is preserved and enhanced'. Nevertheless the Lake District stands on the brink of major landscape modification (5.28 to 5.35). It is clear that government policies, the way the land is managed, and the economic influence of tourism are shaping the Lakeland landscapes of tomorrow. But in which direction? The people who most affect the land, the

farmers who work it, are in the midst of a revolution. Successive governments have subsidised hill farming in difficult upland areas and promoted the production of as much food as possible. These policies have been at the expense of some traditional features of the fellscape as farmers strive to remain profitable in the face of the intensification of agriculture in the EC. Other land uses are becoming more important in the upland landscape of Lakeland, e.g. profitable coniferous plantations and tourist-related developments. Cooperation over the wise use of the Lake District landscape is now a matter of urgency not only for the millions of annual visitors but also for the local communities whose livelihood is dependent upon it.

5.30

5.31

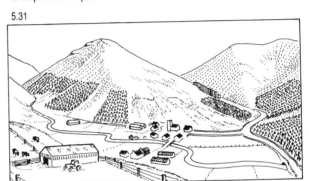

Subsidised livestock landscape. This will emerge if the government continue to subsidise livestock production in the fells. Here there would be a polarisation, with some farms becoming very intensive and others carrying only a few stock to tick over. Meadows would be either intensified for silage or abandoned to scrub and thistles. Moorland would become overgrazed and new conifer plantations would replace old woodlands as investments. Hog houses and walls would disappear.

Agribusiness landscape. With little public money available to maintain fell farming, large agribusinesses could buy out small farms and create large livestock ranches to make quick profits. Modern technology would be used and large sheds and wire fences would replace hog houses and walls. Most meadows would be intensified to produce silage; heather and woodland would be lost through overuse and old woodlands would give way to capital-intensive conifer plantations. Genetically manipulated livestock would be brought in to maximise profits.

5.34

5.35

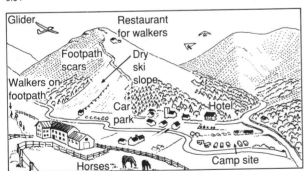

Sporting estate landscape. The fells could be run like a large estate for grouse and pheasant shooting, deer hunting and outdoor recreation. Few locals would farm. Most would work on the sporting estate or in tourism. There would be more moorland and large mixed woodlands for game cover and timber production. Hotels and visitor facilities would be built and some hog houses would be converted for other purposes. Walls might be replaced by fences. Careful control of public access to the fells would be enforced by estate workers.

Wildscape. This would develop if farm subsidies were withdrawn and the land was abandoned or if the fells were setaside as a nature reserve. A few locals could gain employment in tourism. Natural broad-leaved woodland would eventually become the climax vegetation as grazing disappeared. Meadows would be replaced by flowery glades and heather moorland would be succeeded by scrub and bog. Hog houses and walls would collapse and become overgrown.

Some Solutions

'Under pressure from land users and visitors, the fabric of the Lake District is crumbling', states the National Park Protection Plan about the pressures on Lakeland. What can be done?

5.36

Problems

Major congestion problems on narrow roads – trucks, buses cars, caravans

Footpaths severely eroded into visible scars

Noise pollution from low-flying military aircraft

Disturbance of wildlife and sheep by visitors

Military area: access to fells limited for walkers

Blanket conifer plantations

Valley settlements congested: new cafes, car parks, litter problems

Unofficial car park

Rise in number of valley properties bought as second homes

Cars parked on verges and in narrow lanes

New leisure developments (e.g. time-share complexes) spoil landscape

Pollution of lakes by phosphates from sewage and diesel from boats

Public access to forests creates problems of litter, vandalism, fire risks

Valley floor farms given over to camp sites

Ribbon lake intensely used for water sports

Conflicts occur between users of valleys and fells, e.g. farmers/tourists, Water Authority/tourists

New hotel built on lakeside

5.37 Pressure on the Lake District

Solutions

Repair footpaths; restrict use and access

Ban low flying aircraft or restrict flight access

Close roads to traffic; encourage use of cycles, minibuses; separate local and tourist traffic

Fence off areas; educate visitors to reduce disturbance

Place controls on forestry, use mixed species with trees planted along contours

Develop alternative honeypots and direct visitors elsewhere

Reduce congestion on roads using a one-way system

Provide cheap local housing for inhabitants of area

Provide free car parks and litter bins

Reduce use of boat engines; encourage sailing and rowing

Reduce number of leisure complexes; screen all others

Educate visitors, use fire notices, employ park wardens

Open local visitor centre with free parking. Educate visitors about problems. When conflicts arise gain cooperation and agreement through LDNPA

Licence use of ribbon lakes and increase fees for use; separate activities: e.g. water skiing/angling

Screen new hotels, cafes, car parks behind deciduous trees. Use only local stone for building

5.38 Reducing pressures on the Lake District

5.39 Terram: a three-layer carpet to support footpaths

Land users, especially the 12 million annual visitors, must tread carefully in their use of the Lake District (5.36). The pressures are many and diverse (5.37) and arise from both the opportunities provided by the environment and its popularity. Solutions to these problems of land over-use (5.38) have long been the subject of intense debate . They include practical steps, such as screening new leisure developments with trees and other vegetation; using local building stone to blend in to the landscape; and repairing severely eroded footpaths using terram: a supportive 'carpet' (5.39). The LDNPA tries to implement a sensible oversight of all the park land uses, seeking the cooperation of land owners, developers, farmers and visitors to ease the pressure on sites within the Lake District. But there are others who wish stricter action to be taken to protect the environment: including banning new developments; licensing the use of lakes; and introducing a visitor tax to reduce the annual number of people visiting the area.

Questions

Q CHERISHED LAND?

1 (a) Which official and non-official bodies are concerned with the conservation of the countryside?
(b) Prepare your own base map showing Britain's National Parks and NP Direction Areas.
(c) Make your own copy of table 5.2.

Q THE LAKE DISTRICT: ROCK STRUCTURE

2 (a) Describe and illustrate the Lake District.
(b) In which ways does rock type and structure influence the landscape of the Lake District?

Q MOUNTAIN AND LAKE

3 (a) Explain the Lake District radial drainage pattern.
(b) What evidence is there to suggest that the Lake District has been glaciated?

Q STEWARDS OF THE LANDSCAPE

4 (a) Why was the Lake District made a National Park?
(b) Evaluate the changes which have occurred in the Hartsop Valley.

Q LAND USE IN THE LAKE DISTRICT

5 (a) Describe the main land uses of the Lake District.
(b) Do you agree with the development of honeypots in the Lake District? Give reasons.

Q LAKELAND CONFLICTS?

6 (a) Argue the case both for and against the afforestation of the more isolated areas of the central Lake District.
(b) Why is a policy of farm-based tourism seen as vital to maintaining hill farms and the Lake District landscape?
(c) Describe the land use conflicts in the Lake District.

Q SOME SOLUTIONS?

7 (a) Discuss the view that tourism has been a mixed blessing for the Lake District.
(b) Should visitors be asked to pay for using the Lake District? Give reasons for your answer.
(c) What are the main pressures on the Lake District? Suggest solutions to these problems.

Q LANDSCAPES OF TOMORROW?

8 (a) Do you agree that cooperation over use of the Lake District landscape is now a matter of urgency? Why?
(b) What do you think the future holds for the Lake District? Give reasons for your answer.

Exam Style Questions

Q Diagram 1

Diagram 1 shows a glaciated upland area in north-west England.
(a) Describe the elements of the natural environment (relief, drainage, climate, vegetation, soils) which create the opportunity for and, in some cases, limit the development of either (i) forestry (ii) tourism. (7)

(b) Discuss the conflicts in land use which may arise in an area such as that shown in diagram. (15)
(c) What solutions are there to the problems of land use pressure in areas such as that shown in the diagram? (8)

RURAL LAND DEGRADATION

Land Degradation

As world population increases, the demands placed on fragile natural resources such as soil also rise because of the need to grow more food. These demands in recent years have damaged forests, grasslands and the topsoil we depend on. Instead of using our resources well, we are using them up or damaging them beyond recovery. We depend on the world's soils to grow food and timber, yet we are using them so badly that they are being lost through **soil erosion**. More than 75 billion tonnes of soil are washed into the sea or swept away by the wind each year and can never be replaced (6.1). Natural regeneration might take hundreds or thousands of years. Unfortunately erosion is selective, removing first the finer particles of organic matter, clays and silts that are richest in nutrients, leaving behind the coarser material. Currently 7% of topsoil is lost every 10 years. Half of the countries of the world and half of all arable land suffers from some form of soil erosion.

As we have seen in Chapter 4, soil is a very complex ecosystem and one cubic centimetre can take hundreds of years to form. The soil is teeming with life which not only recycles waste but tills, ventilates and refines the soil, keeping it crumbly, capable of holding moisture and therefore able to sustain plant life. All the micro-organisms, fungi, mites and worms, etc. in the soil are essential for soil fertility. Misuse of the land by overgrazing or **monoculture** (growing only one crop) can eventually lead to serious soil erosion.

Heavy modern farming machinery compacts the soil, damaging its structure (6.2). Modern farming practices require the use of artificial fertilisers to maintain productivity as soil fertility declines. Creatures that live off the crops are treated with

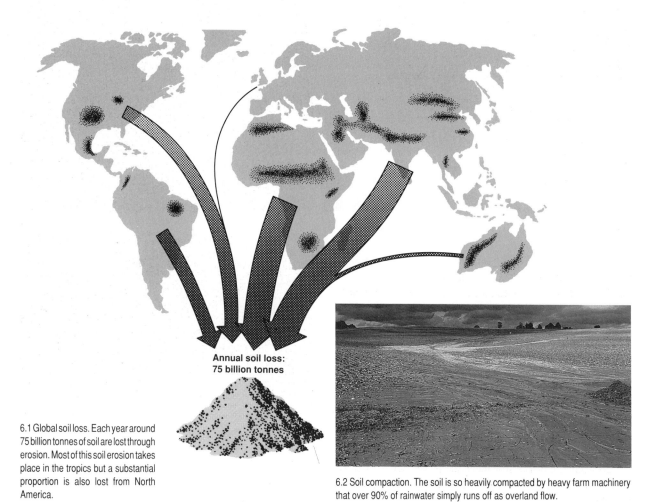

Annual soil loss: 75 billion tonnes

6.1 Global soil loss. Each year around 75 billion tonnes of soil are lost through erosion. Most of this soil erosion takes place in the tropics but a substantial proportion is also lost from North America.

6.2 Soil compaction. The soil is so heavily compacted by heavy farm machinery that over 90% of rainwater simply runs off as overland flow.

pesticides, and weeds are controlled with herbicides. These chemicals damage life in the soil: for example, pesticides attack worms and bacteria. The nutrients in plant and animal waste are not returned to the soil and this reduces soil fertility. Slowly crop production would fall if increasing quantities of artificial fertiliser were not applied. Modern agriculture leaves the soil both depleted and vulnerable: exposed to the rain and wind it is simply washed or blown away. The larger field sizes (with fewer windbreaks) common in modern farming also make wind erosion more likely. In some parts of the USA and UK over half the topsoil has already been lost (6.3).

All soils suffer from erosion as a natural part of landscape development. However if erosion is happening faster than weathering can provide new soil material, the soil begins to **degrade**. **Accelerated erosion** is most serious on cultivated land because the soil is exposed to rain and wind and is no longer held together by deep root systems. Erosion by water is often far more serious than erosion by wind.

Rain breaks up the soil into individual particles by direct impact (**rainsplash**) lifting the particles and dropping them in new positions (6.4). On sloping ground rainsplash tends to shift the soil downhill. Rainsplash can also seal natural soil openings reducing the soil's infiltration capacity.

6.3 Soil erosion in the USA. Over one-third of US cropland is going through a marked decline in long-term productivity because of soil erosion. The map shows the areas most seriously affected by soil erosion.

6.4 Rainsplash. A large raindrop landing on a wet surface produces a miniature crater throwing grains of clay and silt into the air.

Severe: more than 75% topsoil lost

Moderate: 25–75% topsoil lost

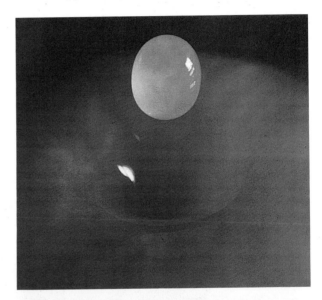

Despite 50 years of soil conservation practice, soil erosion is still one of the USA's most serious environmental problems. Until 1977 the US government was unable to obtain accurate estimates of the damage caused. About one third of cropland in the USA is now suffering a decline in long-term productivity and this will eventually reduce US exports of food by a dramatic proportion. Unfortunately farming in a modern industrialised country is now very much just another business which is regulated by short-term economic considerations that encourage present-day overproduction at the expense of our future environment. Modern farming methods inhibit the structure-forming processes and, as the soil structure deteriorates, water infiltration is reduced, so increasing overland flow, resulting in erosion. As soil fertility declines, the potential for soil erosion increases. Soil erosion can also enhance other problems such as flooding, as was shown in Chapter 2.

CHAPTER 6

Soil Erosion and Conservation

If the amount of rainfall is greater than can be absorbed by the soil, the excess water flows over the surface as overland flow, removing the unprotected topsoil. Overland flow tends to remove soil in rather uniform thin layers, a process called **sheet erosion**. Because of cultivation the impact of sheet erosion is often not noticed until the topsoil is greatly thinned. Where slopes are particularly steep and run-off is significant sheet erosion may progress into a more intense activity called **rilling** where closely spaced shallow channels are scored into the soil (6.5). If these rills are not destroyed by ploughing they may develop into still larger channels called gullies which cannot be so readily recovered (6.6). Sheet and rill erosion only affect the topsoil (approx 30 cm on mature arable soils in the UK) while gully erosion bisects the entire soil profile and often needs special machinery to fill in or control the gullies. Gullies in tropical climates may rapidly progress beyond the stage where they can be filled in.

Water erosion is influenced by the size of the rain storm, the steepness of slopes, amount of vegetation cover and type of soil. The basic principles of **soil conservation** to protect against water erosion are to keep the ground well covered for as long as possible, reduce the steepness of slopes by **terracing**, or alternatively plant grass strips along the contours (see 6.7) to

6.5 Rill and gully erosion. Some of the rills develop into larger gullies.

6.7 Contour ploughing, Parana, Brazil

6.6 A huge gully produced by soil erosion in the Ethiopian Central Highlands

retard water movement, and rough plough to break-up the soil and help infiltration. The ground can be kept covered longer by drilling the seeds for the next crop through the remains of the harvested crop or by **intercropping** (planting crops that ripen at different times of the year in alternate bands across fields). Terracing can be achieved by building retaining walls or by ploughing to produce the same stepped appearance. **Contour ploughing**, i.e. ploughing across the slope, also helps prevent water erosion by retaining the water in the furrows until it drains away (6.7).

In the UK about 21% of the cultivated land suffers from water erosion and in most cases downslope cultivation and soil compaction have been the major contributing factors. With removal of organic matter from the soil and loss of soil structure, in intensively cropped land, even light rain can produce run-off and erosion.

Wind erosion occurs on poorly vegetated soils with the finer particles being lifted by the wind and sand-sized particles being bounced along the ground until they come to rest against buildings or fences, or fill in drainage ditches. The finest, most agriculturally useful, material is carried away completely, leaving behind coarser material and stones. Wind erosion is most effective where strong winds are frequent and there are few obstructions, as in regions of extensive plains. Soils which are poorly stuck together with little organic material are more susceptible to erosion. Certain farming practices can make soils more liable to wind erosion such as: ploughing parallel to the prevailing wind direction; monoculture without the use of organic fertilisers; fine ploughing, which breaks up the topsoil into small particles that can be removed by the wind; stubble burning in autumn (6.8); and inappropriate irrigation practices.

6.8 Stubble burning in the autumn suppresses weeds and pests but the sterile fields are deprived of a vegetation cover, increasing the likelihood of accelerated soil erosion.

6.9 Shelter belts. This windbreak of trees in Niger provides shelter from wind erosion.

Wind erosion can be reduced by a number of short-term and long-term measures. In the long term windbreaks of tall trees and shrubs are effective at reducing the impact of the wind but shelter is only effective for short distances and trees take up space and may shade crops (6.9). Temporary screens can also be used but these are only economic when used to protect high-priced crops.

Intercropping, the planting of root crops in alternate rows with grain crops, can also help by maintaining a crop cover for a longer period with the grain crop protecting the soil until the root crop has established. Covering the ground with a **mulch** of straw or other material can also protect the bare soil helping it to retain moisture. Cultivation machinery can now enable the soil to be loosened below surviving stubble which holds the topsoil together (stubble mulching). As with water erosion, drilling the seeds of the next harvest through the remains of the harvested crop also keeps the soil covered and bound together.

Recent research has shown that the drop in crop yields as a result of soil erosion is most dramatic after the initial erosion. Therefore once farmers have allowed soil to erode by even a small amount they should expect a significant drop in yield. This finding suggests that sheet erosion, which takes away the finer soil particles, is the most insidious. The impact on tropical soils is even more drastic than on temperate soils. For 10 millimetres of soil lost in the corn belt of the USA a drop in yield of 100 kilograms might be expected. In Nigeria the same loss might cause yields to drop by as much as 5.8 tonnes.

This finding has important implications for investment in soil conservation because it shows that it is much more cost effective to invest in conserving soil that has only recently begun to erode rather than in soil which is seriously degraded. Politically and socially this implication may be rather unwelcome because it would suggest spending the money on land which is productive and ignoring the marginal land which is owned by the poor.

Desertification in the Sahel 1

Overgrazing, forest clearance and intensification of agriculture in developing countries has brought about significant soil erosion. **Desertification** in Africa and rainforest destruction in South America are examined in more detail in this chapter to illustrate the impact of human activity on ecosystems, and the physical, social and economic consequences of **land degradation**.

Land degradation is nothing new. In Roman times wheat and vines were cultivated in some parts of what is now the Sahara desert, but eventually through misuse and/or climatic change these areas were turned into desert. The degree of change now appears to be more marked. About one-third of the earth's land surface is arid or semi-arid and these dry lands support about 700 million people. An increasing proportion of this dependent population is having their lives impoverished by land degradation.

Desertification in the Sahel zone of Africa is due to a number of factors, both human and physical. Desert expansion has been speeded up by human interference, with the Sahara now extending southwards by about 9 kilometres a year, according to some more pessimistic estimates. The rate of desertification is still a matter of debate as most recent research into desert expansion uses aerial photographs to determine the boundary of the deserts, and the effects of serious droughts may only be temporary and not a long-lasting change. Previously mapped desert boundaries could also be inaccurate because weather data were limited and satellite photography wasn't available (6.10).

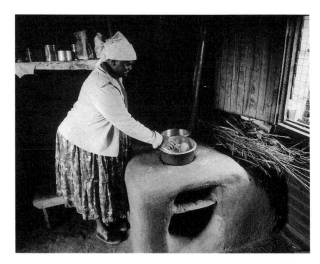

6.11 Fuelwood for cooking. Most wood collected for domestic use in Africa is intended for the cooking stove. Improvements in the design of simple stoves (such as this new one) can cut heating losses by 60%. This simple initiative in Kenya could save millions of tonnes of fuelwood if it was replicated across Africa.

The growth of human population has led to a loss of vegetation as trees are cut for firewood and land is cleared for cultivation (**deforestation**). In the Sahel each person requires about 1 kg of wood each day, for cooking alone (6.11). It has been estimated that a family of five would destroy about a hectare of land a year, even allowing for regeneration of some vegetation. All woodland within 40 km of Ouagadougou, the capital of Burkina Faso, has been felled for firewood and this situation is repeated throughout the Sahel zone. The scarcity of fuelwood has raised its economic value to the point where fuelwood collection and sale is now a commercial enterprise (6.12). In many parts of the Sahel the fuelwood cooking the food costs more than the food in the pot.

6.10 The advance of the desert. 6 million hectares of land are lost to the world's deserts each year. Over 100 countries and about 1 in 5 of the world's population are affected.

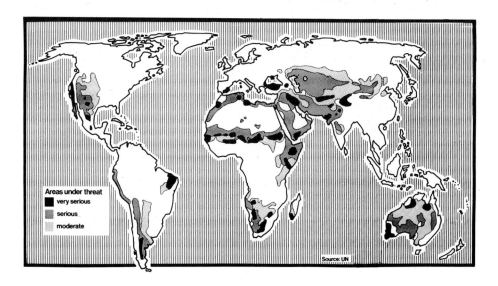

Areas under threat
very serious
serious
moderate

Source: UN

Land use changes since the 1950s

After the 1950s more land was placed under cultivation and herds of grazing animals were increased, encouraged by above average rainfalls. Nomadic herders were encouraged by governments to establish permanent settlements and this increased the pressure on the pastures in the vicinity of the settlements. Traditional attitudes to livestock as a measure of wealth and status encouraged the growth of herds in the 1960s, when many wells were sunk to provide water for growing settlements. Overgrazing resulted in removal of the vegetation cover and compaction of the soil (6.13). The resulting bare soil was exposed to wind and water erosion. The sinking of wells has also caused localised lowering of the water table, which in some areas may have caused changes in the natural vegetation.

Poor irrigation and drainage practices have led to excessive accumulation of salts in some areas and to leaching (resulting in deficient soils) in others. Mismanagement of irrigated areas has pushed cultivation into more marginal areas (6.14).

6.12 Commercialisation of fuelwood supplies. The price of fuelwood has risen by about 600% since the late 1960s in many Sahel countries. Sources of wood near to settlements have largely been exhausted and it is now an economic proposition for entrepreneurs to haul wood from distant sources.

6.13 Sahel droughts. Overgrazing and intensification of agriculture beyond the lands carrying capacity brought disaster and famine when the Sahel region suffered droughts in the 1970s and 1980s.

6.14 Irrigation from a hand-dug well in Niger is necessary to cultivate crops in this arid climate. This traditional irrigation is suited to the environment and less prone to mismanagement than larger-scale irrigation. (The trees in the background act as a windbreak.)

Desertification in the Sahel 2

Land use in the Sahel has been intensified beyond its carrying capacity over the last 30 years, to support the increasing population, and more marginal land has also been brought into production. The best land is used for export crops while subsistence crops are grown on the most marginal land. Traditional farming practices have been abandoned in an attempt to produce more from the land.

6.15 Reforestation in Mali. This tree nursery provides the young plants for reforestation projects in the area.

Gum arabic farming

Traditional gum arabic farmers have been able to eke out a living from marginal arid lands by careful management which evolved over centuries. Traditionally only one-third of the land is used for crops and the other two-thirds is left fallow with an average fallow period of 15 years. Gum arabic trees grow on the fallow land and the farmer collects the resin from the tree for sale as a cash crop. The 'gum' or resin from the tree is used to make cosmetics and chewing gum among other products. Since the 1960s the fallow period has been reduced to about seven years as agriculture has intensified to support the growing population. This reduction in fallow period means the gum arabic trees do not reach maturity and productivity falls. The fertility of the soil is also lowered as the fallow period is reduced.

Another change in the economics of gum arabic farming has put the farmer under increased pressure. The fallow crop, gum arabic, has a lower economic value than it did 10 or 20 years ago, because prices are determined by world markets which the farmer has no control over.

So as the human and animal populations have grown, the soils have deteriorated. Serious droughts in the 1970s and 1980s brought disaster and famine as the misused land was unable to support the population.

This century an area the size of the UK, France and Germany has been lost from production. Each year some 12 million hectares (21 million hectares worldwide) deteriorate to the point where they can no longer be used for agriculture. In money terms agricultural production to the value of $20 billion is lost each year, whereas it would have cost only about $2.5 billion to protect and rehabilitate the land.

Reforestation

The first stage in any land rehabilitation is to restore vegetation cover removed by overcultivation or deforestation. There have been some signs of progress in the Sahel belt but still less than 2% of aid is directed to **reforestation** projects while deforestation continues at an alarming rate. Small-scale local irrigation, drainage and reforestation projects which capitalise on local initiatives have been most successful (6.15). The most successful schemes rely on local control with some technical advice and the minimum of imported technology, often requiring very limited financial assistance. Even the United Nations admitted that these small-scale projects sponsored by non-governmental organisations such as Oxfam and the Six Ss organisation (Se Servir de la Saison Séche en Savanne et au Sahel: Making use of the Dry Season in the Savanna and the Sahel) have been often the most successful in combating desertification. Schemes which have been successful include fencing off reforestation plots with barbed wire and brushwood to keep out grazing animals, and simple water-focusing techniques such as growing the tree seedlings in small hollows which direct water to the seedlings.

Planting trees is not necessarily the best way to protect the soil from erosion because trees have great difficulty in establishing themselves where erosion is continuing and where water supply is short. Drought-resistant shrubs and grasses are quicker to establish themselves and can offer as much protection from erosion (6.16). Some tree species do, however, have other important side effects, and also produce fuelwood. For example, legume species such as acacias 'fix' their own nitrogen from the atmosphere and transfer large amounts of it to the soil making it more fertile. Other tree species produce their own insecticides to protect them from leaf-eating insects. When these trees were

planted among arable crops in trial plots, yields rose substantially.

Once erosion starts it is important to re-establish ground cover of whatever type in order to halt the process and restore the ecosystem. If this does not happen, erosion establishes a hold and causes more erosion by positive feedback. Loss of vegetation cover exposes the soil to the elements increasing run-off and impoverishing the soil (6.17). Establishing a vegetation cover increases the soil's capacity to hold water and provides organic binding agents. In semi-arid areas the shade provided by plants decreases the water lost by evaporation so preventing crusts from forming on the soil surface which would encourage run-off and erosion.

6.16 Soils can be stabilised and desert dunes halted by restoring plant cover. The planting of trees and shrubs in Niger has halted the dunes in the photograph.

6.17 Severe erosion caused by deforestation in Burkina Faso. Poor farming practices combined with fragile soils and torrential rains can destroy a landscape in a couple of years.

Disappearing Rainforests?

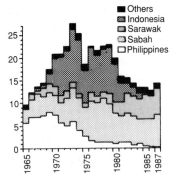

6.19 Changes in the geographical pattern of tropical hardwood supply to Japan, 1965–1987. The changes reflect the large-scale deforestation in Indonesia and the Philippines and the move to fresh reserves in Sabah and Sarawak.

The demand for agricultural land is a major cause of the degradation and disappearance of tropical forest. Vast areas of the rainforest have been cleared for cash crop plantations, cattle ranches and some smallholder cultivation. Demand for wood has also increased over the last 40 years and both commercial forestry and fuelwood gatherers deplete the forest without replacing it. Commercial forestry also opens up areas of previously impenetrable rainforest for agriculture because colonists are able to use the forestry roads to gain access to this land. Currently 35 acres of tropical forest disappear every minute, equivalent to an area the size of Cambridgeshire disappearing every three weeks. This means 1% of the world's rainforest is destroyed each year. 10% of the Amazon rainforest has already gone and will not readily regenerate. Rainforest destruction is a worldwide problem: each year 1.82 million hectares of Asia's 305.5 million hectares; 4.12 million hectares of Latin America's 678 million hectares; and 1.33 million hectares of Africa's 216.6 million hectares are cleared (6.18).

Currently Japan is the world's major consumer of rainforest trees: it uses about 30% of the total. Japan's demand for tropical hardwoods has devastated the forests of the Philippines and Indonesia and now the forests of Sabah and Sarawak are being systematically exploited (6.19). The Japanese are beginning to look to Brazil as a future supplier as the supplies from Asia's forests dwindle. Brazil already exports some timber to Japan and the Japanese are currently proposing to fund a road which will link the Trans-Amazonia Highway with ports on the Pacific coast: the implications of this proposition are clear!

The threat to the Amazon rainforest

Although rainforests are being depleted around the globe, the Amazon Basin, particularly in Brazil, has experienced serious deforestation in response to a wide range of development pressures. The Amazon Basin has been seen by successive Brazilian governments as an underutilised area with great potential for development. The area's vast reserves of timber and mineral resources combined with its agricultural potential have led the

6.18 Disappearing rainforests

Every year the world loses **7.27 million hectares** of tropical rainforest.

That's over 5 times the area of Northern Ireland (1.34 million hectares)

Worldwide

DESTROYED EVERY YEAR

Tropical rainforest

Rainforest frontier under threat

In the time it takes you to read this map 7 hectares of tropical rainforest will be destroyed.

Latin America
4.12 million hectares

DESTROYED EVERY YEAR

Africa
1.33 million hectares

DESTROYED EVERY YEAR

Asia
1.82 million hectares

DESTROYED EVERY YEAR

6.20 Uses of the rainforest. The cartoon illustrates the sort of things the rainforest could provide if preserved. What does the cartoonist indicate about the attitude of the businessman?

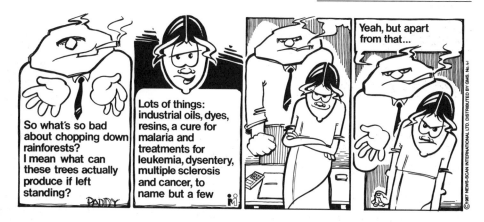

government of Brazil to try to use these riches to fund national economic development. The government sees the rainforest as an area to be 'tamed' and doesn't believe the nation can 'develop' while it is largely covered in forest. Selling the tropical timber brings in foreign currency and opens the land for cultivation of cash crops, cattle ranching or for industrial purposes.

Consequences of deforestation

However, it is now well known that serious environmental and ecological consequences result from this sort of 'development'. When the forest cover is removed, the tropical climate, with high rainfall, leaches out nutrients from the soil and can remove vast quantities of topsoil, leaving the land almost infertile.

On a local level, cleared land increases run-off and erosion which may cause floods. About 20–25% of rainfall flows as run-off in the forest, but this can increase to 75% after deforestation. The forest in effect recycles water with 75% of rainfall returned to the atmosphere by evapotranspiration. This water returned to the atmosphere falls as rain elsewhere. In the case of Amazonia the water is recycled several times as the rains passes from east to west through the region. Eradication of the forest in the east will affect the forests in the interior as less water is recycled and the interior's rainfall decreases.

The rainforests also contain about 50% of the world's plant and animal species and deforestation is causing the extinction of a number of these species. This loss in **bio-diversity** is not just a matter of feeling sad about the species we lose: the rainforest plants have already proved to be an invaluable resource of raw materials for medical drugs. Around one-third of medical drugs have been derived from rainforest plants and there is no telling which plant might prove a useful source in the future (6.20).

The threat of climatic change is another environmental consideration. When rainforest is cleared by burning, this contributes to global warming (see page 26) because carbon dioxide is released into the atmosphere (6.21). The trees help to reduce the amount of carbon dioxide in the air, because they convert it into carbohydrates. (Recent research has shown that the hitherto largely ignored tropical grasslands are just as productive at converting carbon dioxide as the rainforests, and the annual burning of some 700 million hectares of savanna grasslands could be releasing three times as much carbon dioxide into the atmosphere as the burning of the rainforest.)

The environmental arguments have been regarded with some suspicion by the governments of Brazil and other Third World countries who see this as a ploy to stop their development. The developed countries don't have a particularly strong moral case since their forests were largely cleared before the twentieth century and they are the principal buyers of tropical wood!

6.21 Burning the forest. The settler is clearing his 100 hectare plot by burning the vegetation after felling the larger trees.

Changes in the Brazilian Rainforests

Since 1945 the Brazilian government has encouraged the development of agriculture in Amazonia, including ranching, plantation farming and smallholdings. Extension of the road network into Amazonia provided the basic infrastructure for this development (6.22) and enabled large-scale migration to the region to take place. Since the early 1970s the government has encouraged large numbers of migrants to come to Amazonia from the north-east, in the hope that this would relieve the population pressures and social tensions of the north-east (6.23). It was reported that the governor of the Brazilian province of Amazonas gave out free chainsaws to increase support for his political party.

Colonists migrating to Amazonia have typically been offered a free plot of land in the forest. Usually the plot is about 100 hectares in size, but the soil in many of these plots of land is so poor that most farmers abandon their land within a year or so, and move on to clear a new area of forest or work as sharecroppers. In 1981 so much forest was burnt by settlers that the government had to ground aircraft for a time because of the dense smoke. Many of the settlers fail to obtain even one crop from the poor, often sandy, soil left when the rainforest is stripped away. Rainforest soils are relatively thin and poor, with most nutrients in the vegetation. Nutrients in the soil are readily leached away when the trees and plants are removed.

The colonists in most cases received very little help from the government. There were insufficient marketing facilities for any

6.23 The landless poor. A migrant family from the north-east of Brazil arriving in Amazonia, enticed by the offer of 100 hectares of free land. The reality of living in the rainforest is often very different from what they imagined.

produce grown and supplies required for farming were often difficult to obtain. The colonists have usually found themselves isolated without electricity, water supply, health or education services and in some cases endangered by the native Indians. These tribal peoples, who have lived in harmony with the forest for over 25 000 years, have been forced off their tribal lands and are not surprisingly resentful of the new settlers.

Large-scale commercial exploitation

Large projects have suffered in the same way as the small farmer has. Cattle ranching in the Amazon requires 0.4 ha for every head of cattle but productivity tends to decline rapidly. So although cattle ranching is the fastest growing agricultural activity in

6.22 Amazon deforestation. These drawings are based on satellite photographs, and show a 30 km by 30 km area in Rondonia. The forest is the black area with the main road running north-west/south-east. Feeder roads at 5 km intervals run into the forest from the main road. The drawings clearly show the extent of deforestation by colonists between 1976 and 1981.

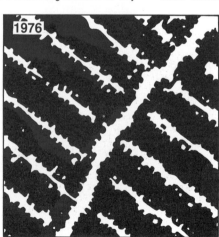

1976

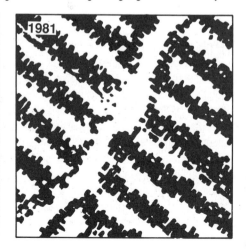

1981

Amazonia, it is unlikely to prove sustainable in many areas of the region (6.24). The growth of pasture grasses is slow because the soil is poor, and they are quickly invaded by inedible weeds which are better adapted to the conditions. Clearing the weeds involves scraping the ground with earth movers which remove some of the topsoil and can lead to further soil erosion. Research has shown that after about five years or so most pastures become so infertile and degraded that it costs more to keep them clear of weeds than the value of the beef produced. By 1978 20% of pasture in Amazonia had been abandoned but this lack of sustainability and inefficient use of the land has not stopped the expansion of cattle ranching. Many of the ranch owners are merely land speculators who obtain large parcels of land with government ranching subsidies and, after ranching is uneconomic, they simply hold onto the land until its value increases. (The value of the land will increase as communications improve and more of Amazonia's minerals and other resources become accessible.)

Despite the destruction and inefficiency the government continues to support ranching because there is a market for the cheap meat in the USA, Europe and Japan (6.25 and 6.26: most of this meat goes into beefburgers and other fast foods), and this export brings in foreign currency.

Large industrial farms producing cocoa and other plantation crops have suffered similar declines in production with loss of soil fertility and attack from pests and diseases. Plantations, however, occupy only a small area of the recently cleared rainforest because initial installation costs are high and most land speculators have preferred the cheaper alternative that cattle ranching offers.

The rainforests and its peoples are not only under threat from agricultural expansion but also from gold prospectors. It has been estimated that some 40 000 prospectors have illegally moved onto Yanomami Indian lands since early 1988. They have brought disease, polluted rivers, reduced the Indians' food supply and undermined their tribal culture. Unfortunately attempts to remove these illegal trespassers have been unsuccessful because of the large numbers involved.

6.24 A cattle ranch in Amazonia

6.25 The rainforest burger

6.26 Clearing the rainforest for cattle

I hear you're cutting down our forest to make room for cattle for your burger bars

That's right

But don't you realise the importance of our forest?

I sure do! How on earth can I graze cattle with all those damn trees in the way?

Extraction without Deforestation

Conservation of the forests has not only been the concern of environmentalists in developed countries and the native Indians. One of the most vociferous and effective groups of protesters has been the local rubber-tappers (*seringueiros*: 6.27). In the most

6.27 A Brazilian rubber-tapper. The *seringueiros* or rubber-tappers cut notches in the bark of rubber trees and collect the latex in tins or bowls which they attach to the tree.

important rubber-tapping province of Brazil, Acre, about one-third of the 380 000 population depend on rubber-tapping for their livelihood. The rubber-tappers have been important in Acre since the turn of the century when many north-easterners migrated into Amazonia to work in rubber plantations controlled by 'rubber barons'. As the rubber trade declined (after the Second World War but particularly since 1960) the 'rubber barons' moved out leaving many of the rubber-tappers free to work for themselves. In the 1970s, faced with near permanent indebtedness because the trade was controlled by middle people who reaped the profits, the rubber-tappers formed a union to fight for their rights and obtain a fair price for their rubber. This union with the help of the new Workers' Party (Partido dos Trabalhadores) was able to win certain rights such as the right to work in the forest where the rubber trees grew; a fair price for their rubber; and elimination of middle people in the rubber trade. As the union gained strength it established cooperatively run schools and medical facilities in the rubber-tapping areas.

The completion of the BR 364 highway into Acre in the mid 1980s brought other types of conflict for the rubber-tappers (6.28 and 6.29). The improved accessibility attracted the interest of

6.28 A highway through the Amazon. The highways through the Amazon are often unpaved and in very wet weather can be impassable.

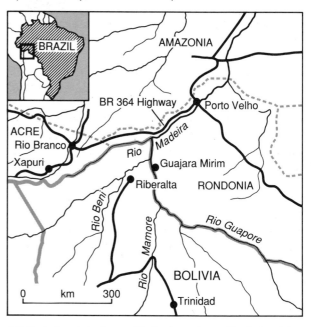

6.29 Roads through the Amazon. The frontier provinces of Rondonia and Acre have been opened up to land speculators with the extension of the road network.

land-hungry outsiders who were intent on clearing the forests for its timber and subsequent cattle ranching or for resale at a profit to new colonists. The rubber-tappers' fight against the large landowners and speculators in the 1980s coincided with a focusing of worldwide attention on the destruction of the rainforests. Francisco (Chico) Mendes (6.30), president of the Rural Workers' Union in Xapuri, leader of the National Rubber-tappers Association, and founder of the Union of Forest Peoples (an alliance of Indians and rubber-tappers), was adopted as a champion of rainforest protection by international environmentalist groups and he was honoured with several international awards.

6.30 Chico Mendes, leader of the rubber-tappers, was murdered on 22 December 1988 because of his fight to restrict exploitation of the rainforest.

However his international fame was not enough to protect his life and he was gunned down by two gunmen outside his simple wooden house on 22 December 1988 (two sons of a local rancher were convicted of the murder in 1991). Chico Mendes' murder was one of over 1000 assassinations since 1980 associated with the land conflict in Amazonia. His death has intensified both international pressure and demands from middle-class Brazilians for more environmentally sensitive government policies. The rubber-tappers have managed to have some forest set aside for 'extractive reserves': for extracting rubber and brazil nuts. However the powerful landowners have so far been able to resist land reform, and rainforest destruction continues, despite the withdrawal of federal government incentives for agricultural development in Amazonia.

If production figures for Acre are examined, the relative value and productivity of the major land uses can be compared. From 1970 to 1982 (the last year for which we have data) rubber was the state's most valuable export followed by brazil nuts. In 1980 rubber accounted for 96% of exports, up from 84% in 1970.

Table 6.31 illustrates that cattle ranching (an unsustainable land use) has been expanding despite the fact that extraction has been more economic in the short term and is sustainable indefinitely. Even agricultural uses are not sustainable without significant inputs of fertiliser and energy, so it has been estimated that the value of extraction yields would outstrip agricultural yields after only 11 years.

The increased productivity of the rubber-tappers since 1970 may in part be the result of the rights and independence they have won for themselves, through their union. They have been able to demonstrate that a living can be obtained from the rainforest without deforestation. However, in the long term, changes in land tenure and income distribution will be required to satisfy the social and economic demands of the people who live in Amazonia.

To arrive at an appropriate development strategy for Amazonia a number of objectives should be met.

- The human and animal population must not exceed the land's carrying capacity.
- Agriculture must be sustainable.
- Land use options should not be subsidised to avoid short-term exploitation.
- Development should aim to achieve a minimum standard of living.
- Development should ensure that undisturbed areas of rainforest are set aside for native Indians.
- Development should minimise loss of biological resources.

The rainforests have been shown to contain a vast range of species. Recent worldwide research has shown that the number of tree species (with a minimum diameter of 10 cm) found in 1 hectare plots varies from 87 to 300. A figure for all species of plant in a 0.1 hectare plot can be as high as 365 species. Studies of rainforest tribes has shown that anything up to 80% of the trees in the forests can be put to some sort of use.

Rainforest fruits and plants are already used in some cosmetics, ice cream and sweets for example. It is hoped current research will identify further extractive potential of the forests without the need to deforest. The research has put a greater economic value on natural forest than any other alternative use. It is now important to convince governments and big businesses of the economic arguments for preserving the rainforests.

6.31 Changes in production and land use in Acre, 1970–80

| | Value of yield/ha ($US) | | Percentage increase 1970–80 | Percentage change in land use 1970–80 |
	1970	1980		
Beef	3.24	3.72	14.80	+ 413.1
Agriculture	14.25	19.42	36.28	+ 57.6
Extraction (rubber & brazil nuts)	2.49	8.99	261.00	− 7.6

Progress in Rainforest Conservation

Despite the ruthless exploitation of many of the world's rainforests, there are some signs that conservation is gaining ground. In April 1988 Virgilio Barco, president of Colombia (6.32), told leaders of the Indian communities 'at last the land which is yours is yours'. He had effectively handed back 6 million hectares of land that had been illegally obtained by the Anglo-Peruvian rubber company at the turn of the century. Today the 70 000 Indians in Colombia own more than 18 million hectares of Amazon rainforest. The Colombian government also has 5.3 million hectares of National Parks, some of this overlapping Indian lands. These measures now protect 22.5 million of the 38 million hectares of Amazonian rainforest in Colombia. That leaves around 10 million hectares of uninhabited, virgin land and 6 million hectares in the foothills of the Andes which have been colonised and deforested over the last 50 years or so (6.33).

The Colombian government has recognised the Indians' ownership of the land because under Colombian law the state does not own lands that were never conquered. The government has also recognised that the best guardians of the rainforest are the people who know how to make a living from it, without disrupting the ecosystem irreversibly. This policy of protecting the forest and its indigenous peoples has been adopted without external pressure and is in sharp contrast to the exploitation

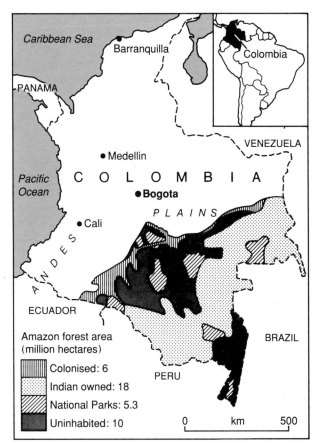

Amazon forest area (million hectares)

||||| Colonised: 6

Indian owned: 18

National Parks: 5.3

Uninhabited: 10

6.33 Colombia's Amazon rainforest

encouraged until recently in neighbouring Brazil. (The government led by Ferdinand Collor elected in March 1990 has committed itself to saving the Brazilian rainforest and its peoples. The appointment of two renowned environmentalists to government posts has raised hopes for positive action.)

The Indians mirror nature in the way they utilise the forest. They clear patches of forest to make gardens or *chagras* (6.34), being careful to choose good soil by examining the vegetation growing in the forest. About three months after felling, the Indians burn the felled wood and prepare their gardens. The Indians grow a variety of crops, including fruit trees which attract birds, whose droppings contain seeds which encourage regeneration of the forest once the *chagras* is abandoned. Even with the Indians' careful management the *chagras* may take 140–200 years to regenerate completely. Including gardens and hunting land an average of 1000 hectares of forest is required by each Indian, in order to make a living.

In peninsular Malaysia there are two areas of protected virgin forest: the Krau Wildlife Reserve (537 square kilometres) into which only scientists are allowed; and the Taman Negara National Park covering 4300 square kilometres, which attracts some 10 000 visitors annually. Conservationists and indigenous peoples

6.32 President Barco

have been campaigning for more than ten years to have more of the virgin rainforest set aside and protected from commercial forestry, in order to preserve the natives' way of life and the species that live in the forests. There has even been progress in the heavily deforested states of Sabah and Sarawak where the World Wide Fund for Nature has supported the establishment of National Parks and nature reserves.

The purchase of land in the tropical forests by conservation groups is one relatively new method used to protect areas from exploitation. Areas in Belize, Venezuela and Equador have been obtained by groups that wish to protect the forest. In Venezuela it is a local initiative while in Belize and Equador international charities and companies are working with the local population. This development is not without its critics but as long as local people provide much of the initiative it is an approach which may achieve some success.

Efforts to restore the rainforests by replanting have also taken strides forward in recent years. When forest is completely cleared the soil is usually so impoverished that native trees cannot recolonise; and in many places where monoculture of one native hardwood has been tried it fails, because the trees run out of nutrients. Plantations of mixed species are likely to be more successful because they mimic the natural forest. Success is more likely if saplings are planted in either partly degraded or secondary forest.

The islanders of the Cape Verde Islands through their own efforts have enthusiastically, year by year, recovered their deforested hills. Other nations are also attempting to recover their degraded forests.

6.34 A *chagras* or garden in the rainforest. The Colombian Indians carve *chagras* from the forest to grow crops and, once abandoned, the *chagras* quickly revert to forest.

Advanced techniques in tree propagation (6.35), cloning of plants and micropropagation are now being applied to produce trees that are productive and commercially desirable. This is one way to guarantee the long-term survival of the virgin rainforest.

6.35 Propagation of trees to restock the rainforest. Triplochiton cuttings take root in a simple propagator in Cameroon.

Q SOIL EROSION AND CONSERVATION

1 (a) Describe the main types of soil erosion by water.
(b) Explain the damage that some modern farming methods cause to cultivated soils.
(c) Outline the main soil conservation methods to prevent soil erosion by water and wind.
(d) Why is sheet erosion so insidious?

Q DESERTIFICATION

2 (a) Describe the process of desertification and outline its possible causes.
(b) Why were the consequences of the Sahel droughts of the 1970s and 1980s so severe?
(c) What human actions since the 1950s have accelerated the desertification process?
(d) What can be done to halt or reverse the process of desertification?

Research and Further Work

(a) Find out about the problems of soil erosion in North America.
(b) What differences in soil conservation strategies would you expect to find between developed and developing countries?
(c) What effect has climate variability had on land degradation?
(d) Find out about the inappropriate irrigation techniques that lead to soil degradation.

Q THE RAINFORESTS

3 (a) Which country is the major consumer of rainforest timber?
(b) What is the fastest growing agricultural activity in the Brazilian rainforest and why is this the case?
(c) Look at 6.25 on page 000. What point is the cartoonist making?
(d) What groups of people can obtain a sustainable living from the rainforest and why?
(e) Why are some governments, in countries with rainforest territory, suspicious of conservationist arguments?
(f) In what way does timber extraction open up the rainforest for other uses?
(g) Why is the loss in biodiversity so worrying for conservationists?
(h) How do the native Indians utilise the rainforest?

Q THE RAINFOREST FRONTIER ZONE (PAGES 000–0)

Look at the photographs and maps on pages 168–9, showing deforestation in part of Rondonia in Brazil.
4 (a) Make a copy of map 1 on page 000, which shows forest clearance in this part of Rondonia.
(b) With reference to the evidence in the photographs on page 000, explain how the invasion of the rainforest is advancing.
(c) With the edge of the rainforest becoming closer to Indian reservations, what impact would you expect this to have on the Indians' way of life?
(d) What are your views on the Rondonia Development Project, which opened up the rainforest in this way, for cultivation?

Exam Style Questions

(a) Describe the world distribution of rainforests. (4)
(b) Explain why the rainforests are being exploited. (6)
(c) Outline the physical, social and economic consequences of rainforest deforestation. (10)
(d) With reference to specific examples you have studied, discuss the attempts being made to preserve the rainforests. (10)

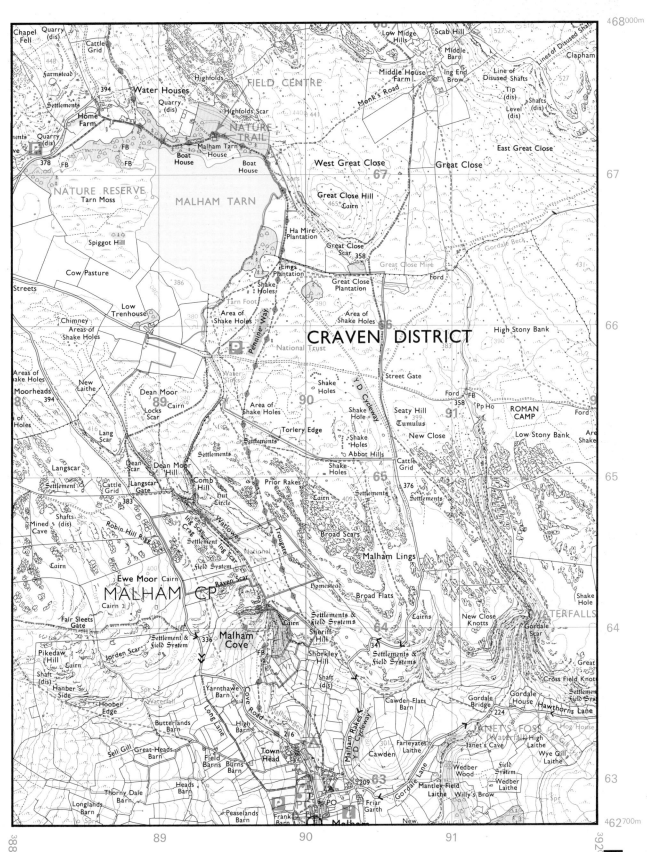

Photograph 1. Rondonia, June 1976

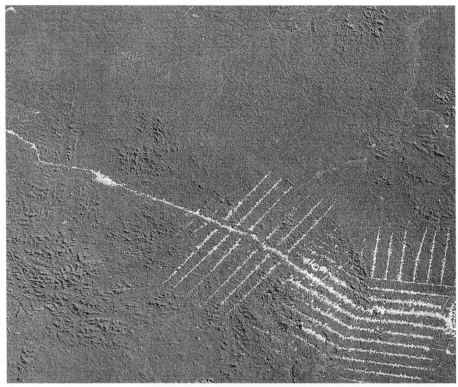

These landsat images show the rainforest in the area of the Rondonia Development Project in western Brazil. Photograph 1 was taken in 1976, and photograph 2 was taken in 1981. Although at slightly different scales, the photos show roughly the same area. Undisturbed forest appears brown/red; cleared land appears white/blue. The photographs clearly show the extent of deforestation that occurred between 1976 and 1981. The central roadway, and sets of parallel side roads, were cleared through the forest in preparation for the families of 'slash and burn' farmers, whom the government relocated in Rondonia. These poor landless farmers left other regions of Brazil because of severe poverty. Burning felled wood releases some nutrients but the soil is soon impoverished by growing crops, so the farmers are forced to move on and clear a new plot of land elsewhere.

Photograph 2. Rondonia, September 1981

Map 1. Forest clearance in the Rondonia Development Project

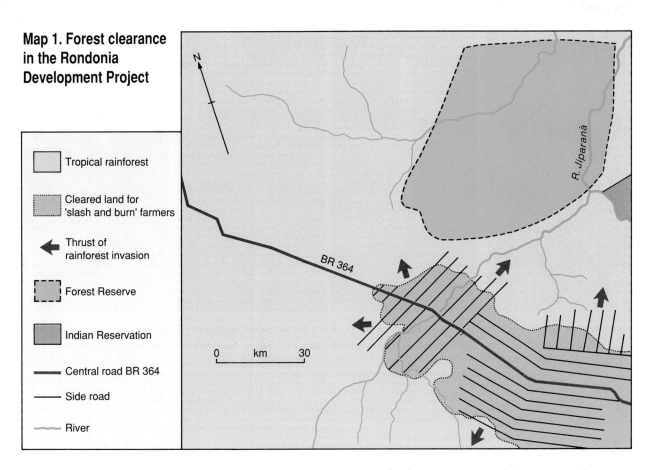

Legend:
- Tropical rainforest
- Cleared land for 'slash and burn' farmers
- Thrust of rainforest invasion
- Forest Reserve
- Indian Reservation
- Central road BR 364
- Side road
- River

BR 364

R. Jiparaná

N

0   km   30

Map 1 shows the same area as in the photographs on page 168, and map 2 shows the location of this area in Brazil. The BR 364 road has opened up the rainforest allowing farmers to settle there.

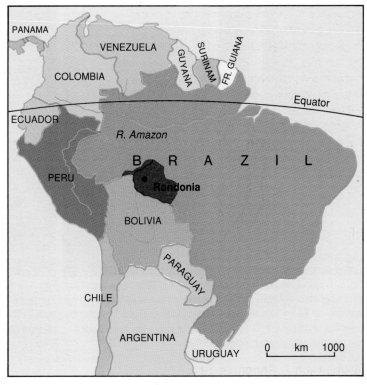

PANAMA

VENEZUELA

GUYANA

SURINAM

FR. GUIANA

COLOMBIA

Equator

ECUADOR

R. Amazon

B R A Z I L

PERU

• Rondonia

BOLIVIA

PARAGUAY

CHILE

ARGENTINA

URUGUAY

0   km   1000

Map 2. Location of Rondonia in South America

Soil profiles

Fig. 1. **Gley soil** from Canada. Iron in soil is in a reduced form because of poor drainage and lack of oxygen.

Fig. 2. **Podzol soil** from the Soviet Union. Iron pan clearly seen as a red band below the ash-grey A horizon. Surface has acid humus (**mor**) layer.

Fig. 3. **Grey-brown forest soil** from south-east England. Brown layers in B horizon below thick A horizon. Iron pan clearly seen in mid B horizon.

Fig. 4. **Chernozem soil** from Ulyanovsk, USSR. Deep humus-rich A horizon is about 1 metre deep. Some calcium concretions can be seen in the lighter B horizon.

Fig. 5. **Tropical red soil** from East Africa. Light brown A horizon due to leaching by heavy rainfall. Rapid chemical weathering in B horizon has resulted in deep red staining by iron oxides.

Fig. 6. Irreversible hardening of iron oxides in the soil as they dried out gives rise to iron hard crust after the material above has been eroded.

Fig. 7. **Rendzina soil** from Yugoslavia. Intrazonal: shallow humus-rich soil lying over limestone parent material. This profile lacks a B horizon.

Fig. 8. **Terra rossa soil** from the Mediterranean area. Intrazonal: note the A horizon has little organic matter. Residual iron oxides give the dark colour. Lighter horizons below with concretions of $CaCO_3$ (hardened calcretes).

INDEX